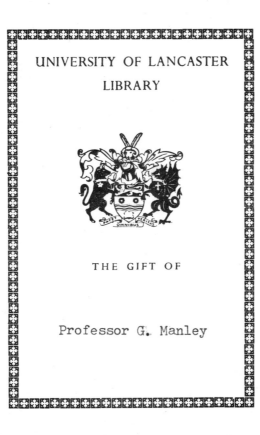

The Climate of
New Zealand

THE CLIMATE OF NEW ZEALAND

A Geographic Survey

BY

B. J. GARNIER

LONDON

EDWARD ARNOLD (PUBLISHERS) LTD

PRINTED IN GREAT BRITAIN BY
W. & J. MACKAY & CO. LTD
FAIR ROW, CHATHAM

PREFACE

I COLLECTED the material for this book between 1945 and 1951 when I was on the staff of the University of Otago, Dunedin. A move to West Africa early in 1951 left me with little time for writing about New Zealand, and it was not until towards the end of 1953 that I was able to start sorting and arranging the material I had collected. Fortunately climatic information does not become rapidly out of date, but the delay between collecting material and writing it up explains why the book contains no illustrations of climatic phenomena taken from occurrences of the past six years.

In New Zealand I received help from many sources. In particular I want to say how grateful I am to the Director of Meteorological Services, Wellington, for allowing me to consult so much unpublished material and for enabling me to work in the Meteorological Office, very often out of office hours. I am especially grateful to the staff of the 'Climat. Section' for their unfailing courtesy, good humour, and co-operation in the face of my many and varied requests.

I would also like to thank the Research Grants Committee of the University of New Zealand for a grant which enabled me to carry out field work, especially in south Canterbury and north Otago. During this field work I met and stayed with many runholders and farmers from whom I received much valued assistance.

That this book has been written as soon as it has is mainly due to my wife. Both before and after our marriage she encouraged me continually and spent many hours helping me with the manuscript, proof reading, and the index. To her I owe a deep debt of gratitude.

Finally, I would like to acknowledge the encouragement I received from Professor R. O. Buchanan, of the London School of Economics, who read and advised on the manuscript, and to express my thanks to the publishers for undertaking to produce this work and for their patience and co-operation in meeting my various requests.

June, 1957   B. J. GARNIER

CONTENTS

FIGURES

In the text

page

LIST OF PLATES

INTRODUCTION

LITERATURE about the weather and climate of New Zealand is widely scattered in journals and books. Some of it is now out of print, some of it is difficult to obtain, and some of it, in mimeographed form, is known only to a small group of students whose particular interests lie in the fields of meteorology and climatology. A portion of this material has recently been collected under one cover,[1] but Kidson's contribution to the Köppen-Geiger *Handbuch der Klimatologie* still remains the most comprehensive single work on the subject.[2]

Kidson's approach is that of a physical climatologist. His book is a masterly explanation of the country's climate, element by element, in the course of which he draws attention to the way in which single elements vary from place to place. There is, however, no attempt to discuss the climate in regional terms, either by drawing attention to the particular combination of climatic phenomena which makes the country unique, or by discussing the way climate varies in its character and significance in different localities.

It is the purpose of the present volume to fill this gap in climatological literature, by examining New Zealand's climate from the geographical point of view. In doing so it will adhere to the most ancient traditions of geography as a chorographic science, since the emphasis will be upon the inter-relation of different climatic features as manifested in the various regions of the country. It begins, therefore, with a broad survey of the land's distinguishing climatic qualities, followed by a discussion of how these have been produced by the combined effect of its position and physiography. This forms a background for the regional studies which constitute the bulk of the book. These are designed to explain how each area is distinguished by its special combination of climatic phenomena, and how the significance of climate as an element of the geographic landscape varies in each locality.

The use of this method is intended also to demonstrate how systematic geography may be more clearly differentiated from the other systematic sciences than is commonly the case. Confusion arises because it too often pursues objectives which are difficult to distinguish from those of kindred sciences like geology, climatology, agriculture, and botany. In these, attention is properly focused upon individual phenomena such as rocks, climatic elements, crops, and plants, and in examining them systematic scientists must, as the logical outcome of their work, explain their character and distribution. But this is all that many geographers working along systematic lines themselves attempt, whereas the development of their subject as an independent discipline requires the realization of its traditional aims, which are to understand the distinctive interrelations of phenomena within different areas.[3] These aims are perhaps most obviously perceived in regional geography. But those geographers whose interests lie in examining a particular kind of phenomenon, such as climate or vegetation, are in fact achieving identical ends if they explain how the phenomenon they are studying displays in different localities a unique combination of features, and has varying significance in relation to the other characteristics of the area in question.

It is from this standpoint that the climate of New Zealand will be treated here. The volume, therefore, should be regarded primarily as an exposition of an important aspect of the country's geography, and secondarily as an attempt to show how studies in systematic geography may make their particular contribution to the field of learning.

[1] B. J. Garnier (ed.): 'New Zealand Weather and Climate', *N.Z. Geogr. Soc. Spec. Pubn., Misc. Ser.* No., 1, 1950.

[2] E. Kidson: 'The Climatology of New Zealand', in Köppen-Geiger *Handbuch der Klimatologie*, Band IV, Teil S, Berlin, 1932.

[3] The author's views on the nature of geography are outlined in B. J. Garnier: 'The Contribution of Geography; an inaugural lecture given at University College, Ibadan, on November 17, 1951', Ibadan, 1952.

I

CLIMATIC CHARACTERISTICS

THE climate of New Zealand is often described as 'insular' or 'oceanic', and classified as 'warm temperate'. According to Köppen's widely recognized system of climatic grouping it is Cfb. But such statements are true only in the broadest sense. They imply, moreover, a resemblance to the climate of places in comparable latitudes which does not in fact exist, and overlook the differences which writers on New Zealand have noted from the earliest days of European immigration. Grimstone, writing in the mid-nineteenth century, for example, reports:[1]

> The climate and season differ so materially from a similar parallel in Europe, and in our own country, that the early settlers, who merely transposed the months to suit the change of hemisphere, found themselves continually surprised in their anticipation, sometimes agreeably, at others the contrary.

In similar vein, Dieffenbach refers to:[2]

> the remarkable feature of the continual chasing of clouds, and sudden alternations of rain and sunshine, which follow each other in far more rapid succession than is ever experienced in England, which has been so unjustly accused of having the most changeable weather in the world.

Such remarks emphasize what is, from many points of view, the most notable characteristic of New Zealand's climate: the many ways in which it differs from what is 'normal' to 'warm temperate, maritime conditions', and does, in fact, fail to conform to the qualities of Cfb climates elsewhere.

Probably the best approach to the study of this climate is to consider it in terms of five general features: its windy and sunny nature; its changeable weather; its temperature régime; its plentiful but variable rainfall; and, finally, its great range of climatic type, with big changes occurring over short distances. In the peculiarities of these five elements lies the essence of New Zealand's climatic personality. Each will be examined briefly.

It is often said that New Zealanders can be recognized by the 'crows' feet' at the corners of their eyes, caused, say the pundits, by their always having to screw them up in the face of the wind. Others will say that they are distinguished, especially if they come from Wellington, by a habit of clutching their hats when rounding a street corner for fear of disaster in the face of a sudden gust. Whatever the truth of these sayings, they do at least recognize that New Zealand is on the whole a windy place. Moreover, the man in the street is fully, if unconsciously, aware of the importance of wind in the country's climate. The daily conditions are commonly described in terms of wind systems: the farmer and townsman alike speak of 'westerly weather', a 'northwester', or a 'southerly', and add descriptive comments which leave no doubt that the speaker understands the import of such winds for the day's weather.

Over New Zealand the atmosphere is rarely still. In places very strong winds occur but they are normally confined to exposed mountains or to the extremities of the ranges, particularly in the area between the North and South Island, and at the southern end of the latter. Elsewhere their average

[1]S. E. Grimstone: 'The Southern Settlements of New Zealand: comprising statistical information from the earliest period to the close of the year 1846, etc. etc.', Wellington, 1847.
[2]Ernest Dieffenbach: 'Travels in New Zealand, with contributions to the Geography, Geology, Botany, and Natural History of the Country', 2 Vols., London, 1843.

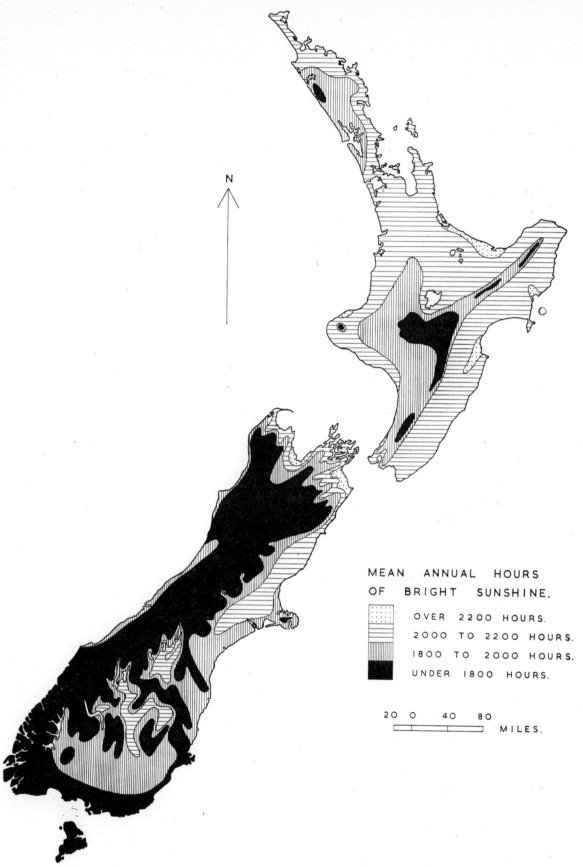

MEAN ANNUAL HOURS
OF BRIGHT SUNSHINE.

OVER 2200 HOURS.
2000 TO 2200 HOURS.
1800 TO 2000 HOURS.
UNDER 1800 HOURS.

20 0   40   80
MILES.

FIG. 1. Mean Annual Hours of Bright Sunshine in New Zealand.

velocity rarely exceeds Force 5 on the Beaufort scale, but owing to topographic influences they are gusty.[3] They blow down valleys and through gaps, varying greatly in strength and direction over short distances, so that they are far more noticeable than their average velocity suggests.

These characteristics have two principal causes: the country's oceanic position in the westerly wind belt of middle latitudes, and its high mountain ranges and youthful physiographic forms. These features are also responsible for another important climatic characteristic: plentiful sunshine. Since the air over New Zealand gets mixed to considerable heights, flowing up and down, over and round the mountain ranges, a continuous cloud layer is rarely maintained for any great length of time. Consequently there is abundant sunshine. Nearly all the country averages more than 1,800 hours of bright sunshine a year, and some favoured parts, in the lee of mountain ranges, average above 2,200 hours (*Fig.* 1). Lower values are experienced only on the principal mountain ranges, and along the coast of the South Island, from Puysegur Point to Dunedin. Here, about 1,700 hours, rather less than 40 per cent of the possible annual total, are normally received. Even so, this amount corresponds to that of the 'sunny south' of the British Isles. Clear skies are thus common in New Zealand. Though they may be covered for a time by rain-clouds, sunshine soon returns, and many are the days on which a sky of almost Mediterranean blue occurs, with the scattered clouds appearing white and bright in the rain-washed atmosphere. Solar radiation is accordingly considerable for the latitude, and helps to maintain the greenness of the vegetation and the vigorous growth which characterizes it.

But if local, surface-controlled winds, gusty in character and variable in direction, play a large part in establishing a fundamental quality of New Zealand's weather, the general air movement across the country is no less important to the overall conditions prevailing at any given time. The New Zealander who speaks of a 'northwester day' or of 'southerly weather' is giving colloquial expression to fundamental climatic controls. Weather characteristics, and therefore climate, are powerfully influenced by prevailing wind systems. Southwesterly winds following a cold front, northwesterly influences in the rear of a departing anticyclone and preceding a cold front, or 'easterlies' associated with the southern sector of a depression moving along New Zealand's Pacific coast—each control, in their own particular way, the weather of the land. Their effects are not uniform over the country, for New Zealand is rugged territory and its different parts react differently to each particular influence.[4] But the onset of a northwesterly, for example, heralds certain well-recognized types of weather in different places: warm weather for the North Island, rain for the west coasts of much of both islands, and clear, hot, dry conditions across the Canterbury plains. Similarly the arrival of a southwesterly frequently portends falling temperatures and rain in many places, while easterly or southeasterly winds spell rain and cold in eastern districts, but probably fine weather in the west.

New Zealand weather is thus very much the consequence of local exposure to the dominant flow of air in the free atmosphere over the country. Between periods of marked wind movement, however, there are times of comparative calm. This is when the country is under the influence of an anticyclone. Within its area of influence the weather is fine, and clear skies, large diurnal temperature ranges, and, in winter, frost at night are characteristic. Such weather does not last very long. With the slow movement of the anticyclone eastwards winds freshen once more and weather changes follow.[5]

Changeable weather of this nature is common also to other mid-latitude countries, especially in maritime situations. In this respect, therefore, the country does not differ materially from others

[3]It is only above about 4,000 ft. of elevation that the steadier flow of the free atmosphere is encountered. Below this height the speed and direction of the wind is very much controlled by local relief. See E. Kidson: 'The Elements of New Zealand's Climate', in *N.Z. Weather and Climate*, op. cit., pp. 45–83.

[4]I. E. M. Watts: 'Forecasting New Zealand Weather', in *N.Z. Weather and Climate*, op. cit., pp. 26–44.

[5]ibid.

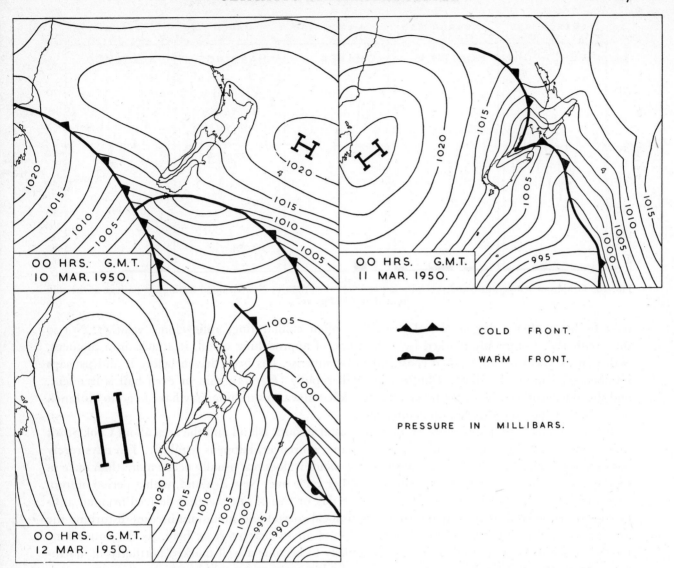

FIG. 2a. Map illustrating the passage of a cold front across New Zealand, 10–12 March 1950.
Note. All maps of the general weather situation given in this book show pressure in millibars and warm and cold fronts by the symbols used for *Fig. 2a.*

in the same climatic group. However, even so it has two peculiarities: the 'southerly' change and its effects, and the exceptional regularity of the weather sequences. These are characteristic of New Zealand and form an integral part of its climatic personality.

The onset of a 'southerly' and its effects are familiar to all New Zealanders. The word is used loosely to cover any change of wind to a southerly quarter; southwest, south, and southeast winds are all included under the one term. In this way the New Zealander recognizes that any of these winds may bring cold and probably rainy weather, which arrives suddenly following in most parts upon warm, and in the east upon fine, conditions. For a 'southerly' occurs after the passage of a cold front (*Fig. 2a*). The winds preceding such a front are from a northerly quarter, and may set in across the land gradually, almost imperceptibly, over a period of two or three days. Thus the 'northerly', although in the end it may reach gale force in Canterbury as the 'northwester', and howl across the plains whipping up dust like a mad thing, on the whole takes possession of New Zealand quietly,

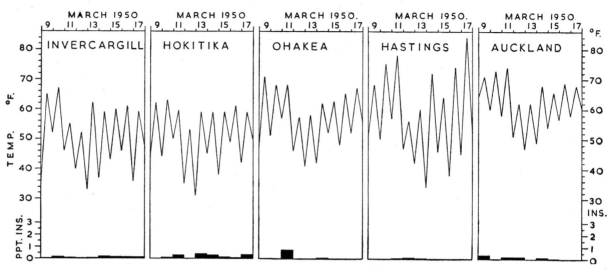

FIG. 2b. Graphs of temperature and precipitation at selected stations in New Zealand during the passage of the cold front shown in *Fig. 2a*.

hour by hour, after a day or two of clear, fine, often exhilarating, anticyclonic weather. Not so the 'southerly'. Commonly marked by a dark line of approaching cloud, it attacks in a moment, and many a yacht on an exposed coast, taken by surprise, has been driven before it and perhaps smashed on some rocky shore. Temperatures fall rapidly (*Fig. 2b*), rain or even hail is frequent, and the office worker who leaves home after breakfast in warm sunshine may have to go to his lunch in a squally wind, and driving, drenching rain.

Such a change is probably more dramatic in eastern South Island and the area about Cook Strait than elsewhere. But it is noticeable everywhere, and, moreover, happens regularly. Ten days rarely pass without a change to the south; on the other hand, it does not usually occur more than once in six days. There is, in other words, a regular weather cycle over New Zealand, with a period of from six to ten days.[6] A typical sequence begins with a day or two of fine weather derived from an anti-cyclone over the land. It is calm and sunny, with local coastal and mountain breezes disturbing the atmosphere and maintaining the incessant motion of air so characteristic here. As the anticyclone moves off, winds begin to freshen into what is likely to become a well-marked northerly or north-westerly air stream. This indicates the presence of a low-pressure trough, in which a depression may or may not form. But in any case, the middle of the trough will be marked by a cold front whose passage will bring a change to the south, or southwest, or southeast, the intensity of the change being controlled by the intensity and vigour of the cold air behind the front, and its direction by the lie of the isobars. Then, after a period of decreasing southerlies with the approach of another anti-cyclone, fine weather arrives again.

In spite of many possible variations upon this general theme, the nature of which will become apparent in later pages, a weather cycle of this kind is remarkably common. It is interrupted for an appreciable length of time when a series of depressions passes from west to east some miles south of the land, and a high-pressure ridge lies over the north (*Fig. 3*). The passage of the depressions causes, in that part of the country lying south of Cape Egmont and Mount Ruapehu, what is popularly known as 'westerly weather'. There, winds blow alternately from north of west and south of west. They bring variable weather, perhaps best described as 'never very good, and never very bad'. 'Showers with bright intervals', 'moderate to strong westerly winds', 'cool and rather cloudy' are the phrases applied to it. At the same time, the high-pressure ridge in the north keeps conditions fine

[6] E. Kidson: 'The Theory of the Polar Front', *Austr. N.Z. Assn. Adv. Sci.*, Vol. 16, 1923.

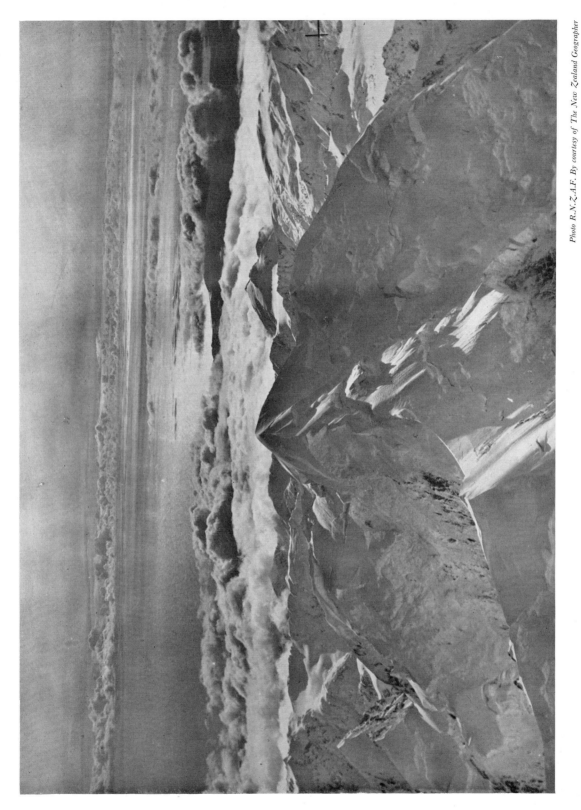

Photo R.N.Z.A.F. By courtesy of The New Zealand Geographer

PLATE I. Orographic cloud forming west of the Southern Alps as an anticyclone moves eastwards to begin a characteristic New Zealand weather sequence.

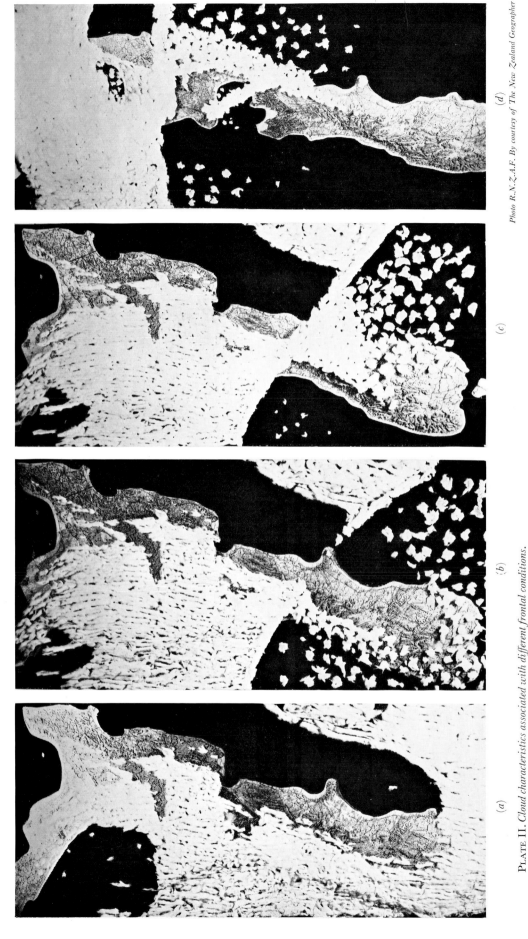

(a) (b) (c) (d)

PLATE II. *Cloud characteristics associated with different frontal conditions.*

(a) Cloud distribution in a northwesterly air stream. Clouds extend gradually northwards as the northwesterlies become more general but the east coast of both islands has clear skies. (b) A cold front followed by southwesterly conditions. Behind the front there is scattered cloud in the west and south; ahead of it there is the cloud formation typical of northwesterly conditions. (c) A cold front followed by southerly or southeasterly winds. Behind the front there is a redistribution of cloud from west to east. (d) A cold front followed by southerly or southeasterly winds usually dissipates rapidly north of Taranaki. It maintains cloud and rainfall on the east coast for some distance behind it.

Photo R.N.Z.A.F. By courtesy of The New Zealand Geographer

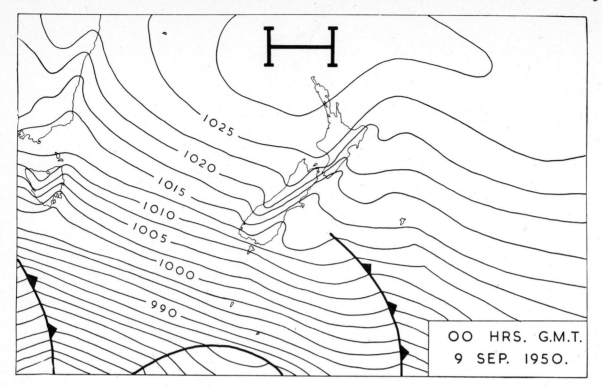

FIG. 3. Map illustrating high pressure to the north of New Zealand with 'westerly weather' in the south.

there. Any fluctuations in the intensity of the ridge are marked by slight increases in wind and cloud, which mildly modify the generally clear days and nights. The whole system lasts for upwards of a week, until a vigorous cold front sweeps it all away and a following anticyclone from the Tasman Sea restores the customary sequence.

Wind systems and weather sequences, however, are not the sole viewpoints from which to regard New Zealand's climatic character. Climate is expressed quantitatively by certain well-recognized elements, notably temperature and precipitation, and these now require some attention.[7]

Temperatures in New Zealand are like those of other oceanic lands in middle latitudes in several ways. Mean monthly values lie between 40°F and 65°F, and the mean annual range is generally below 20F°.[8] Extreme annual temperatures at most places are normally between 90°F and 25°F, while snow falls in appreciable quantities only in the mountains, and frost, though widespread in winter, occurs on less than a hundred days of the year, at least in the inhabited parts of the country.

The distribution of mean annual temperatures is shown in *Fig. 4*.[9] The map indicates the combined influence of latitude and differences in elevation upon surface temperatures. The former is exemplified by the steady decrease in temperature from north to south, when allowance is made for altitude, and the latter by the contrast between the pattern of surface temperatures of the two main islands. The South Island, with its great physiographic diversity, has a much more intricate pattern than the North Island, and about half of it has an average annual temperature under 45°F. By contrast,

[7]A note on statistical sources and climatic statistics for numerous stations will be found in Appendix C. Information given in the text should always be read in conjunction with the details given in this appendix, particularly as to the duration of records and the location and altitude of the stations.

[8]The use of F° to represent a temperature difference and of °F to represent actual temperature follows a suggestion made by V. Conrad: 'Methods in Climatology', 1st edn., Harvard U.P., 1946, p. 13 and note.

[9]In making this and other temperature maps a good deal of interpolation for places of higher elevation was necessary. The method used and the results obtained are given in Appendix A.

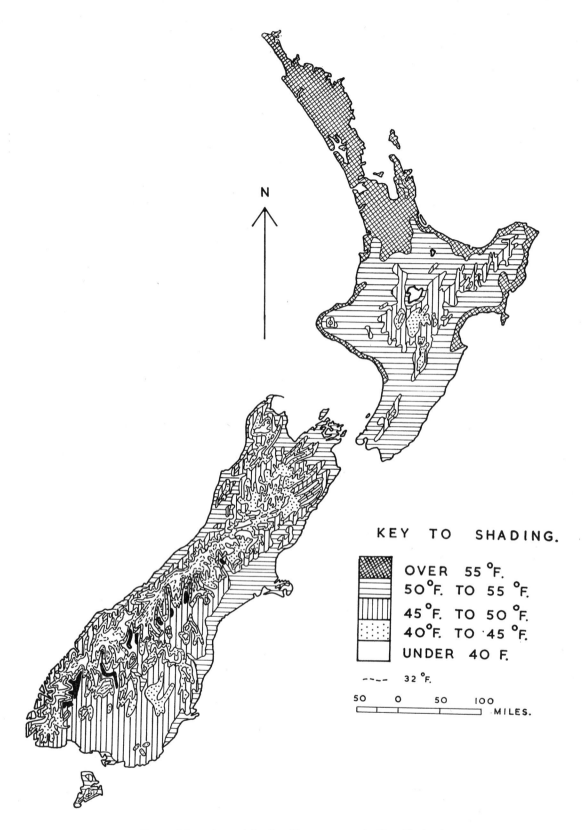

KEY TO SHADING.

	OVER 55 °F.
	50°F. TO 55 °F.
	45°F. TO 50 °F.
	40°F. TO 45 °F.
	UNDER 40 F.

---- 32 °F.

50   0   50   100
MILES.

FIG. 4. Mean Annual Surface Temperatures in New Zealand.

Table 1

TEMPERATURE CONTRASTS BETWEEN NORTHERN AND SOUTHERN NEW ZEALAND DURING WINTER AND SUMMER

Station	Altitude ft.	Latitude °S	Mean Temp. °F July	Jan.	Mean Temp. °F Winter	Summer
Auckland	160	36° 51′	51.4	66.4	52.2	65.6
Alexandra	520	45° 15′	36.3	61.7	38.5	61.1
		Diff:	15.1	4.7	13.7	4.5
Te Paki	200	34° 30′	52.6	64.7	53.3	64.4
Timaru	56	44° 24′	41.4	60.6	42.5	59.8
		Diff:	11.2	4.1	10.8	5.6
Invercargill	32	46° 24′	40.9	56.9	42.3	56.4

Table 2

A COMPARISON OF MEAN TEMPERATURES DURING AUTUMN AND SPRING FOR PLACES IN DIFFERENT LATITUDES

Station	Latitude	Mean Temp. °F Autumn	Spring	Difference
Te Paki	34° 30′	60.9	57.2	3.7
Auckland	36° 51′	60.9	57.4	3.5
New Plymouth	39° 04′	57.6	54.3	3.3
Hastings	39° 39′	56.8	55.1	1.7
Karioi	39° 28′	50.3	48.4	1.9
Masterton	40° 59′	54.3	52.7	1.6
Nelson	41° 17′	55.7	53.9	1.8
Hokitika	42° 43′	53.8	51.9	1.9
Christchurch	43° 32′	53.1	52.7	0.4
Alexandra	45° 15′	50.5	52.0	1.5*
Dunedin	45° 52′	52.1	51.4	0.7
Gore	46° 05′	50.1	50.4	0.3*
Invercargill	46° 24′	50.1	50.3	0.2*

* Spring warmer than autumn.

very little of the North Island is below this figure and most of the lowlands exceed a mean annual value of 55°F. The same kind of contrast exists at each of the four seasons of the year,[10] when, however, some additional features of the temperature may be noted.

The difference between the two islands in both summer and winter is well marked (*Fig.* 5). But whereas in winter it comes about through the combined influence of latitude and elevation, in summer it is largely the consequence of differences in elevation alone. Mean sea-level isotherms reveal this distinction. That for 45°F in July lies across the northern end of the South Island and that for 50°F is just south of Auckland City. In January, on the other hand, whereas the mean sea-level isotherm of 60°F reaches well to the south, that for 65°F barely touches even the far north and has not been drawn on the map.[11] This suggests that, allowing for altitude, there is a greater contrast between the two islands in winter than there is in summer. As *Table* 1 indicates, this is true for a comparison of places in the north of New Zealand with those in the latitude of Timaru and Alexandra. Summer in north Auckland, indeed, is not a great deal warmer than it is in south Canterbury or central Otago. But from the latter area southwards mean summer temperatures rapidly decrease, so that in January the difference in mean temperature between Alexandra and Invercargill is 4.8F° and between Timaru and Invercargill it is 3.7F°. These values are commensurate with the differences

[10]The months of the year have been grouped into seasons as follows: Winter—June, July, August; Spring—September, October, November; Summer—December, January, February; Autumn—March, April, May.

[11]The mean sea level isotherm of 65°F in January could be drawn for small areas in the Bay of Plenty and for the northern part of the north Auckland peninsula. (See E. Kidson: 'The Elements of New Zealand's Climate', op. cit.) Very few stations in New Zealand record a mean temperature of 65°F in January, and only Auckland (66.7°F) and Te Aroha (66.8°F) exceed a mean temperature of 66°F during this month.

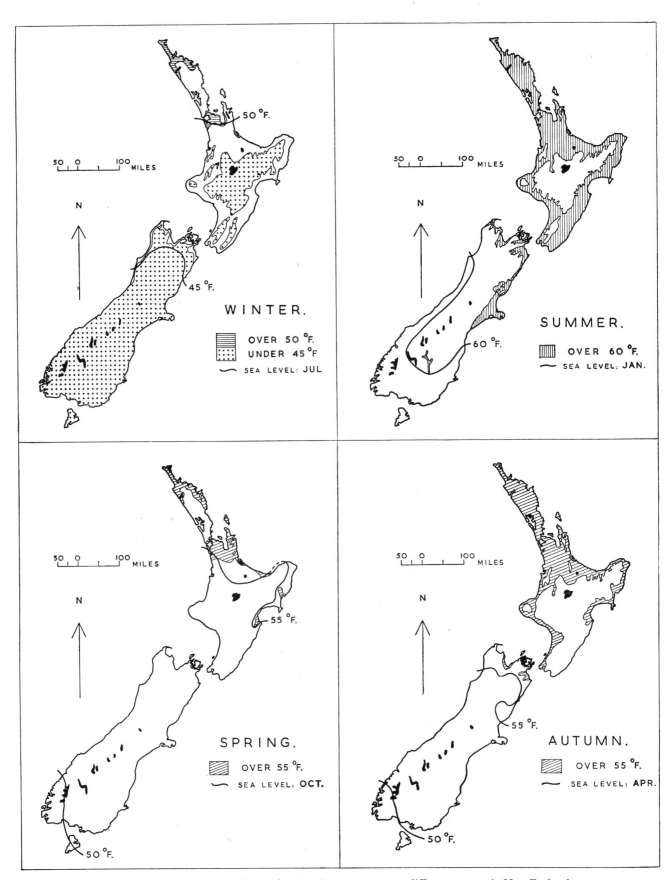

FIG. 5. Aspects of mean surface and sea-level temperatures at different seasons in New Zealand.

Table 3

SOME MEAN TEMPERATURE RANGES IN NEW ZEALAND

Station	Altitude	Latitude	Mean Annual Range	Mean Ann. Diurnal Range	Mean Ann. Extreme Range
	ft.	°S	F°	F°	F°
(a) Western Exposure					
Te Paki	200	34° 30'	12.7	13.9	47.4
Auckland	160	36° 51'	15.3	11.7	43.8
New Plymouth	160	39° 04'	13.6	12.9	48.1
Hokitika	12	42° 43'	15.1	14.2	48.5
Invercargill	32	46° 24'	16.0	16.6	59.6
mean	113		14.5	13.9	49.5
(b) Easterly Exposure					
Gisborne	14	38° 40'	17.4	18.8	62.0
Hastings	45	39° 39'	19.4	21.9	65.5
Blenheim	12	41° 30'	18.7	19.1	67.2
Christchurch	22	43° 32'	19.1	16.9	63.5
Timaru	56	44° 24'	19.2	17.9	64.9
mean	30		18.8	18.9	64.6
(c) Interior Positions					
Rotorua	931	38° 09'	17.7	19.1	60.6
Karioi	2,125	39° 28'	17.2	20.1	61.2
Hanmer	1,225	42° 31'	21.2	21.8	73.8
Lake Tekapo	2,350	44° 00'	23.1	20.4	70.8
Ophir	1,000	45° 07'	25.4	22.2	75.3
mean	1,526		20.9	20.7	68.3

in mean temperature between Auckland and Alexandra, and between Te Paki and Timaru during the same month.

The comparative uniformity of mean temperature at places of similar elevation which is characteristic of summer does not continue into autumn months, when the northern part of the North Island is clearly warmer than the rest of New Zealand.[12] From Auckland City northwards at this time mean temperatures are close to 60°F, only a few degrees lower than they normally are in summer, and over the North Island lowlands generally they exceed 55°F. Mean temperatures in the South Island, on the other hand, are virtually all below 55°F. This contrasts with the situation in spring when the difference between north and south is somewhat less. *Fig.* 5 shows that, whereas the location of the mean sea-level isotherm of 55°F moves from the northern part of the South Island in April to north of the central plateau of the North Island in October, that of the mean sea-level isotherm for 50°F in these two months remains approximately the same. In other words, the difference in temperature between autumn and spring, which is quite large in northern New Zealand, gets steadily less as we proceed southwards, until in the southern parts of the South Island it disappears (*Table* 2).

When the distribution of temperature ranges in New Zealand is considered it is found that, unlike mean temperatures, the main contrasts are between west and east on the one hand, and between coast and interior on the other. This is illustrated in maps of the mean annual range, and of the mean annual extreme range of temperature (*Fig.* 6 and inset), and also in the statistics of *Table* 3. The lowest values are found in areas exposed to westerly winds. The mean annual range of temperature at Te Paki, New Plymouth, or Invercargill, for instance, is from three to five degrees less than that at coastal stations east of the mountains, such as Gisborne, Blenheim, and Timaru. A like contrast exists between the mean annual diurnal ranges, while the mean annual extreme range

[12]B. J. Garnier: 'The Seasonal Climates of New Zealand', in *N.Z. Weather and Climate*, op. cit., pp. 105–39.

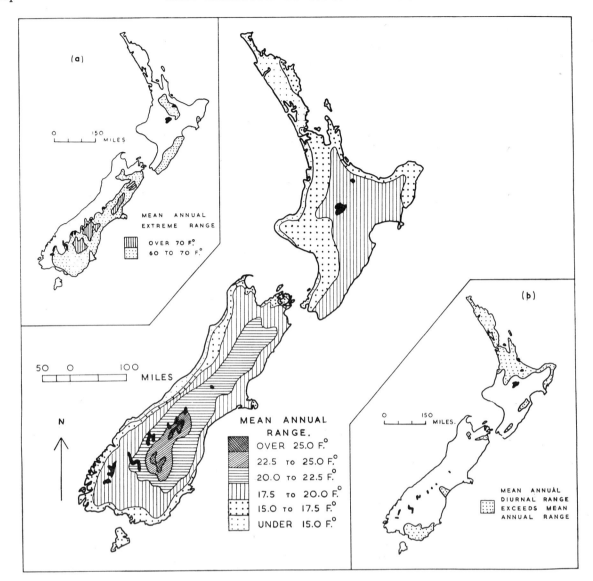

FIG. 6. The Mean Annual Range of Temperature in New Zealand. Inset maps show (a) the mean annual extreme range of temperature, and (b) areas where the mean annual diurnal range of temperature is greater than the mean annual range.

along the west coast is from fifteen to twenty degrees lower than that along the east coast. On the other hand, places in the interior tend to have higher values still. This is especially marked in the South Island, where the intermontane basins of central Otago and of Canterbury have the largest temperature ranges in the country. At Ophir, for example, the mean annual range of temperature is 25.4F°, the mean annual diurnal range is 22.2F°, and the mean annual extreme range is 75.3F°, while the corresponding figures at Hanmer, in north Canterbury, are 21.2 F°, 21.8F°, and 73.8F°.

Temperatures in New Zealand are distinguished in three further respects: by the way they change with the passage of a cold front, by diurnal ranges which are rather large for a mid-latitude, oceanic region, and by the absence of prolonged hot or cold spells.

The dramatic effects produced by the arrival of a cold front have already been mentioned, and in later pages we shall examine the sudden drop in temperature which can accompany its movement across particular localities. Here we shall consider the more general consequences to temperatures

Table 4

MINIMUM TEMPERATURES AT DIFFERENT PLACES IN NEW ZEALAND, 9–17 MARCH 1950 (°F)

Station	9	10	11	12	13	14	15	16	17
Invercargill	35	52	46	40	33	37	43	46	36
Hokitika	44	44	50	35	31	45	38	49	42
Ohakea	48	51	57	46	41	42	52	48	52
Hastings	51	50	57	47	42	34	46	38	45
Auckland	64	60	58	51	47	49	54	57	58

through the country. The graphs which are found in *Fig. 2b*, show what happened during the second week of March 1950, when, on the 11th, a typical cold front moved across the country. Beforehand, temperature conditions had been warm, with daytime maxima between 65°F and 70°F in the south, and above the latter figure in the north. More significant, perhaps, were the night minimum temperatures, which exceeded 50°F in most lowland localities. As the front passed, however, temperatures fell sharply, and continued low for about thirty-six hours. Thereafter it grew warmer as an anti-cyclone from the Tasman Sea moved on to the land. The temperature conditions are especially well illustrated by the figures for minimum temperatures (*Table 4*). These show a sequence typical of the passage of a cold front: the big contrast between the temperature before and after it goes over, the short period of cold in the subantarctic air it brings, and the subsequent slow recovery to warmer conditions. Furthermore, the figures indicate how the effects of the front are not uniform over the country. Temperatures reacted more sharply at Invercargill, Hokitika, and Hastings, for instance, than they did at Ohakea and Auckland. This is characteristic, and illustrates how the effects of a frontal passage are generally more noticeable in the southwest, south, and east of the country than they are in the north and west of the North Island.

The range of diurnal temperature is rather large in New Zealand because of the clear skies which result from there being so much wind and air turbulence. Like other temperature ranges, it is greater in the east and in the interior than in regions exposed to westerly winds. In most localities, the mean annual value at a given station is generally within two degrees of the local mean annual range. As a rule, the latter is the greater, but in some places the reverse is true. This is particularly so in the northern half of the North Island (see inset map in *Fig.* 6). Except for one or two places, such as Auckland City, all stations there record mean diurnal ranges which are two degrees or more higher than the mean annual range. At Waipoua, for example, the excess is 3.1F°, at Tauranga it is 2.2F°, at Rotorua it is 1.4F°, and at Ruakura (Hamilton) it is as much as 4.0F°. A like relationship between mean diurnal and mean annual ranges occurs here and there in other parts, as a rule in places of comparatively low mean annual range, such as the lowlands of Southland and south Otago. It is, however, a comment on the tendency towards high diurnal ranges everywhere, to realize that some places, even in inland and eastern districts, have a mean annual diurnal range which is greater than the mean annual range. Such a place is Hanmer, for example, where the former value is 21.8F°, and the latter is 21.2F°.

Finally, we should note the absence of prolonged hot or cold spells over the country. This reflects its oceanic position and the regularity of its weather sequences. There is not, as in the case of the British Isles, for example, a large neighbouring continental mass to obtrude its influence upon New Zealand's climate. Consequently, there is no possibility of persistent periods of continental weather, and temperatures fluctuate continually, in sympathy with the regular movement of the air streams and pressure systems which pass across the land.

Let us consider next the fourth of the 'five general features' of New Zealand's climate: its rainfall. World climatic surveys often classify the country as a land where rainfall is plentiful, well-distributed through the year, and reliable in occurrence. This may sum up conditions well enough for such broad purposes, but it is inadequate here because from many points of view the most significant

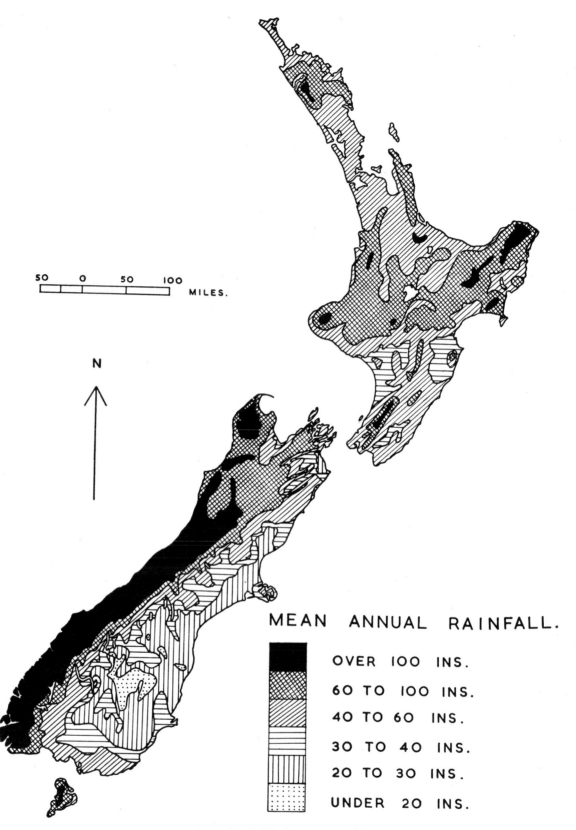

MEAN ANNUAL RAINFALL.

OVER 100 INS.
60 TO 100 INS.
40 TO 60 INS.
30 TO 40 INS.
20 TO 30 INS.
UNDER 20 INS.

50   0   50   100
MILES.

N

FIG. 7. The Mean Annual Rainfall of New Zealand (after Kidson).

26

Table 5

SOME EXAMPLES OF HEAVY RAINFALLS IN NEW ZEALAND

Region	Station	Date	Amount of Fall (in.)	Duration	Rate per hour* (in.)
Middle N.Z.	Nelson	23/2/33	0.67	25 min.	1.61
	Inglewood	12/10/43	12.16	24 hrs.	....
	Bainham	2/4/31	19.43	24 hrs.	....
	Otorohanga	25/1/36	1.41	20 min.	4.23
Western Sth. Is.	Milford Sound†	17/4/39	22.00	24 hrs.	....
	Lake Kanieri	19/2/35	14.50	24 hrs.	....
	Greymouth	23/2/31	12.50	24 hrs.	....
Northern N.Z.	Whangarei	14/2/24	0.88	20 min.	2.64
	Matamata	27/1/30	1.37	10 min.	8.22
	Waihi	4/2/38	16.50	24 hrs.	....
Southern N.Z.	Dipton	25/12/08	1.00	30 min.	2.00
	Whare Flat	19/3/29	1.45	1½ hrs.	....
Eastern Nth. Is.	Wellington	17/3/35	0.56	10 min.	3.36
	Rissington	11/3/24	20.14	10 hrs.	....
	Cape Runaway	22/3/33	1.55	30 min.	3.10
	Hastings	11/4/31	1.00	30 min.	2.00
Eastern Sth. Is.	Pleasant Point	1/2/42	1.42	15 min.	5.68
	Buccleugh	20/12/37	0.67	10 min.	4.02
	Rudstone, Methven	8/3/37	0.60	15 min.	2.40
	Stag and Spey	6/5/23	19.69	24 hrs.	....
Central Nth. Is.	Château Tongariro	31/12/32	1.21	20 min.	3.63
	Rotorua	28/1/1886	1.47	45 min.	1.96
Inland Sth. Is.	Alexandra	12/1/30	2.00	30 min.	4.00
	North Lowburn	20/1/33	2.00	15 min.	8.00
	Benmore	24/1/26	1.60	30 min.	3.20
Upland Sth. Is.	Hermitage, Mt. Cook	19/12/13	13.25	24 hrs.	....
	Arthur's Pass	4/11/26	12.70	24 hrs.	....

*The rate per hour is only given in the case of falls lasting less than one hour.

†Milford Sound is strictly located in Upland South Island, according to the regions of this book, but is included in Western South Island as an example of coastal rainfall.

feature of New Zealand's rainfall is its unequal distribution in both time and space. As *Fig.* 7 shows, mean annual totals vary from under 20 inches in central Otago to over 100 inches in the adjacent highlands. Moreover, two farming seasons rarely have the same amount of rain, and notable differences occur in the monthly or even daily totals of closely located areas. Its intensity and incidence, too, vary greatly from place to place, so that of all the elements significantly distinguishing the country's climatic personality, it is the one which is the least amenable to generalization and to treatment on a country-wide scale.

Warm fronts and cold fronts are both active in New Zealand, but of the two the latter produce the most widespread rains, since rain from the former tends to be confined to areas west of the mountains. Consequently, a high proportion of the country's rainfall comes from the passage of cold air across it.[13] Such rainfall is often heavy but rarely prolonged. It occurs in irregular showers with water falling in large drops, especially east of the ranges.[14] The average intensity of rainfall is therefore high, and the number of days on which it falls is comparatively low.[15] Both these features are illustrated in the maps of *Fig.* 8. Such maps, however, fail to give sufficient weight to one of New Zealand's

[13]F. Bondy and C. J. Seelye: 'Temperatures Associated with Rainfall in New Zealand', *N.Z. Journ. Sci. and Tech.*, Vol. 28, Sec. B, 1947, pp. 253–8. See also E. Kidson: 'The Theory of the Polar Front', op. cit.

[14]K. B. Cumberland: 'Soil Erosion in New Zealand; a geographic reconnaissance', 2nd edn., Wellington, 1946.

[15]The definition of a day with rain may be stated as 'a period of twenty-four hours between observation times, i.e. 9.30 a.m. local time, during which a minimum of 0.005 in. of rain is recorded'.

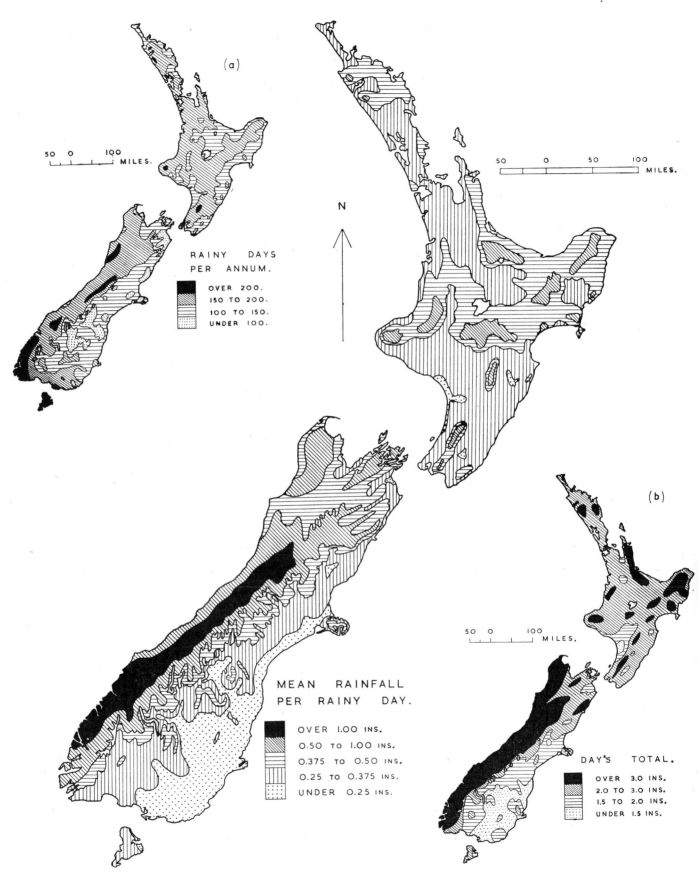

FIG. 8. The mean amount of rain falling per rainy day in New Zealand with insets illustrating (a) the mean annual number of rainy days and (b) the maximum amount of rainfall in a day equalled or exceeded on the average once a year. (Inset (b) is simplified from Seelye.)

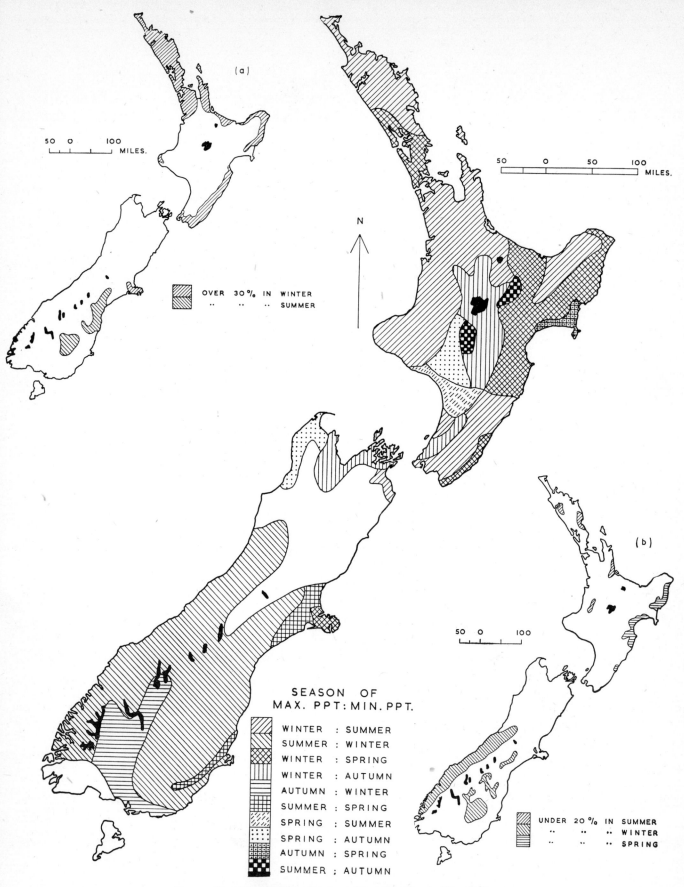

(a)

50 0 100
MILES.

OVER 30% IN WINTER
·· ·· SUMMER

N

(b)

50 0 50 100
MILES.

50 0 100

SEASON OF
MAX. PPT: MIN. PPT.

WINTER : SUMMER
SUMMER : WINTER
WINTER : SPRING
WINTER : AUTUMN
AUTUMN : WINTER
SUMMER : SPRING
SPRING : SUMMER
SPRING : AUTUMN
AUTUMN : SPRING
SUMMER : AUTUMN

UNDER 20% IN SUMMER
·· ·· WINTER
·· ·· SPRING

FIG. 9. The Seasonal Distribution of Precipitation in New Zealand.
The main map shows the principal features of the seasonal distribution; areas left blank on this map have little seasonal variation, every season of the year receiving not more than 27 per cent and not less than 23 per cent of the annual total. Inset map (a) indicates regions with a marked maximum (over 30 per cent) in a given season; inset map (b) indicates regions with a marked minimum (under 20 per cent) in a given season.

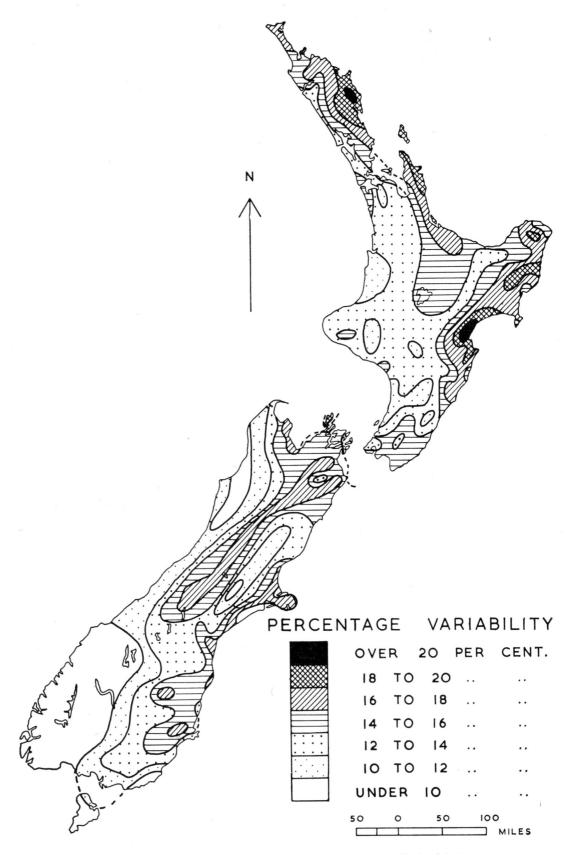

PERCENTAGE VARIABILITY

OVER 20 PER CENT.
18 TO 20 .. ..
16 TO 18 .. ..
14 TO 16 .. ..
12 TO 14 .. ..
10 TO 12 .. ..
UNDER 10 .. ..

50   0   50   100
MILES

FIG. 10. The Mean Annual Percentage Variability of Precipitation in New Zealand (redrawn from Seelye).

most singular rainfall characteristics—the phenomenal amount which may occur during an hour, during a day, or during a period of two or three consecutive days.[16] *Table* 5 indicates statistically what can sometimes happen. Rainfall of this nature is local in occurrence but, as the table shows, takes place often enough in a sufficiently large number of regions to warrant mentioning it here as a general characteristic of the country.

There is a fairly even distribution of precipitation through the year, no area normally receiving more than 35 per cent, or less than 15 per cent, of its annual total in any one season. However, sufficient variation occurs for it to be of some climatic significance, especially in the north, east, and south (*Fig.* 9). Northern and eastern areas of the North Island, and Banks Peninsula in the South Island, for example, receive more than 30 per cent of their annual fall in the three winter months of June, July, and August. In central Otago and south Canterbury, on the other hand, nearly a third of the year's rain comes in the summer quarter. Much of the same area, along with the west coast and mountains of the South Island, has, on the average, less than 20 per cent of its mean annual total in winter. Elsewhere the seasonal contrasts are less marked, but it is only in the northern part of the South Island that no appreciable variation occurs (*Fig.* 9).

Although statistically small, these variations are regionally important, especially when regarded from the standpoint of moisture effectiveness.[17] In much of the South Island, east of the ranges, for example, most rain comes when it is least effective, owing to increased evaporation during the summer period. It follows, moreover, a winter of minimum precipitation during which there has been little opportunity for the soil to build up a reservoir of moisture. In northern territories contrasts between the incidence of rainfall in winter and summer are accentuated further by the temperatures of the two seasons. Thus, the winter is wetter and the summer is drier than the rainfall statistics suggest.[18]

But if the seasonal distribution of rainfall is relatively even, and like that of Cfb climates generally, the same cannot be said for the variation in total from year to year. This exceeds, on the average, 12 per cent of the mean annual quantity nearly everywhere, and in northern territories and in the east of both islands, it is above 16 per cent rising to a mean value of over 20 per cent in mid-Hawke's Bay (*Fig.* 10).[19] Although there is a tendency for the degree of variability to get less towards the south, the major contrasts lie between east and west. Where rainfall is derived principally from westerly winds, the mean variability is low, since these winds are the most reliable sources of precipitation in the country. On the other hand, if an area is exposed to the more wayward 'easterly', or to the erratic arrival of tropical disturbances, then the incidence of rainfall from year to year, and from month to month, is unpredictable.[20]

Throughout the discussion of this chapter there has run a common thread: the way in which the various climatic elements vary within a general framework conditioned by the atmospheric influences surrounding New Zealand. Southerly, northerly, and easterly wind systems have different climatic expression in different parts of the land; sunshine and cloud have no uniform pattern; temperatures alter radically according to elevation and exposure; and precipitation varies from quantities associated with semi-arid conditions to amounts commensurate with the world's rain-drenched lands.

[16]K. B. Cumberland: 'Soil Erosion in New Zealand . . .', op. cit. C. J. Seelye: 'The Frequency of Heavy Rainfalls in New Zealand', Report of the Sixth N.Z. Congress, 1947, published in *Trans. Proc. Roy. Soc. N.Z.*, Vol. 77, Pt. 5, 1949, pp. 66–70.

[17]B. J. Garnier: 'The Application of the Concept of Potential Evapotranspiration to Moisture Problems in New Zealand', *N.Z. Geogr.*, Vol. 7, 1951, pp. 43–61.

[18]*idem*: 'The Seasonal Climates of New Zealand', op. cit.

[19]C. J. Seelye: 'The Variation of Annual Rainfall in New Zealand', *N.Z. Journ. of Sci. and Tech.*, Vol. 22, Sec. B, 1940, pp. 18–21.

[20]*idem*: 'Variations of Monthly Rainfall in New Zealand', *N.Z. Journ. Sci. and Tech.*, Vol. 27, Sec. B, 1946, pp. 397–405. Dispersion diagrams for rainfall at selected stations during the period 1935–54 are given in *Fig.* 11.

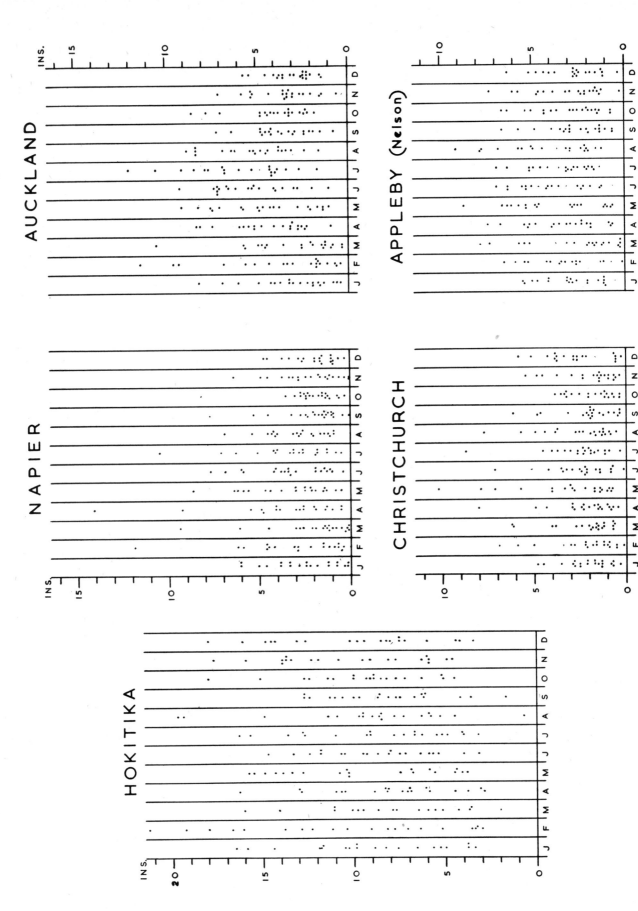

Fig. 11. Rainfall dispersion diagrams for five places in New Zealand for the period 1935–54.

The range of climate produced by this is considerable. Speaking broadly, the North Island consists of warm or cool, superhumid and humid territory, without a great deal of diversity (*Fig.* 12). In contrast to this is the climatic jigsaw of the South Island where all the major climatic types represented in New Zealand are found. Moreover, the alterations between one district and another are particularly noticeable in comparatively lowlying areas. Within 1,000 feet of sea-level, superhumid, humid, subhumid, and semi-arid conditions are all found—a lowland diversity, also present to a small degree in the North Island, which is especially significant for the country's farming economy. Altogether, as has been shown elsewhere, there are upwards of a dozen kinds of climate within the 103,000 square miles of mountain, valley, plain, and plateau which constitute New Zealand.[21]

This diversity is no haphazard affair. It can be given order and meaning in terms of two dominant controlling influences: one is the character of the atmospheric circulation where New Zealand lies, and the other is the country's structure and surface configuration. These two factors, working together, produce the diverse qualities of the climate of New Zealand. They provide the next two chapters with their subject matter.

[21]B. J. Garnier: 'The Climates of New Zealand: according to Thornthwaite's classification', in *N.Z. Weather and Climate*, op. cit., pp. 84–104.

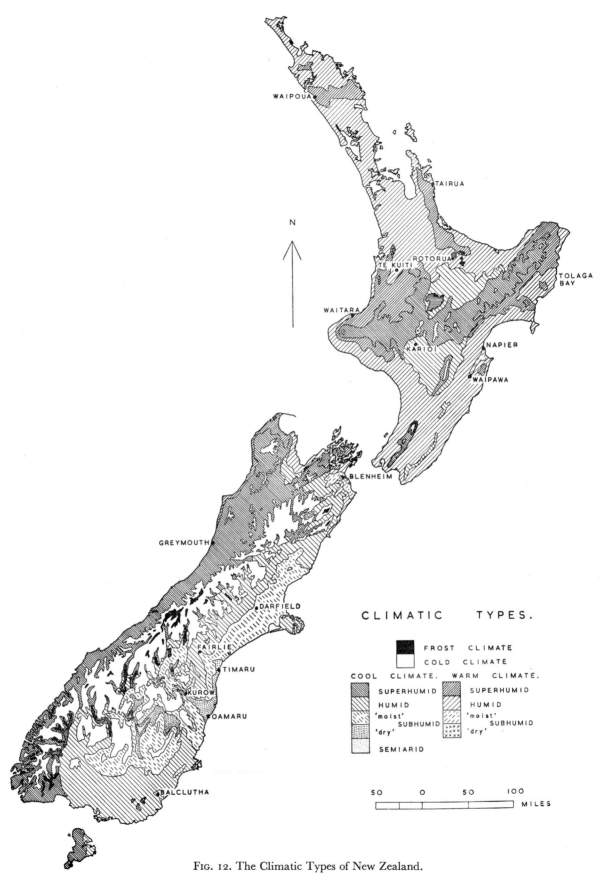

CLIMATIC TYPES.

FROST CLIMATE
COLD CLIMATE

COOL CLIMATE.   WARM CLIMATE.

SUPERHUMID   SUPERHUMID

HUMID   HUMID
'moist'   'moist'
      SUBHUMID   SUBHUMID
'dry'   'dry'

SEMIARID

50   0   50   100
MILES

FIG. 12. The Climatic Types of New Zealand.

34

2

LOCATION

NEW ZEALAND lies between latitudes 34° 04′ S. and 47° 02′ S. It is surrounded by many miles of water, and a hemisphere centred on Wellington consists almost entirely of ocean (*Fig.* 13). Australia, 800 miles to the west, and the ice-covered wastes of Antarctica, nearly twice that distance to the south, alone break the uniformity of the surrounding seas. Otherwise the only landfalls are the eastern littoral of Asia, the southern part of South America, and the multitude of islands of the western Pacific Ocean.

The climatic significance of this location is best examined against a background of the general

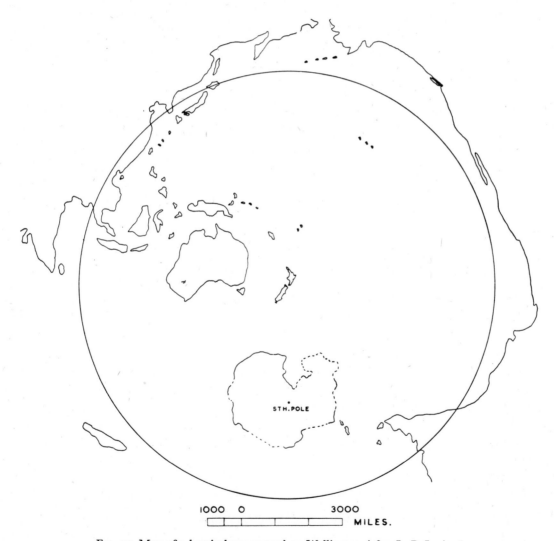

1000   O   3000

MILES.

Fig. 13. Map of a hemisphere centred on Wellington (after L. P. Lee).

global circulation. This has been well described by Rossby, who emphasizes the cellular structure of the earth's atmosphere.[1] In equatorial regions there is an area of convective instability, with rising air carried aloft to great heights. This upper air spreads out towards the poles and its descent maintains the subtropical high-pressure cells located twenty to thirty degrees north and south of the equator. These, fed from above, act as source regions for air which moves both towards the poles and towards the equator. At the other extreme are the cells of cold air above the poles. Here is heavy air, sinking earthwards and travelling in its lower layers towards the equator, but being continually replenished from above by air from warmer regions.

These major cells of high pressure fundamentally control the world's surface circulation. At lower levels, the air which moves towards the equator appears as an easterly wind, and that which moves away from the equator as a westerly wind. Between the polar air cells and those of the subtropics lies a region of surface low pressure, where westerlies predominate both at the surface and aloft. Here a conflict takes place between polar and subtropical air, which reaches its greatest intensity between latitudes 50° and 60° in both hemispheres. This brings frequent precipitation and rapid transitions of temperature, as the warm conditions of subtropical regions battle for supremacy with the cold air of polar parts.

An arrangement of this kind may be observed in both hemispheres of the world. In the southern one, where there are no large continental areas to modify the general scheme, the pressure belts move north and south with the seasons, following the sun in a straightforward manner. Moreover, strong westerlies develop between latitudes 50°S. and 60°S. which produce especially rapid and regular weather sequences in the middle latitudes of this part of the world. Another important point is the influence of Antarctica. This is a huge area of very cold air, and it is estimated that over 18,000,000 square miles, centred on the south pole, have more than a hundred days a year in which temperatures remain below freezing point.[2] The outflow of air from this frigid reservoir is powerful and, even in mid-summer, incursions of cold, polar air may be felt far from their source, often as far away as 30°S.

Where does New Zealand stand in relation to this general climatic scheme? Its extent through thirteen degrees of latitude means that it reaches from just to the south of the subtropical high-pressure belt into that of the vigorous westerlies. It is placed, therefore, within the zone of conflict between subtropical and polar air. The regular migration of the pressure belts, however, produces some significant seasonal changes. In winter, all the land lies within the region of predominant westerlies. The major depression centres, however, pass some miles to the south, and it is the elongation and subsequent modification of their accompanying cold fronts which influence the country's weather, rather than the depressions which form on the polar front itself. In summer, the pressure belts move south so that the North Island becomes closely associated with the zone of relatively dry, subtropical air, whereas the South Island remains more truly within the area of conflicting air masses and under the influence of cold fronts.

The country's longitude is such that it lies about midway between Australia and the remarkably stable high-pressure cell of the central and eastern south Pacific Ocean. This cell, with its axis along 30°S., is prevented from moving eastwards by the high South American cordillera. It acts, therefore, as a gigantic receptacle for the migratory anticyclones which travel from the west, and it also directs the movement of approaching wave-depressions towards the south east. Over Australia, on the contrary, there is no such stable system. Although the continent is a major land area and the chief source of tropical continental air in the southern hemisphere, so powerful is the westerly trend of the atmosphere in these parts that the high pressure systems which form from time to time are propelled eastwards.

[1] C. G. Rossby: 'The Scientific Basis of Modern Meteorology', in 'Climate and Man', *U.S. Dept. Agric. Year Book of Agric.*, Washington, 1941.
[2] J. Gentilli: 'Air Masses of the Southern Hemisphere', *Weather*, Vol. 4, 1949, pp. 258–61; 292–7.

The existence of this procession of migratory anticyclones in the Australia-New Zealand area was first recorded in 1893 by Russell, who reported:[3]

> The leading fact that our investigations have brought to light is that Australian weather south of 20° south latitude is the product of a series of rapidly moving anticyclones, which follow one another with remarkable regularity and are the great controlling force in determining local weather.

Since Russell's day the phenomenon has been studied by numerous workers.[4] While a full explanation of them is still awaited, the facts of their occurrence and the paths which they follow are now well established. They appear to arise from outward surges of polar air and get carried along in the strong westerly air currents of the south Indian and south Pacific oceans. The paths they follow and the speed at which they travel vary somewhat according to the time of year (*Table* 6).[5] Broadly speaking, they move along the south coast of Australia between latitudes 30°S. and 35°S. and then into the Pacific Ocean, their centres passing either across northern New Zealand, or between the country and Norfolk Island. They travel faster in spring and early summer than at other seasons, with an average speed of about 450 miles a day in November and December, but only about 300 miles a day during May. The size of each one varies, but, as a rule, is such that one will cross New Zealand or pass just to the north of the country once every six to ten days.

Table 6

MEAN LATITUDINAL POSITION OF ANTICYCLONES AT DIFFERENT LONGITUDES
(from Kidson)

Long °E.	Jan.	Feb.	Mar.	Apr.	May	June	July	Aug.	Sept.	Oct.	Nov.	Dec.	Year
120	35.3	35.9	35.5	33.8	31.9	30.1	29.9	30.4	31.0	32.7	34.3	34.9	33.0
130	36.1	36.6	35.8	34.1	31.7	29.5	29.8	30.3	31.3	33.0	34.7	35.6	33.2
140	38.2	38.9	37.9	35.7	34.2	31.9	31.6	32.2	33.1	34.2	36.2	37.3	35.1
150	38.6	39.5	38.7	36.2	34.9	33.6	33.4	33.1	32.8	34.3	35.7	37.5	35.7
160	37.1	38.3	38.0	36.4	35.2	34.8	34.8	33.3	31.9	32.7	33.7	35.8	35.2
170	36.3	38.5	38.4	37.2	36.7	35.8	35.9	34.5	32.8	32.7	33.4	35.3	35.6
mean	36.9	38.0	37.4	35.6	34.1	32.6	32.6	32.3	32.2	32.9	34.7	36.1	34.6
Velocity*	8.6	8.5	8.5	7.6	6.6	6.7	7.0	7.8	8.1	9.0	9.1	9.1	7.9

*This is the mean velocity, given in degrees per day.

Note: The above table is based on thirty years of observations.

The nature of the air on the east and west sides of the anticyclones is important to the character of the weather over New Zealand. That on the east is from the south or southwest, according to the trend of the isobars, and is cold, maritime air derived from antarctic sources. On the western side, however, the air is subtropical in origin, and forms a warm, humid, and unstable current from the north or northwest. The two air streams meet in the trough of low pressure which exists between successive anticyclones. Here there are unstable conditions: low cloud, and rapid wind and temperature changes occur as the warm, moist, uprising northwesterly air gives way at the surface to the polar, maritime air which precedes the passage of the next anticyclonic system. The junction generally maintains an extended cold front, which in its southern part is joined to one of the major depressions circling the globe outside the Antarctic Circle. These 'trailing' fronts can stretch a long way, and in the extreme case may reach from the Antarctic to the equator. The formation of a wave, or

[3]H. C. Russell: 'Moving Anticyclones in the Southern Hemisphere', *Quart. Journ. Roy. Met. Soc.*, Vol. 19, 1893, pp. 23–34.

[4]See in particular C. E. Palmer: 'Synoptic Analysis over the Southern Ocean', *N.Z. Meteor. Off. Prof. Notes*, No. 1, 1942. This work contains a very complete discussion of the problem and an extensive bibliography.

[5]E. Kidson: 'Daily Weather Charts extending from Australia and New Zealand to the Antarctic Continent', *Austr. Antarct. Exped. 1911–14, Sci. Rep. Ser. B*, Vol. 7, Sydney, 1947. Also *idem*: 'The Elements of New Zealand's Climate', op. cit.

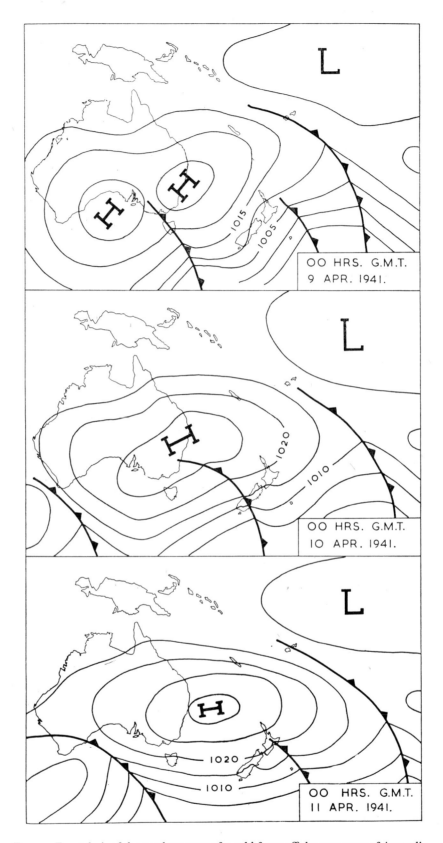

OO HRS. G.M.T.
9 APR. 1941.

OO HRS. G.M.T.
10 APR. 1941.

OO HRS. G.M.T.
11 APR. 1941.

Fig. 14. Frontolysis of the northern part of a cold front off the east coast of Australia.

'kink', on this long front may create a wave-depression on it. This happens commonly in the vicinity of Lord Howe Island, especially if the northern portion of the front gets retarded without losing its identity, while the southern portion continues on its way. In this case the wave-depression moves along the line of the front, through the low-pressure trough, towards the area south and east of the Chatham Islands.

New Zealand weather is thus largely the consequence of two fundamentally contrasting situations: the anticyclones on the one hand and the low-pressure troughs which lie between them on the other. The former approach the country from slightly south of west and travel in a direction which is somewhat north of east. The intervening low-pressure troughs are generally elongated northwest to southeast, and we must now consider what developments are likely within them.[6]

It has already been shown that these troughs nearly always contain a cold front, the northern part of which is commonly retarded east of Australia where a wave-depression may develop as the southern half moves eastwards. Should such a depression not develop, then the trough fills in from the north and only a cold front passes across New Zealand (*Fig.* 14). If a wave-depression does form, however, it moves towards New Zealand following a track which depends on what had happened to the front before cyclogenesis took place. The most common occurrence is for the wave-depression to come into being when the front has already passed on to the South Island. If this happens, it passes across the middle of the country towards the low pressures southeast of the Chatham Islands (*Fig.* 15). It is not unusual for a series of such wave-depressions to move over the land in this way, before the low-pressure area in which they are forming is obliterated by higher pressures from the north or west. Under these circumstances, New Zealand is traversed by both the warm and cold fronts of the wave-depressions, although as a rule the former are effective only in the middle sector of the country, whereas the latter pass across the whole area from Puysegur Point to Auckland and East Cape.

When a wave-depression forms on a cold front while it is quasi-stationary over the Tasman Sea, the resulting track is southwards between Tasmania and the South Island and then eastwards, generally some miles south of New Zealand (*Fig.* 16). On the other hand, if the cold front has already passed across the country, then the wave-depression moves eastwards some distance north of north Auckland, and then towards the southeast (*Fig.* 17). In both these cases New Zealand is, as a rule, affected by a cold front only. From time to time a tropical cyclone, approaching from the north, may induce a frontal wave which then develops into a very violent disturbance. This is most likely to occur in summer and early autumn, and its effects are normally confined to northern districts.[7] It can, however, happen at any season and follow a more southerly course, like that of other wave-depressions.

At this point it is advisable to draw attention to three modifications of the general situations outlined above. Firstly, there is the effect of a high-pressure ridge lying across the Tasman Sea and North Island of New Zealand, which is commonly associated with a series of depressions which travel eastwards between latitudes 50°S. and 60°S. Secondly, there is a tendency for local anticyclones to develop over the South Island. They are created in the cold air behind a cold front when part of it is held stationary.[8] This occurs normally only in winter and is responsible for periods of cold, clear, frosty weather over southern New Zealand. Thirdly, there is the possibility that a cold front may be

[6]The comments which follow, together with the maps used in illustration, have been derived from C. E. Palmer: op. cit. A useful summary of Palmer's work, giving more examples than are provided here, will be found in M. A. Garbell: 'Tropical and Equatorial Meteorology', London, 1947.

[7]M. A. F. Barnett: 'The Cyclonic Storms in Northern New Zealand on the 2nd February and 26th March, 1936', *N.Z. Meteor. Off. Notes*, No. 22, 1938. J. W. Hutchings: 'Tropical Cyclones in the Southwest Pacific', *N.Z. Geogr.*, Vol. 9, 1953, pp. 37–57.

[8]I. E. M. Watts: 'The Relation of New Zealand Weather and Climate: an analysis of the westerlies', *N.Z. Geogr.*, Vol. 3, 1947, pp. 115–29.

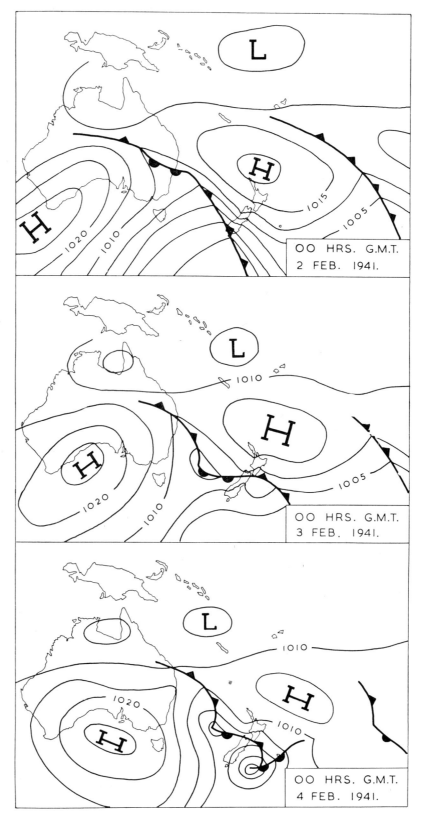

OO HRS. G.M.T.
2 FEB. 1941.

OO HRS. G.M.T.
3 FEB. 1941.

OO HRS. G.M.T.
4 FEB. 1941.

Fig. 15. Formation of wave-depressions off the east coast of Australia after a
cold front had passed on to New Zealand.

FIG. 16. Formation of a wave-depression on a cold front before it has passed on to New Zealand.

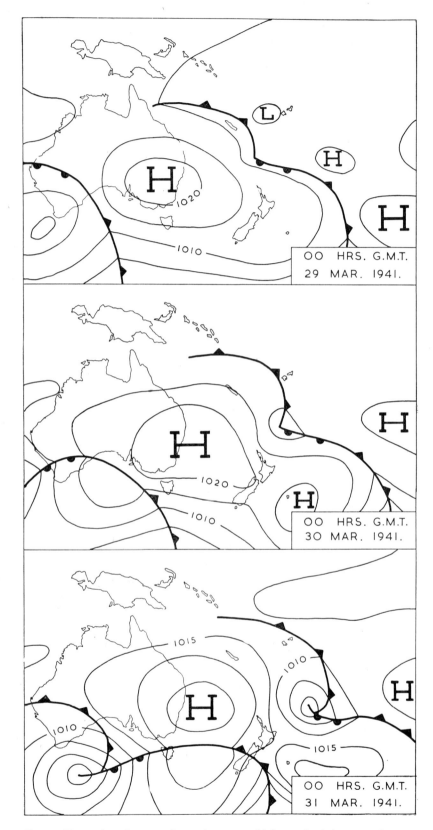

OO HRS. G.M.T.
29 MAR. 1941.

OO HRS. G.M.T.
30 MAR. 1941.

OO HRS. G.M.T.
31 MAR. 1941.

FIG. 17. Formation of a wave-depression on a cold front after it has passed across New Zealand.

deformed in passing across the mountains of the South Island.[9] This produces a wave in it immediately east of New Zealand, which may cause cyclogenesis like that which takes place east of Australia. The resulting depression passes southwards off the east coast with marked effect upon the weather of eastern districts.

Table 7

PERCENTAGE OF DAYS UNDER MAJOR CONTROLLING INFLUENCES, JULY 1943–JUNE 1946

Controlling Factor	North	Centre	South
Northwesterly, westerly, and southwesterly	39	41	37
Southerly to easterly	14	21	21
Anticyclone	28	19	20
Moist northerly	5	4	3
Depressions, warm fronts, and stationary fronts	14	15	19

Note: The areas are defined as follows:—

North—north of a line from New Plymouth to Napier.
South—south of Farewell Spit and Cape Campbell.
Centre—the remainder of the country.

Some of the major climatic contrasts within New Zealand result from the frequency of these controlling influences in different parts of the country. This frequency is indicated in *Table 7* which is derived from an analysis of the 6 a.m. daily weather charts from July 1943 to June 1946.[10] Westerly conditions are clearly the most prevalent for the country as a whole, and they controlled the weather on over 35 per cent of the days in the period analysed. In the north, anticyclones came next in importance, but elsewhere there was an even distribution of days between the remaining major controls, except that moist northerlies were by far the least frequent influence everywhere. One feature masked by the table is the relative frequency of cold fronts in the south. Throughout the country these occur more than twice as often as warm fronts, but their dominance increases enormously in the southern part of the South Island. During the period covered by *Table 7*, they were experienced on 5 per cent of the days in the centre and north; on the other hand, they had a frequency of 10 per cent in the south. This gave a ratio of 3 : 1 between cold fronts and warm fronts in the south, in contrast with that of other parts where it was 2 : 1 or less.[11]

[9] J. W. Hutchings: 'Orographical Cyclogenesis over New Zealand', *N.Z. Meteor. Off. Notes*, Series A, No. 8, 1944.
[10] This table has been abstracted from Watts (see note 8).
[11] These ratios have been calculated from information given in Watts (see note 8). If separate statistics for the area south of the Waitaki river were available the ratio of cold fronts to warm fronts for that area might be higher than that given here for the south. We shall see in later pages that Otago and Southland rarely experience the passage of a warm front.

3

PHYSICAL CHARACTER

ALTHOUGH New Zealand is too small to affect the major circulation of the atmosphere which surrounds it, the detail of its weather, and therefore of its climate, is profoundly influenced by the character of the land itself. The surrounding atmosphere, with its anticyclones, low-pressure troughs, and fronts, provides the material, which local surface characteristics mould into the multitude of climatic types peculiar to New Zealand. Structure and relief are the two agents acting in this way. Their influence is combined, but, for the sake of convenience, it may be examined here in two sections: firstly, the influence of structure, along with the direction of the main mountain ranges, and secondly, the influence of elevation and the diversity of relief.

New Zealand lies at the southwestern extremity of the great mountain chain which circumscribes the Pacific Ocean. Its gigantic mountain ranges were produced by earth movements in late Tertiary times.[1] This 'Kaikoura' orogeny occurred during the pliocene period, following upon the depositions of earlier days, and caused the uplift of a series of earth-blocks, of varying shapes and sizes, which have been subsequently eroded by glaciers and subaerial denudation into the steep-sided and intensely rugged mountains of the present day. These mountains are arranged along a major axis which trends southwest to northeast. There is also a minor axis in the north, however, which controls the direction of the Auckland peninsula, pointing northwestwards like an out-stretched arm. New Zealand is thus a curved and narrow territory. At its widest part only one fifth of its total length, it is shaped like an arc, concave to the west. Almost exactly in the middle the arc is broken by Cook Strait. This turns the land into two main islands: the southern one is long, narrow, and mountainous, and the northern one is squarer and less rugged. It is important to notice that the two islands overlap. Cape Palliser, the southern extremity of the North Island, is nearly seventy miles nearer the South Pole than Cape Farewell, the northern point of the South Island; Nelson is west, not south, of Wellington City. This means that Cook Strait is oriented almost due north and south; it means also that the southern North Island is open to southerly influences, for due south of Wellington Harbour there is no land until the Antarctic continent.

New Zealand, then, a long, curved, narrow, mountainous territory, lies across the path followed by the migratory anticyclones, and athwart the orientation of the low-pressure troughs between them. At first sight, this implies strong contrasts between west and east. In particular, western districts appear likely to be wet and eastern ones relatively dry. This is only true up to a point. When the influences are from a westerly or northwesterly direction this type of contrast is marked; under southerly or southwesterly conditions, however, the difference may not be so great.

The greatest contrasts between west and east are thus derived either from a northwesterly air stream following the departure of an anticyclone, or from the passage of a depression across the country. In the first instance the west coast is generally wet, while on the east coast the weather is clear and sunny. During the passage of a depression, however, the distinction is not so straightforward, since the actual path followed, the intensity of development, and a variety of other factors complicate the picture. The details of these can safely be left to later chapters. Generally speaking, the onset of

[1]C. A. Cotton: 'Structure and Later Geological History of New Zealand', *Geol. Mag.*, Vol. 3, 1916, pp. 243–9; 314–20. W. N. Benson: 'An Outline of the Geology of New Zealand', *Journ. Geol.*, Vol. 30, 1922, pp. 1–17.

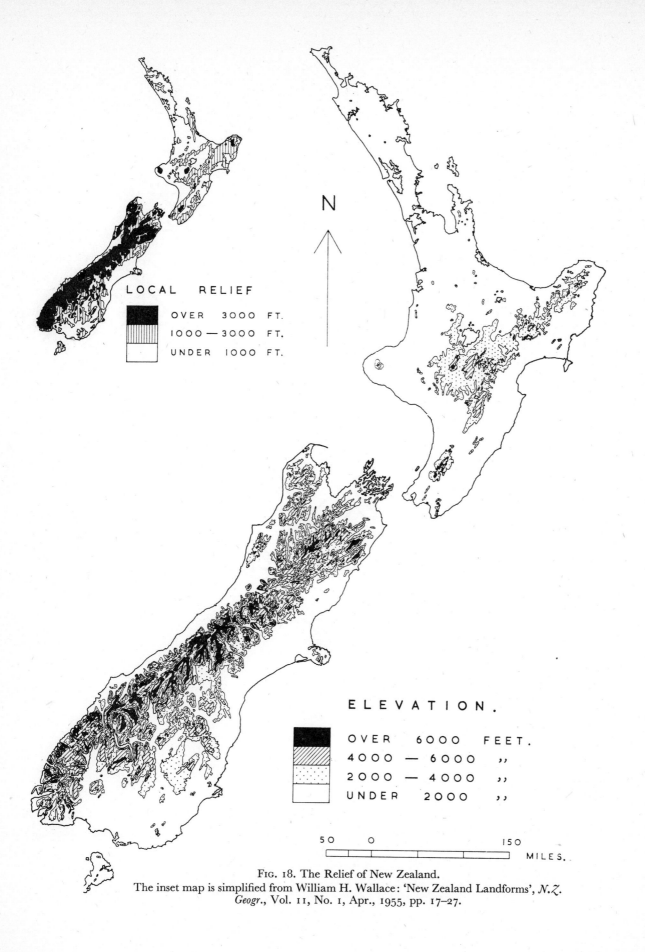

LOCAL RELIEF

OVER 3000 FT.
1000 — 3000 FT.
UNDER 1000 FT.

N

ELEVATION.

OVER 6000 FEET.
4000 — 6000 ,,
2000 — 4000 ,,
UNDER 2000 ,,

50   0   150
└──┴──┴──┴──┴──┘ MILES.

Fig. 18. The Relief of New Zealand.
The inset map is simplified from William H. Wallace: 'New Zealand Landforms', *N.Z.*
Geogr., Vol. 11, No. 1, Apr., 1955, pp. 17–27.

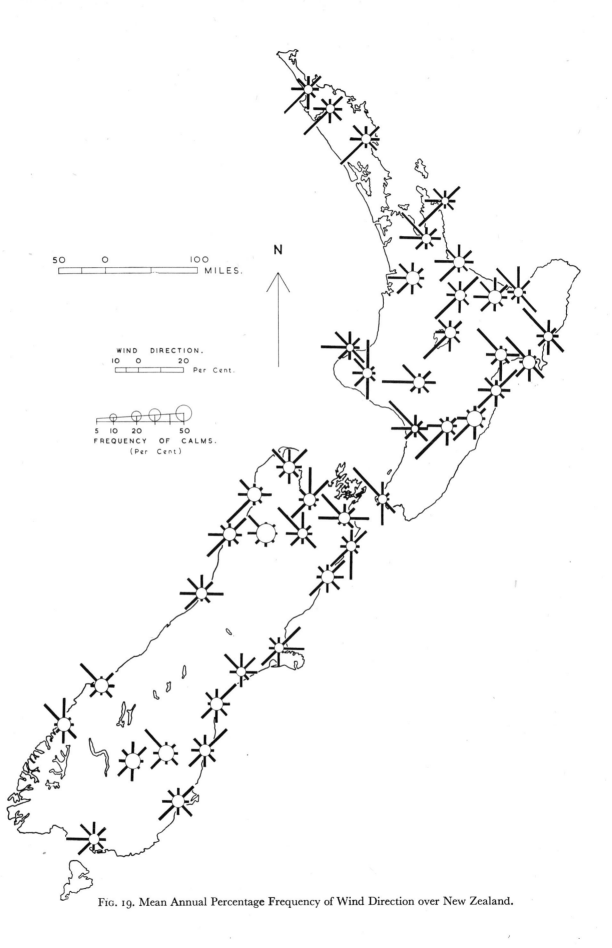

FIG. 19. Mean Annual Percentage Frequency of Wind Direction over New Zealand.

a depression from the Tasman Sea brings rain to the west and not to the east, but when a depression lies off the east of the country the contrast is in a reverse direction.

Southerly or southwesterly conditions follow the passage of a cold front. As a rule such fronts are elongated parallel to the country's minor axis, but travel across the area along the line of the major structural axis. The actual direction of the winds that follow them depends on the orientation of the isobars behind.[2] When these are in the vicinity of 220°, which is the general bearing of the South Island, the effect of the following wind is more or less similar on both sides of the land. Rain and low temperatures occur in both the east and the west, and, provided no frontal deformation occurs, and it passes right across New Zealand, any rain-shadow effects are local ones. If the isobars are appreciably west of 220° more truly west winds occur, and consequently conditions are likely to be wetter on the western side of the country than on the east. The opposite occurs, however, if the isobars are oriented appreciably east of 220°.

Two other effects of structure in association with the main mountain ranges remain to be noticed: their effect on the passage of fronts, and their effect on the direction and force of the wind. For the former the orientation of the Southern Alps is of chief significance, although that of the east coast ranges of the North Island is also of some importance. The Southern Alps frequently deform a front as it passes across them. This is especially true of cold fronts. The warm front is not so influenced, partly because it is less extensive than the cold front, and partly because it moves in from the northwest and is thus uniformly delayed in its passage by the mountains. Cold fronts, on the other hand, approach from the southwest. Their movement, therefore, is along the line of the mountains, and while the western part of the front moves freely, that portion which encounters the ranges is held back a little. This causes differences in the time of its arrival on either side of the mountains (*Figs. 2a* and *2b*), which may also mean the development of a wave-depression east of New Zealand.

Winds below 4,000 ft. of elevation are strongly affected by the direction of the mountain ranges in both islands (*Fig. 19*).[3] There is a concentration of air through Cook Strait and around the southern end of the South Island, so that both these areas experience an abnormally large number of gales.[4] Moreover, a southwest wind along western South Island, for example, may curve through Cook Strait as a northwest wind, and then appear as a northeasterly on the coast of Marlborough as far south as Kaikoura. From Jackson's Bay southwards, on the other hand, there is a tendency for winds to move south around Puysegur Point, where they join with the general westerly and southwesterly air movements common to Southland and south Otago. Farther north, however, they may appear as southerly or even southeasterly winds, in conformity with the general lie of the mountains in these parts.

In summing up the effects of structure and the mountain ranges, we can say that their chief one is to control the kind of exposure which different parts of New Zealand experience. This is as much the consequence of the barrier-like nature of 8,000-ft. ranges as of the direction in which they lie. This brings us to the second aspect of the climatic effects of New Zealand's physical character: the nature and importance of elevation and relief.

The uplifting forces during the late Tertiary (Kaikoura) orogeny were powerful ones. They elevated the submarine depositions of earlier times to great heights, and subsequent erosion has carved up the land into very rugged territory, spreading sediments over the margins of the mountains so as to create the narrow, peripheral plains of the present day. This in itself would be enough

[2]I. E. M. Watts: 'Forecasting New Zealand Weather', op. cit.

[3]Above 4,000 ft. the air flow is more like that of the free atmosphere. See E. Kidson: 'The Elements of New Zealand's Climate', op. cit.

[4]E. Kidson: 'The Elements of New Zealand's Climate', op. cit. I. E. M. Watts: 'The Relation of New Zealand Weather . . .', op. cit. N. G. Robertson: 'Notes on Weather Factors affecting Electric Power Transmission in New Zealand', *Trans. Elect. Supply Author. Engin. Inst.*, Vol. 22, 1952, pp. 97–102.

to promote a very irregular surface outline. It has been added to by volcanic activity which occurred in both islands, but which was more marked in the North Island than in the South Island. Three-quarters of the country is more than 1,000 ft. above the sea, and about an eighth is above 3,000 ft. of elevation (*Fig.* 18). Relief forms are irregular, and skylines are uneven. Mountain ranges, pierced by narrow, gorge-like valleys, slope steeply down to level plains. The contrast between rugged land-scapes and comparatively flat land is very sharp. Within the space of a mile one can pass from a flat-floored, open valley or coastal plain, of no appreciable relief, into a world of steep, 40 per cent slopes, which lead to towering mountain masses. This type of contrast is responsible for very high figures of relative relief. They exceed 1,000 ft. over about a fifth of the North Island, and three-quarters of the South Island, and in the main ranges of the latter area they rise to 3,000 ft. and more (inset to *Fig.* 18).

Although there is such relief intensity, however, the overall pattern of mountain and plain is comparatively simple. The loftiest ranges are in the South Island. Here the Southern Alps, lying close to the western seaboard, rise in their central parts to elevations commonly in excess of 9,000 ft., with Mount Cook (12,349 ft.), the Maori's 'Aorangi', towering above them all. To north and south, heights are somewhat less, but only in the extreme north, in the Sounds–Nelson area, do mean ele-vations fall below 6,000 ft. These ranges trend southwest to northeast, following the main struc-tural direction of the land. Several ridges, high and steepsided, splay out like fingers towards the southeast in Otago province, and create the enclosed basins which constitute the South Island's semi-arid interior. Around these highlands lie coastal plains, narrow in extent and flat in general appearance. The major ranges of the North Island are found on the east. They are neither so high nor so rugged as the Southern Alps, and their elevation is commonly below 5,000 ft. above sea-level. They are flanked and penetrated on the east by local flat plains; westwards they are bounded by the extensive volcanic plateau, over 1,000 ft. high, which connects with the seaward-sloping, steeply dissected peneplain of inland Taranaki. North of these central highlands is rolling country, generally under 1,000 ft. above sea level, which stretches northwest to occupy the land area which makes up Auckland province.

The maps of rainfall and climatic types given in Chapter 1 (*Figs.* 7 and 12), sum up very well the effect of New Zealand's physiography upon its climate, and the cross-sections in *Fig.* 20 illus-trate it further. The major temperature differences through the country, for example, are largely created by differences in elevation. To some extent latitude is important, but the greatest contrasts result from elevation. This works both directly and indirectly: directly by the normal falling-off in temperature with an increase in altitude, and indirectly through its effect on precipitation which, being heavy, maintains snow and ice in the main mountain ranges and so lowers temperatures still further. In like manner, the presence in close proximity of high mountains and neighbouring plain, differentially exposed to prevailing wind and weather influences, is responsible for the precipitation contrasts over very short distances. Finally, the general contrast between the climatic patterns of the North and South Islands closely follows the contrasts in their physical character.

SECTION FROM ALBATROSS PT. TO MID-HAWKE'S BAY.

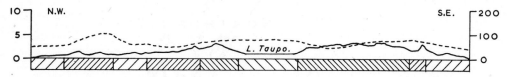

SECTION FROM CAPE EGMONT TO MID-HAWKE'S BAY.

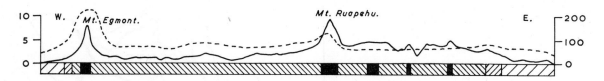

SECTION FROM HOKITIKA TO L.ELLESMERE.

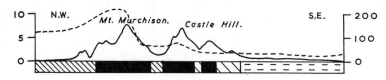

SECTION ACROSS SOUTH ISLAND THROUGH C.OTAGO.

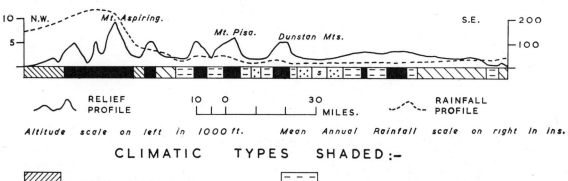

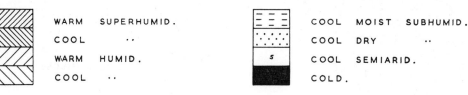

Altitude scale on left in 1000 ft. Mean Annual Rainfall scale on right in ins.

CLIMATIC TYPES SHADED:—

WARM SUPERHUMID.	COOL MOIST SUBHUMID.
COOL ‚‚	COOL DRY ‚‚
WARM HUMID.	COOL SEMIARID.
COOL ‚‚	COLD.

FIG. 20. Cross-sections illustrating the relationship between relief and climate in New Zealand.

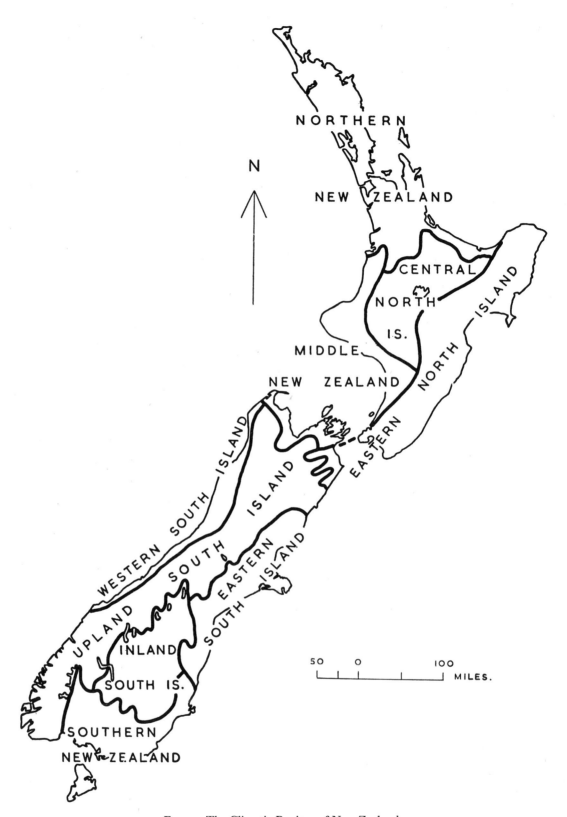

FIG. 21. The Climatic Regions of New Zealand.

4

CLIMATIC REGIONS

THE previous three chapters have presented a general description of the character and causes of New Zealand's climate, and have stressed that contrasts arise from the way in which controlling influences act differently in different parts of the country. It is now necessary to examine these contrasts in somewhat greater detail by discussing the land's climate region by region.

The division of an area into 'regions' is standard geographical procedure. It is made in order that the interrelationships of phenomena existing together over the earth's surface may be studied more easily. There is a vast literature on how such a division should be made, which need not concern us here. Since there is a good deal of controversy on the subject, however, it is desirable to state that the view of regional division taken in this volume is that it is simply a convenient way of grouping the subject matter of a particular study. As Unstead has written:[1]

> We may reasonably divide the earth's surface in whatever way is most useful at a given stage of our work.

The delimitation of regions, therefore, whether they are climatic, physiographic, economic, or social, is largely a matter of subjective judgement, made in conformity with the purpose behind the division.

In the present instance we are trying to understand how the climate of New Zealand differs in character and geographic significance from place to place. A division into 'climatic regions' for this purpose is best made by considering, in particular, two aspects of the country's climate: the way its elements vary over the land, and the degree to which they express the major controlling factors. So far as is possible the delimitation of the regions has been made statistically. The final decision on where to draw the regional boundaries, however, has been taken after judging not only the statistical evidence, but also that derived from field observations and the experience of those who live and work in different places in the country.

After reflections of this nature, and having regard to the amount of detail possible in a volume of this kind, it has been decided to divide New Zealand into the nine climatic regions which are shown in *Fig.* 21. Each one differs from every other because of the peculiar combination of climatic features it contains. Each of them, on the other hand, possesses characteristics found in one or more of the others. This may be illustrated by assigning letters to certain climatic characteristics and then using them to express some of the qualities of each region as follows:

W   'Westerly' influences are the dominant ones, being expressed particularly in plentiful and reliable rainfall, and relatively small mean annual ranges of temperature.

E   'Easterly' influences are the dominant ones, being expressed particularly in a high variability of rainfall, and relatively large mean annual ranges of temperature.

T   Subtropical influences are particularly marked in the area from time to time.

A   Antarctic influences are particularly marked in the area from time to time.

X   Although occasionally affected by 'external' subtropical and/or antarctic influences, neither are predominant.

[1] J. F. Unstead: 'A System of Regional Geography', *Geography*, Vol. 18, 1933, pp. 175–87.

I   Inland situation is reflected in relatively large diurnal ranges of temperature, and a tendency for a rainfall maximum in summer.

M   Effects of elevation within the region are marked, and expressed especially in cold winters and high rainfall totals.

M*   Effects of high mountains bounding the region are apparent in excessive precipitation.

D   A region characterized by considerable diversity of climatic types.

H   A generally homogeneous climatic unit.

K   A region with moderate diversity of climatic types, but not forming an intricate pattern as expressed by the letter D.

The foregoing list of characteristics is by no means exhaustive, but it will serve to exemplify the point being made. By using it we may assign climatic qualities to the various regions of the country as follows:

Middle New Zealand	WXK	Eastern South Island	EAH
Western South Island	WXM*H	Central North Island	WXIMK
Northern New Zealand	WTH	Inland South Island	AID
Southern New Zealand	WAH	Upland South Island	WAMD
Eastern North Island	ETD		

From these groupings it can be seen that westerly influences, for example, are dominant in every region of the North Island, except Eastern North Island, and that they are also dominant in Southern New Zealand and Upland South Island. They provide these areas with a certain degree of similarity. Three of these six regions, Middle New Zealand, Western South Island, and Central North Island, are similar to each other, but differ from the other three, in lacking marked characteristics derived from 'external' sources. Middle New Zealand and Central North Island are also like each other in having a moderate diversity of climatic types, whereas Western South Island, by contrast, is a homogeneous climatic unit. The climate of Central North Island, nevertheless, has certain features not found in Middle New Zealand: those derived from its upland position and its inland situation are instances. This area thus becomes climatically unique because of the combination of characteristics which it possesses. As a further example of the same kind of individuality, we may compare Eastern North Island and Eastern South Island. These are similar in that easterly influences are dominant, but whereas the former is open to subtropical effects and possesses a diversity of climatic type, the latter has external relationships with the antarctic and is a homogeneous climatic unit. Neither of these two areas is unique in any of its three major climatic qualities, but each one is without parallel in the combination it displays.

Each region of New Zealand, therefore, derives its climatic personality from the interrelationship of several phenomena.[2] It will be the aim of the next nine chapters to illustrate this, and in doing so, to demonstrate not only that each region differs from the other climatically, but also that the significance of climate varies in different places according to the other features of the geographical landscape. Without dealing with the latter aspect no geographical account would be complete.

[2]If we denote 'climatic personality' by the letter P, and use the letters as given in the text to indicate the phenomena creating it, the relationship may be expressed by a formula of the following nature: $P = f(W, X, K \ldots)$

The idea of expressing 'climatic personality' in this way was obtained from reading Jenny's study of the factors of soil formation, in which he uses the same method to illustrate the interrelation of the soil forming factors in the creation of the character of individual soil types. See H. Jenny: 'The Factors of Soil Formation', New York, 1941.

A similar method has been adopted in an elementary treatment of the nature of regional geography by Cumberland. See K. B. Cumberland: 'Geographic Regions of New Zealand; the nature of regional geography', *N.Z. Post-Primary School Bulln.*, Vol. 4, No. 8, 1950.

5

MIDDLE NEW ZEALAND

IT is better to begin the analysis of the climatic regions of New Zealand by studying Middle New Zealand, rather than by following the more conventional way of working systematically through the country from north to south. This is because the area's climatic qualities epitomize, to a remarkable degree, those of the country as a whole. Here are sunny, windy conditions, and a plentiful rainfall evenly distributed through the year. Moderate as the mean temperatures undoubtedly are, they represent averages derived from fairly large diurnal and extreme ranges. Finally, the exposure of the region to westerly influences, and its susceptibility to the whole gamut of the weather contrasts associated with the passage of migratory anticyclones, combine with the foregoing factors to make it in effect a miniature of the whole country's climate. In this respect, Middle New Zealand is unique, since no other region conforms so closely to the average conditions associated with New Zealand as a whole.

Mean temperatures in Middle New Zealand are moderate. Their annual value is between 50°F and 55°F nearly everywhere, while in winter they fall below 45°F over only 15 per cent of the territory, and in summer lie within a few degrees of 60°F in all but the most elevated districts. This means that the region is one of mild winters and warm summers, and that the mean annual range of temperature is relatively small. It is below 20F° throughout the area, and at New Plymouth is as low as 13.6F°. Snow rarely occurs, but frost is more common, except on the west coast where there are on the average only two or three screen frosts a year and less than twenty ground frosts.[1] Elsewhere, however, the latter can be expected about fifty times a year, although their frequency varies very much from place to place. The mean annual number of ground frosts at Wanganui, for example, is 13, whereas at Tangimoana, a few miles along the coast, it is 57, at Appleby, near Nelson, it is 76, and at Nelson itself it is 61.

Table 8
MEAN DIURNAL RANGES OF TEMPERATURE IN MIDDLE NEW ZEALAND
(F°)

Station	Winter	Spring	Summer	Autumn	Year
New Plymouth	12.2	12.4	13.8	13.4	12.9
Palmerston North	14.2	14.9	16.3	15.6	15.3
Kapiti Island	10.4	11.8	13.6	11.7	11.9
Nelson	17.1	16.8	16.9	16.9	16.9

Like the rest of the country, the region displays comparatively large mean diurnal ranges of temperature. At most stations their annual average is close to 15F°, but there are noteworthy differences between one part of the area and another (*Table* 8). In the vicinity of Nelson, and in the Manawatu (near Palmerston North), for example, they are greater than those where westerly exposure accentuates maritime influences, as at New Plymouth and Kapiti Island. Another of their characteristics is that they tend to be greatest in summer and least in winter. Again, this is not universal

---

[1] E. Kidson: 'The Frequency of Frost, Snow, and Hail in New Zealand', *N.Z. Journ. Sci. and Tech.*, Vol. 14, 1932, pp. 42–53. It is desirable to mention here that Mount Egmont is an exception to these statements. This ancient, volcanic cone is over 8,000 ft. high, so that it achieves a permanent snowline and a small unit of 'frost climate' within Middle New Zealand.

through the region. At Nelson, for example, there is virtually no difference between the seasons in respect of the mean diurnal ranges of temperature.

When extreme temperature ranges are examined they are found to exhibit a similar kind of contrast to that displayed by mean diurnal ranges. They are large enough everywhere, however, to show that these parts are no exception to the general rule that New Zealand is occasionally subject to very cold or very hot weather conditions. In fact it is only on Kapiti Island that temperatures normally stay above freezing point all the year round, while everywhere below 1,000 ft. of elevation there is generally a maximum of 80°F or more each twelvemonth. The frequency of low temperatures is greater than that of high ones, however. The latter usually occur no more than two or three times a year, whereas freezing point is as a rule crossed on more than a dozen occasions annually. Low temperatures, moreover, can be caused by an out-of-season cold snap: on 30th September, 1949, for example, the screen temperature fell to 31.9°F at New Plymouth, and to 31.3°F at Nelson; in 1927 a temperature below freezing point was recorded at Tangimoana three weeks before Christmas.

This brief account indicates that temperatures in Middle New Zealand combine the equable qualities common to mid-latitude oceanic climates generally, with the more extreme conditions peculiar to New Zealand. The same kind of combination is observable in the region's precipitation characteristics. Its rainfall totals, and their seasonal distribution, unite it with comparable climates elsewhere, and its annual variability, its relatively small number of rainy days, and its high intensity of rainfall over short periods link it with its particular milieu.

The mean annual rainfall exceeds 30 inches everywhere, and in four-fifths of the area it is more than 40 inches. The lower values are experienced on the lowlands of Nelson and the Manawatu. The latter area, indeed, often displays moisture conditions commensurate with the recognizably sub-humid sectors of the North Island.[2] Where mountain ranges are directly exposed to westerly influences, on the other hand, the mean annual total rises to over 100 inches. This happens on Mount Egmont, on the ranges inland from Kawhia, and on the mountains where Middle New Zealand joins Western and Upland South Island; altogether these occupy but 5 per cent of the land area.

As a general rule, precipitation is evenly spread through the year. There is a maximum in winter, and a minimum in summer or autumn. Neither of these is pronounced, however, except near Cape Egmont, where rather more than 30 per cent of the annual total occurs in the three winter months.[3] Its mean annual and monthly variability, moreover, is commensurate with that for New Zealand generally. The former value lies between 12 per cent and 14 per cent in most places, and the latter is in the neighbourhood of 40 per cent each month, although it tends to be above this in summer months and below it in those of winter and early spring (*Fig.* 22).[4] Within the region, however, there are some local contrasts. Variability is greatest near Nelson which, being an area of northeasterly exposure, is liable to experience occasional downpours from cyclones of tropical origin, especially in late summer and early autumn. By contrast, the Manawatu, across the water from Nelson, experiences the lowest mean annual and monthly variability in the region, since this area derives the greater part of its relatively low rainfall totals from westerly winds.

The incidence of rainfall in the area is also typical of New Zealand. There are, on the average, between 125 and 175 rainy days a year at most stations, and much of the precipitation is derived from cold fronts. The region is, however, occasionally subject to the prolonged, heavy, and finely

[2]B. J. Garnier: 'The Climates of New Zealand . . .', op. cit.

[3]The principal maximum commonly occurs in May or June, and there is a secondary one in October, when westerly winds are strongest and most persistent. This secondary maximum is particularly apparent in the Manawatu, where spring rains total a higher percentage of the annual fall than do those of Taranaki. E. Kidson: 'The Annual Variation of Rainfall in New Zealand', *N.Z. Journ. Sci. and Tech.*, Vol. 12, 1931, pp. 268–71; *idem*: 'Climatic Notes: New Zealand districts', *N.Z. Meteor. Off. Notes*, No. 17, 1937.

[4]C. J. Seelye: 'The Variation of Annual Rainfall . . .', op. cit.; *idem*: 'Variations of Monthly Rainfall . . .', op. cit.

divided rains associated with the passage of warm fronts.[5] It lies in the path of wave-depressions whose warm and cold fronts affect it, and it is particularly liable in its western parts to receive the deluges which occur when warm, moist, uprising northwesterly air associated with a front of the former nature comes into contact with the New Zealand mountain system. These soaking rains are regionally important and one of the climate's more individual aspects.

Sunshine, like rainfall, is plentiful in Middle New Zealand. The apparent paradox of this statement is resolved partly because of the points just mentioned, and partly because of the windiness of the area, which keeps the atmosphere in constant motion and prevents a cloud layer from maintaining overcast conditions for very long. In general terms, we can say that sunshine here is, both annually and seasonally, either close to or somewhat above the average for the whole country. Thus, rather more than 2,000 hours of bright sunshine a year are normally experienced, which is about 47 per cent of the possible annual total. Most is received in summer and least in winter:

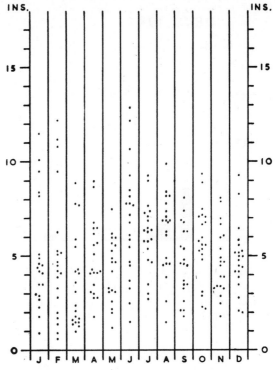

FIG. 22. Rainfall dispersion diagram for New Plymouth, 1935–54.

the region's average for the former season is about 650 hours, which is over 50 per cent of the possible sunshine for the time of year, and the average for the latter season is some 200 hours less than that for summer, which represents, nevertheless, 45 per cent of the possible total for the period owing to the shorter days. A good deal of local contrast is found. Nelson is very sunny, the Manawatu lowlands are relatively cloudy, and western Taranaki has more sunshine than might be expected from its rainfall totals (*Table* 9).

Table 9

MEAN HOURS OF BRIGHT SUNSHINE IN MIDDLE NEW ZEALAND

(a) Mean hours received.
(b) Percentage of the possible total for the season.

Station	Winter		Spring		Summer		Autumn		Year	
	(a)	(b)	(a)	(b)	(a)	(b)	(a)	(b)	(a)	(b)
New Plymouth	431	47	549	47	695	53	536	52	2,211	50
Palmerston North	339	37	479	38	593	45	428	42	1,839	41
Nelson	503	56	658	54	744	57	585	57	2,490	56

Finally among its climatic elements, let us consider the question of wind in Middle New Zealand. Like the rest of the country, it is windy here, and the winds, gusty in character, are orographically controlled in their direction. At Stratford, for example, the predominance of winds from north and south is related to the existence of Mount Egmont west of the town and also to the way it lies open to the southerlies passing through Cook Strait. Prevalent winds at Nelson are from three directions: from the north, in view of the open bay in that direction, and from the southwest and northeast respectively along the line of the valleys and mountain ranges near the town. The predominance of northwest and west winds at Ohakea and of northwest winds through Cook Strait at Wellington,

[5]K. B. Cumberland: 'Soil Erosion in New Zealand . . .', op. cit.

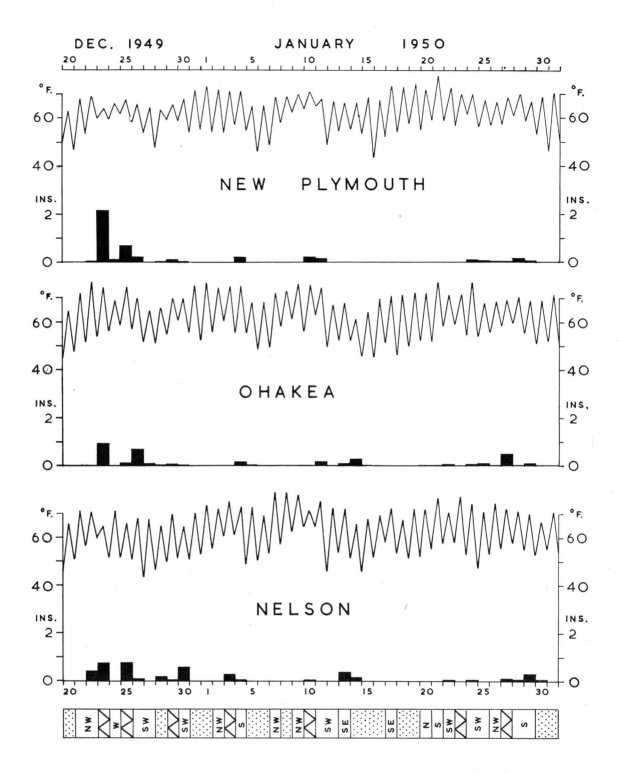

Fig. 23. Daily Temperature and Precipitation during part of the summer of 1949–50 at New Plymouth, Ohakea, and Nelson.

illustrates further how orographical control affects local winds, whose momentum and general direction have been derived from conditions in the free atmosphere.

A rather high proportion of winds are strong ones. At most stations more than 20 per cent are over Force 5 on the Beaufort scale. Moreover, a large number of gales, generally more than twenty-five each year, blow through Cook Strait, and when these are from the south they are widely felt through Middle New Zealand. Strong winds from northwest and west are common also, but the strongest appear to come from a southerly quarter. Nearly everywhere gusts of 80 miles an hour or more have been recorded at low levels, and the majority of these are from the latter direction (*Table* 10).[6]

Table 10

Highest Gusts of Wind at Different Places in Middle New Zealand
(recorded by Dines Pressure Tube Anemometer and corrected to January 1951)

Station	Period	Highest Gust m.p.h.	Direction degrees from nth.	Date
New Plymouth	1939–51	89	170	18 Aug. 1947
Ohakea	1939–51	94	200	15 Feb. 1947
Milsom	1940–51	69 (twice)	160	11 Mar. 1942
		..	170	15 Apr. 1947
Shannon	1937–51	84	130	26 Aug. 1942
Levin	1942–43	76	300	24 Sept. 1942
Paraparaumu	1937–39; 1946–51	88	180	15 Feb. 1947
Kelburn	1928–51	87	315	5th Oct. 1938
Nelson	1940–51	94	60	22 Feb. 1944

We have already seen that New Zealand's climatic character is derived fundamentally from the passage of migratory anticyclones and the nature of the atmosphere in the intervening low-pressure troughs. Middle New Zealand exemplifies this remarkably well. It is located in the path of the majority of wave-depressions which pass over the land, but is also regularly influenced in turn by conditions predominantly connected with the depressions of the far south on the one hand, and the anticyclonic systems or tropical disturbances of the north on the other. Certain typical weather sequences are illustrated in *Figs.* 23 and 24.[7] They illustrate day to day changes of temperature and rainfall of a kind so characteristic of New Zealand that it is worth examining them in some detail.

The first example (*Fig.* 23) is from the summer of 1949–50. The first eight days of the period shown were dominated by two deep depressions in the south. Cold fronts extended well to the north and, prior to the arrival of the first of them, there was a well-marked northwesterly air stream across Middle New Zealand, during which temperatures reached 69°F at New Plymouth and 76°F at Ohakea. The passage of the first front was accompanied by heavy rain and a fall in temperature. Afterwards, temperatures rose a little, but then declined again on Christmas Day which, as another cold front passed over, was wet that year but not unduly cold. After this there was a period of about a fortnight during which short spells of anticyclonic weather were separated from each other by the disturbed conditions associated with the passage of cold fronts. The first of these fronts was related to a small depression, which crossed quickly over the South Island three days before New Year's Eve, but the remainder were attached to depressions moving eastwards well to the south of the country. Each front brought some rain and a fall in temperature, but otherwise the weather was fine and warm.

[6]Nelson provides an exception to these general statements: it is somewhat sheltered here, so that the lowlands experience few strong winds. On the average less than 20 per cent are above Force 5 on the Beaufort scale, and the highest gust recorded has come from the northeast.

[7]The reader is referred to Appendix B for a general description of these, and of the other similar diagrams which are used in this book.

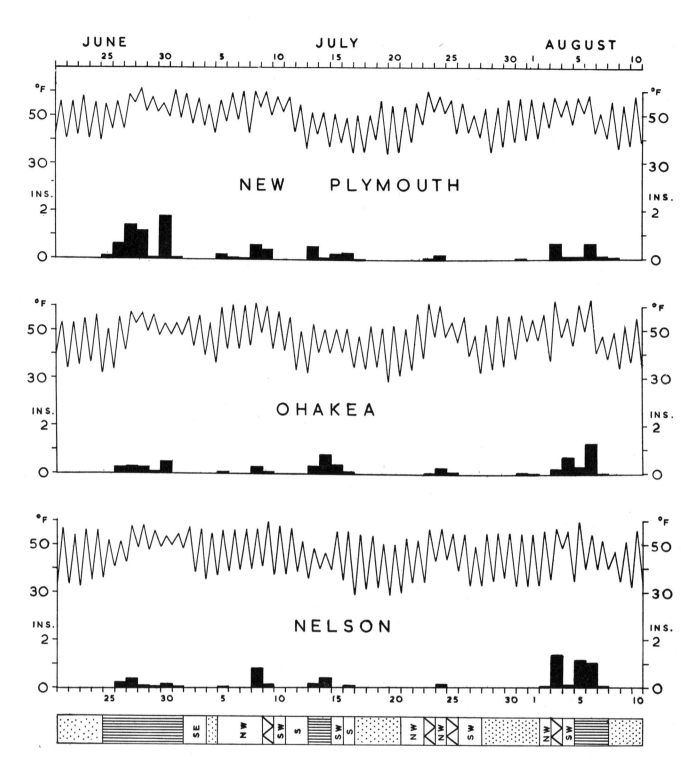

FIG. 24. Daily Temperature and Precipitation during part of the winter of 1950 at New Plymouth, Ohakea, and Nelson.

This pattern lasted until 11 January, after which there came a change. Over the Tasman Sea there lay a ridge of high pressure, elongated north and south, on the eastern side of which southerly winds were blowing. Western Taranaki, on the eastern edge of the ridge, was rainless, but the eastern and southern parts of Middle New Zealand came within the orbit of a cold front which crossed the South Island, and there was rain, first at Nelson and later at Ohakea. Eventually the Tasman ridge of high pressure moved on to New Zealand, bringing with it fine weather which culminated, on 21 January, in the highest day temperatures of the month. But this preceded an unsettled interval which lasted almost to the end of January. First came a depression, moving slowly along the east coast of the country from the north; this was followed by a high-pressure ridge, which settled over the Tasman Sea and north of New Zealand, with westerly and southwesterly winds along its southern side, while depressions travelled eastwards some miles south of the country. One cold front crossed Middle New Zealand; temperatures were low for the time of year, and rain fell in small quantities, varying in total from locality to locality. Altogether this was a typical sequence of 'westerly weather'. Before the month ended, however, there was a change and the last two days again displayed the blue skies, the high diurnal ranges, and the clear air of anticyclonic conditions.

During the period of this analysis, almost the full range of possible weather phenomena has been illustrated. It reveals the effects of the movement of anticyclones, followed by a northwesterly build-up and then by the passage of cold fronts; it shows how the region is affected in turn by the passage of depressions well to the south, and by influences mainly northern in origin; finally, it illustrates occasions when depressions east of the country have made their influence felt here. Altogether a total of seven cold fronts passed over in the forty-three days; the shortest interval between any two was 60 hours, and the longest ten days. Practically all of these fronts were related to depressions to the south of the country, although one, on 11 January, was attached to a wave-depression which had developed east of the ranges in Canterbury, on an extensive cold front which reached from a sub-antarctic centre. Several periods of predominantly anticyclonic weather, one of 'westerly weather', and the effect of a depression which originated north of Auckland, and moved southwards east of the land, complete a picture which well fits the theoretical framework of weather cycles over New Zealand.

There is not a great deal of difference in the seasonal weather patterns of Middle New Zealand. During both summer and winter, migratory anticyclones and low-pressure troughs cross the area with more or less similar frequency and similar general effect. That this is so may be perceived by comparing *Fig.* 23 with *Fig.* 24, which refers to a fifty-one day period during the winter of 1950. The main characteristics of the weather sequences shown in this diagram are so like those of *Fig.* 23 that there is no need to describe them. Attention should, however, be drawn to the number of days when Middle New Zealand was under the influence of depressions. These are not as common in the area during the summer as they are in winter, when they are responsible for a high percentage of the rainfall in the latter season. They often have well-developed warm fronts and cold fronts, the former of which cause especially heavy rain in districts with westerly exposure. Such was the case, for example, on 27 and 29 June, 1950, as shown in the diagram.

Although one of the characteristics of Middle New Zealand is its slight climatic diversity, it is possible to make a division between the west and east which is based principally on differences in moisture conditions, as revealed by an analysis of the water balance.[8] In the west rainfall is plentiful,

---

[8]A full discussion of the water balance and its computation is given in C. W. Thornthwaite and J. R. Mather: 'The Water Balance', *Pubns. in Climat.*, Vol. VIII, No. 1, 1955. This is a mimeographed publication of the Drexel Institute of Technology's Laboratory of Climatology, Centerton, New Jersey, U.S.A. Less complete accounts will be found in C. W. Thornthwaite and J. R. Mather: 'The Water Budget and its use in irrigation', in 'Water', *U.S. Dept. of Agric. Year Bk.*, Washington, 1955; C. W. Thornthwaite and F. Kenneth Hare: 'Climatic Classification in Forestry', *Unasylva*, Vol. 9, No. 2, June, 1955; and C. W. Thornthwaite: 'An Approach toward a Rational Classification of Climate', *Geogr. Rev.*, Vol. 38, No. 1, Jan., 1948, pp. 55–94. Reference to conditions in New Zealand will be found in B. J. Garnier: 'Thornthwaite's New System of Climate Classification in its Application to New Zealand', *Trans. Proc. Roy. Soc. N.Z.*, Vol. 79, 1951, pp. 87–103; and *idem*: 'The Application of the Concept of Potential Evapotranspiration . . .', op. cit.

with no month in which precipitation is, on the average, less than potential evapotranspiration (*Fig.* 25). This is true, even allowing for the amount by which rainfall may vary from its normal for a given month. The lowlands from Patea eastwards, however, are regions of lower rainfall total than elsewhere. At Wanganui, for example, rainfall is on the average less than potential evapotranspiration in summer and early autumn. As a result, water in the soil is drawn upon by plants to such an extent that there is a slight moisture deficiency, which, in March, may become significant for agriculture. Across the water, at Nelson, also, the average rainfall from December to March is less than mean potential evapotranspiration. But here the difference is generally so small that moisture deficiencies do not normally occur.

To some extent these climatic contrasts are reflected in the region's geographic personality. On the well-watered lowlands of Taranaki, for example, are found some of the most mature agricultural landscapes in the country.[9] Little more than a century ago, it was a wilderness of forest, scrub, and waterlogged swamp, in which groups of Maoris had built their scattered villages.[10] Dieffenbach, for instance, describes the area by saying:[11]

> Everywhere vegetation appeared most vigorous, and the primeval forest was often almost impenetrable, on account of thick creepers, and the thorns, tataramoa (rubus), of which several species are found, and which tore our hands and faces severely. We scarcely ever obtained a view of the sun, and the shade of the trees produced a delightful coolness . . . We did not see many birds, and I need scarcely repeat that the most perfect silence reigned through the forest.

Today lowland Taranaki's rolling hills are covered by the green of vigorously growing perennial ryegrass and white clover pastures, and dotted with the fawn and brown backs of Jersey cattle, or with the white fleeces of lambs being fattened for the market. Paddocks, ten acres in size, are divided by hedges, which likewise line the roadsides and surround the red-roofed, white-walled, suburban-looking, wooden homestead or farmhouse, which is so typical of the lowlands of rural New Zealand. It is a well-roaded and closely settled district. Dairy factories, mainly for cheese production, are evenly scattered through it, and agricultural production is intense on farms which are small by New Zealand standards, being not above 200 acres.

This intensely green and settled land is in contrast with those areas where rainfall is less, and where there are four months of the year when precipitation is commonly less than potential evapotranspiration. Dairy farming is still dominant in these parts, but there are browner countrysides, with danthonia pastures, larger farms, and a greater proportion of sheep among the livestock units.[12] Both cattle fattening and lamb fattening are found, and in some localities grain and fruit growing are important also. For example, practically all the small amount of wheat grown in the North Island is found in the area near and west of Palmerston North, and Nelson is well known for its fruit growing, tobacco culture, and mixed farming.

The chief geographic contrasts in Middle New Zealand, however, are not between the west and the east, but between the lowlands and the adjoining highlands. In the latter areas, sheep rearing on large estates is practised. This is particularly true of the steeply-dissected, soft Tertiary mudstones of inland Taranaki and Wanganui. Here, store sheep are maintained on rough pasture, to be used for wool and as a reservoir for keeping up the supply of lambs for fattening on the neighbouring lowland grasses. For these purposes, the land was cleared rapidly of its virgin forest cover. Axe and fire achieved their quick destruction, and almost before the ashes had cooled, English grasses had been

[9]K. B. Cumberland: 'The Agricultural Regions of New Zealand', *Geogr. Journ.*, Vol. 112, 1948, pp. 43–63.

[10]K. B. Cumberland: 'A Century's Change: natural to cultural vegetation in New Zealand', *Geogr. Rev.*, Vol. 31, 1941, pp. 529–54; *idem:* 'Aotearoa Maori: New Zealand about 1780', ibid., Vol. 39, 1949, pp. 401–24.

[11]Ernest Dieffenbach: op. cit.

[12]E. A. Madden: 'The Grasslands of the North Island of New Zealand', *N.Z. Dept. Sci. Ind. Res. Bulln.*, No. 79, 1940; K. B. Cumberland: 'The Agricultural Regions of New Zealand', op. cit.

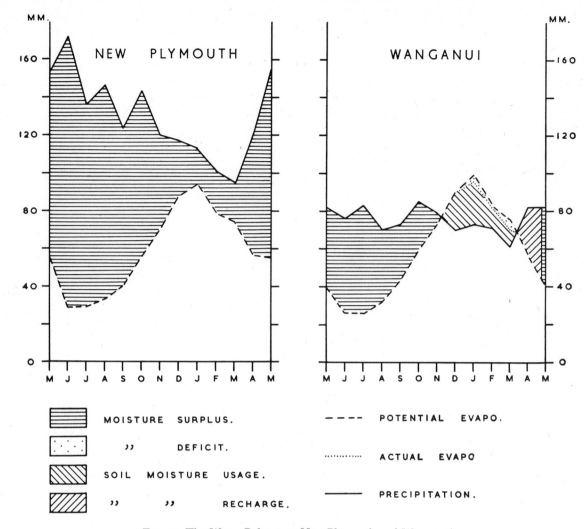

FIG. 25. The Water Balance at New Plymouth and Wanganui.

sown and the soil was being trampled by the feet of Romney ewes.[13] Nature reacted violently to the onslaught. Under the impact of heavy rains, whole hillsides slipped away; under the influence of plentiful moisture, bright sunshine, and moderate temperatures, a vigorous 'second growth' of shrubs, young trees, and weeds asserted itself. Thus farmers here, instead of achieving the rich grazing lands they sought, preserve their rough pastures only by waging a continual battle against soil erosion, and the attacks of blackberry, thistle, ragwort, and gorse, in addition to the quickly-growing young, native 'bush'. In sum, therefore, the landscapes of the highlands of Middle New Zealand generally, and of inland Wanganui and Taranaki in particular, are disorderly ones. They contrast strongly with the well-ordered adjacent lowlands. Yet there is no substantial climatic difference between the two areas. Very much the same amount of sunshine and rainfall, and the same moderate temperatures are experienced in both western and inland Taranaki, for example. Yet whereas in the former area, in association with easy slopes and local agricultural practices, they have promoted a landscape of rich pastures, in the latter area, in association with a different set of factors, they have achieved a wilderness of tortured slopes and rank, unruly vegetation.

[13]K. B. Cumberland: 'Contrasting Regional Morphology of Soil Erosion in New Zealand', *Geogr. Rev.*, Vol. 34, 1944, pp. 77–95; *idem*: 'Soil Erosion in New Zealand . . .', op. cit.

6

WESTERN SOUTH ISLAND

WESTERN South Island extends from Kahurangi Point to Jackson's Bay. Physically it consists mainly of a hummocky, gravel-strewn plain, between the Tasman Sea on the west and the Southern Alps on the east. As a climatic unit, it is widely regarded as a very wet place: 'rainy Westland', it is commonly called. Undoubtedly precipitation is heavy. Daily falls of two or three inches are common, and the mean annual total is over 100 inches nearly everywhere. Nevertheless, it is not so very much wetter than several other parts of the country, and this characteristic should not be allowed to overshadow three other noteworthy aspects of the climate: the low temperature ranges, the mild winters and cool summers, and the comparatively large number of hours of bright sunshine. To begin with, however, let us consider its better-known feature: its wetness.

The only part of Western South Island where the average annual rainfall is less than 100 inches is north of Westport. Thus, at Karamea it totals 73 inches and at Westport 76, in contrast to mean annual totals of 115 inches at Hokitika, 134 at Ross, and 187 at Jackson's Bay. These statistical differences are insigificant climatically, and we can safely describe Western South Island as superhumid everywhere. Moreover, it is annually superhumid. The mean variability from year to year is under 12 per cent of the annual total, which in such large quantities is unimportant, and the mean variability in any month is likewise insignificant.[1] On the whole precipitation is evenly spread through the year, but there are some differences in the seasonal distribution between different parts. North of Greymouth, for instance, the maximum occurs in spring and the minimum in late summer and early autumn. South of the town, however, there is a minimum in winter, which becomes pronounced south of Ross, where less than 20 per cent of the mean annual total is found at this time of year. Moreover, the proportion of the mean annual total arriving in summer increases the farther south we go, until at Jackson's Bay it is slightly in excess of that which comes in spring (*Table* 11).

Table 11

PERCENTAGE SEASONAL DISTRIBUTION OF RAINFALL IN WESTERN SOUTH ISLAND

Station	Winter	Spring	Summer	Autumn	Annual Total (in.)
Karamea	24.4	27.5	24.0	24.1	73.4
Westport	26.0	26.4	23.6	24.0	76.4
Hokitika	23.8	26.9	24.7	24.6	115.4
Jackson's Bay	18.6	27.4	27.7	26.3	186.7

The general rainfall characteristics of Western South Island reflect the interplay of several factors, of which the dominant ones are, firstly, the interrelationship of wind systems and the relief bounding the area, and, secondly, the annual migration of the pressure belts. The first explains the heavy total precipitation and its general reliability, and the second the details of its seasonal distribution.

The high annual rainfall totals here are caused by the frequent occasions on which air, already unstable through frontal activity, is lifted further in the face of high, steep-sided mountain ranges. Petterssen's text-book diagrams can, indeed, be applied without modification to the explanation of rainfall over Western South Island.[2] Furthermore, any low-pressure trough, whatever its detailed

---

[1]C. J. Seelye: 'The Variation of Annual Rainfall . . .', op. cit.; *idem*: 'Variations of Monthly Rainfall . . .', op. cit.
[2]S. Petterssen: 'Weather Analysis and Forecasting', New York, 1940.

structure or the path of its main centre, tends to give rain in this region.[3] Thus, the warm, moist, uprising northwesterly air, which streams across the Tasman Sea in the wake of a retreating anticyclone, or the cold, unstable, atmosphere derived from polar, maritime sources, which precedes the arrival of a high-pressure system, are both likely to produce precipitation as they meet the 8,000-ft. barrier of the Southern Alps. Moreover, just as westerly exposure explains the quantity of precipitation received, so does it explain its reliability. Everywhere in New Zealand, areas which derive their rainfall from the west tend to a greater reliability than those of easterly exposure. No region in all New Zealand depends more than this one on winds of western origin for its rainfall. Easterlies, saturating the mixed farmlands of Canterbury and north Otago, bring fine, sunny weather to the west coast; northeasterlies, associated with an extra-tropical cyclone, may bring a deluge to parts of the northern South Island, but they leave Western South Island untouched by rain. Only winds from a westerly quarter are effective rain-makers here, and they are the most reliable of New Zealand's diverse wind sources.

Western South Island is long enough in a north to south direction for it to be affected by the seasonal migration of the pressure belts. This is responsible for the detailed differences in the seasonal distribution of rainfall, which we can think of in three groups for explanatory purposes: firstly, there is the spring maximum, which is particularly apparent from Ross northwards; secondly, there is the winter minimum from Greymouth southwards; and thirdly, there is the tendency towards a summer maximum in the south, and the occurrence of a minimum in late summer and early autumn in the north.

The first of these is explained by the increasing activity of westerly winds during spring. Kidson has shown that the north to south pressure gradient is steepest when the circulation system is moving southwards, and reaches its maximum in October.[4] Consequently, spring is the season of maximum windiness at low levels, and northwesterlies in particular are more common at this time. These are felt all along the coast and are responsible for the plentiful rainfall experienced here at this season.[5]

The second feature, the winter minimum south of Greymouth, has a double cause. In the first place, there are the anticyclones which form over the South Island from time to time in the cold air behind a front at this time of year, especially if it is extensive and lying across Middle New Zealand, or farther north, with a generally west to east orientation.[6] Weather is clear under these circumstances and light, cold easterlies, katabatic winds coming down from the icefields of the Southern Alps, are experienced on the west coast. In the second place, temperatures over the land are relatively low, so that convective instability is reduced. Thus, fronts, especially cold fronts, do not produce such heavy individual falls as they do at other times of the year. In combination, therefore, the two influences produce the minimum rainfall characteristic of the period in question.

The contrasting situation through the region in summer and early autumn may be explained by the fact that the anticyclonic systems are now farthest south, but that fronts are still active in the southern part of the South Island. Moreover, air over the land is now warmer than that over the sea, so that convective instability increases the amount of rainfall normally associated with them. The combined effect of fronts, orographic lifting, and thermal contrasts is thus apparent in the tendency towards a summer maximum in south Westland. The area north of Greymouth, however,

[3]C. J. Seelye: 'Variations of Monthly Rainfall . . .', op. cit.

[4]E. Kidson: 'The Climatology of New Zealand', op. cit. It should be noted that the increased wind velocity during spring is a low-level phenomenon. Upper winds, above 10,000 ft., reach their maximum speed in winter (July). See J. F. Gabites: 'Mean Westerly Wind Flow in the Upper Levels over the New Zealand Region', *N.Z. Journ. Sci. and Tech.*, Vol. 34, Sec. B, 1953, pp. 384–90.

[5]At this time of year many places east of the ranges have their minimum precipitation. The spring minimum is especially marked in parts of Eastern South Island.

[6]I. E. M. Watts: 'The Relation of New Zealand Weather . . .', op. cit.

experiences less frontal activity, and borders upon the general region where precipitation is least in summer, which extends over the North Island as a whole.

The seasonal variation in precipitation, however, is nowhere substantial, and the colloquial expression, 'rainy Westland', is true at all times of year. Even when it is not actually raining, the atmosphere is well-charged with moisture. Relative humidity at 9.30 a.m. averages more than 80 per cent during most of the year, and the saturation deficit is generally under 4.0 millibars. Moreover, these figures do not alter appreciably during the day, so that even in the early afternoon at Hokitika mean relative humidity remains in the vicinity of 75 per cent or over and the saturation deficit averages less than 5.0 millibars (*Table* 12). Thus, 'wetness' is an integral part of the region's

Table 12

ATMOSPHERIC HUMIDITY IN WESTERN SOUTH ISLAND

(a) Temperature, °F. (b) Vapour Pressure, mbs.
(c) Saturation Deficit, mbs. (d) Relative Humidity, per cent.

Station		Jun.	Jul.	Aug.	Sept.	Oct.	Nov.	Dec.	Jan.	Feb.	Mar.	Apr.	May	Year
Westport[1]														
	(a)	46.1	45.0	46.9	51.2	53.7	56.6	58.6	60.6	60.5	59.1	55.0	50.5	53.7
	(b)	9.1	8.5	9.0	10.5	11.3	12.1	13.6	14.5	15.2	14.2	12.3	10.7	11.7
	(c)	1.5	1.7	1.5	2.3	2.8	3.6	3.8	3.5	2.8	2.9	2.5	1.9	2.6
	(d)	85.0	83.0	82.0	82.0	80.0	78.0	81.0	80.0	83.0	83.0	84.0	85.0	82.0
Hokitika[2]														
	(a)	42.5	41.3	44.2	49.7	53.5	56.7	58.5	61.0	60.3	58.3	53.0	47.2	52.2
	(b)	8.2	7.7	8.5	10.1	10.9	12.0	13.3	14.7	14.8	13.7	11.9	9.8	11.3
	(c)	1.1	1.1	1.4	2.1	3.1	3.7	3.5	3.6	3.0	2.9	1.9	1.7	2.4
	(d)	88.0	87.0	85.0	84.0	78.0	77.0	79.0	80.0	83.0	84.0	87.0	88.0	83.0
Hokitika[3]														
	(a)	52.1	51.5	51.6	53.5	56.0	58.8	60.5	63.1	62.9	62.5	59.3	56.5	57.4
	(b)	9.4	9.8	9.4	10.4	11.8	12.6	14.0	15.6	15.3	14.7	12.6	11.4	12.3
	(c)	3.9	3.2	3.6	3.6	3.5	4.4	4.0	4.2	4.3	4.6	4.6	4.2	4.0
	(d)	71.0	75.0	72.0	74.0	77.0	74.0	78.0	79.0	78.0	76.0	73.0	73.0	75.0
Jackson's Bay[4]														
	(a)	44.2	43.0	45.9	49.3	52.1	54.8	56.8	59.3	58.8	57.5	53.3	48.3	51.9
	(b)	8.5	8.1	8.8	9.8	10.5	11.6	12.6	14.2	14.3	13.6	12.0	10.2	11.2
	(c)	1.4	1.3	1.7	2.2	2.8	3.0	3.2	3.0	2.6	2.6	1.9	1.3	2.3
	(d)	88.0	87.0	84.0	82.0	79.0	80.0	80.0	82.0	83.0	84.0	87.0	88.0	84.0

[1]Average of 9.30 a.m. observations at Westport Signal Station, 1938–44, and at Westport Airfield, 1945–50.
[2]Average of 9.30 a.m. observations at Hokitika Town, 1938–44, and at Hokitika Airfield, 1945–50.
[3]Average of 2 p.m. observations at Hokitika Airfield, 1946–50.
[4]Average of 9.30 a.m. observations, 1938–48.

climate. We must not, however, overrate its importance. Equal or greater amounts of precipitation are found in Upland South Island generally, and in many parts of the North Island also; the reliability of moisture from year to year is matched in Southern New Zealand; even the marked winter minimum from Greymouth southwards is part of a general climatic characteristic common to the country south of the latitude of Christchurch. The superhumid qualities of Western South Island, therefore, should not be so stressed as to exclude recognition of the region's other notable climatic features, particularly its temperature régime and sunshine characteristics.

The temperature régime of Western South Island is distinguished by ranges which are lower than elsewhere in the country. This is true whether we are considering the mean annual ranges, the mean annual or monthly extreme ranges, or the mean diurnal ranges (*Table* 13). These low temperature ranges are developed from a régime of mild winters and cool summers. The mean daily

Table 13
MEAN RANGES OF TEMPERATURE IN THE DIFFERENT REGIONS OF NEW ZEALAND

Note: The figure for each region has been obtained by averaging the statistics of all stations in that region. Some of these, because of their borderline location, can be used for more than one region, which explains why the number of stations for New Zealand is less than the sum of the numbers for individual regions. All figures are in degrees Fahrenheit.

(a) *Mean Monthly Temperatures:*

Region	No. of Stations	Mean Temperature Warmest Month	Mean Temperature Coolest Month	Mean Annual Range
Middle New Zealand	16	62.0	45.6	16.4
Western South Island	5	58.9	44.5	14.4
Northern New Zealand	24	64.8	49.1	15.7
Southern New Zealand	11	57.8	40.6	17.2
Eastern North Island	14	63.0	45.1	17.9
Eastern South Island	16	60.4	41.0	19.4
Central North Island	11	59.8	41.2	18.6
Inland South Island	11	59.2	35.4	23.8
Upland South Island	7	59.1	38.3	20.8
All New Zealand	107	60.6	42.3	18.3

(b) *Mean Annual Extreme Temperatures:*

Region	No. of Stations	Maximum	Minimum	Extreme Range
Middle New Zealand	8	81.4	27.8	53.6
Western South Island	3	75.4	30.1	45.3
Northern New Zealand	10	82.5	27.6	54.9
Southern New Zealand	3	85.7	24.9	60.8
Eastern North Island	10	86.0	25.9	60.1
Eastern South Island	11	88.7	22.5	66.2
Central North Island	6	82.1	22.5	59.6
Inland South Island	4	84.9	12.3	72.6
Upland South Island	5	83.9	19.2	64.7
All New Zealand	60	84.1	24.1	60.0

(c) *Mean Diurnal Temperature Ranges:*

Region	No. of Stns.	Mean Value of Diurnal Ranges Wi.	Sp.	Su.	Au.	Year	Index Values: Wi.=100 Wi.	Sp.	Su.	Au.	Year
Middle N.Z.	15	14.9	15.9	17.2	16.7	16.1	100	107	115	112	108
Western Sth. Is.	4	14.0	14.3	13.0	13.7	13.3	100	102	93	98	95
Northern N.Z.	24	15.7	16.4	18.5	17.0	17.2	100	104	118	108	109
Southern N.Z.	8	15.9	16.5	19.9	17.7	18.2	100	104	125	111	114
Eastern Nth. Is.	14	16.4	18.4	20.2	17.9	18.2	100	112	123	109	111
Eastern Sth. Is.	14	17.2	19.8	20.5	18.8	19.0	100	115	119	109	111
Central Nth. Is.	11	16.4	19.2	21.2	19.0	18.8	100	117	123	116	115
Inland Sth. Is.	9	17.9	21.3	23.1	21.3	20.9	100	119	129	119	117
Upland Sth. Is.	7	17.7	20.6	22.1	19.9	20.3	100	116	125	112	115
All New Zealand	97	16.1	17.7	19.4	17.8	17.9	100	110	121	111	111

minimum temperatures of the coldest months are several degrees above freezing point, but even at the height of summer the mean daily maximum temperature is less than 70°F. There are normally less than ten screen frosts a year, although ground frosts average over fifty annually. At times, also, an icy wind, known locally as 'the barber', blows through the mountain passes from the east.[7] Such cold conditions, however, are local and rarely prolonged, and the extreme annual minimum temperatures, which average about 30°F in this region, tend to be above those of other parts of the country.

But if winters are distinguished by their mildness, so are summers by their coolness. Mean extreme maximum temperatures for the year are rarely very great here. At Hokitika, for example, they are not above 77°F and the highest temperature recorded since 1913 is 84.5°F. Figures for the

[7]It occurs behind a cold front lying across the northern part of the South Island with an orientation of from slightly north of west to south of east. See I. E. M. Watts: 'Forecasting New Zealand Weather', op. cit.

C.N.Z.—E

whole region are commensurately low. They are as much as ten degrees behind the corresponding values of several other regions and, when considered in relation to the minimum figures already discussed, show that there is more difference between summer temperatures here and elsewhere, than between winter ones.

Let us consider next the hours of bright sunshine in the area. The mean annual average is between 1,800 hours and 2,000 hours in most parts, which represents rather more than 42 per cent of the possible yearly total, and is only slightly below the average for the whole country. These are higher values than might be expected in an area with so much rain. The mean annual hours of bright sunshine at places like Westport (1,996 hours), and Hokitika (1,898 hours), for example, compare favourably with those at Timaru, where sunshine averages 69 hours less a year than at Westport, in spite of there being only a quarter of the rainfall. Indeed, the mean annual sunshine totals of Western South Island are not far off those of recognized holiday centres such as Rotorua (2,061 hours) and Thames (2,067 hours).

The region, therefore, is by no means a sunless spot, and in spite of so much rain there are not long periods of grey and cloudy skies. Instead, once the rain is over the sky soon clears; the Southern Alps, invisible for a time in a grey world of pelting water, can be seen once more, clouds enveloping their summits; and out of a blue sky, patched with scattered, white clouds, the sun shines brilliantly again on the green and dripping vegetation, and on the shining, rain-soaked houses, upon whose corrugated-iron roofs water had been beating so mercilessly and noisily a short time before. On the average, more than half an inch of rain falls each rainy day on the west coast. The number of wet days, therefore, is not great, and is generally under 200 a year. Hokitika, for example, with an annual average of 115 inches of rain, receives it on 188 days, which is barely thirty days more than at Dunedin, where there is about one-third the rainfall. No wonder, then, that the rain falls drenchingly when it comes. Indeed, all through the area one can annually expect at least one occasion when there will be three inches or more in twenty-four hours.[8]

Some characteristic features of the daily weather are shown in *Fig.* 26. It illustrates how several inches of rainfall can be concentrated into the space of one or two days, and also how clear and sunny conditions set in again soon after the rain is over. During the two months covered by the diagram, particularly heavy rains were associated with the warm air of moist, northwesterly winds, and nearly every time more than an inch fell in a day it was brought about in this way. Characteristic-ally, too, a cold front followed on each occasion, and once it had passed fine conditions rapidly set in. The general weather features illustrated are, in short, developed from the anticyclonic and frontal sequences already discussed at some length in the previous chapter, and need not be enlarged upon further here.

Western South Island is thus seen as a region of abundant moisture, plentiful sunshine, mild winters, and cool summers. Throughout the area there is a good deal of climatic uniformity. Such small differences as exist result mainly from differences of latitude rather than of relief. This is in itself a point of regional differentiation, since in nearly all the other regions of New Zealand such internal contrasts as occur are the result, either of local relief conditions, or of contrasting exposure to prevailing winds. Neither of these factors is particularly important in Western South Island. A second point to notice is that it is the only lowland area of the country which is superhumid; com-parable moisture conditions are elsewhere confined to highland areas, and neither are they such a universal characteristic of any other single region.

Familiarly known as 'the Coast', Western South Island is a region of distinctive geographic personality. Much of this has arisen from its general isolation and the particular form taken by its economic development and history. The former is largely due to its inaccessibility. Rail and road communication with the rest of the South Island has been established only with difficulty, and is

[8]C. J. Seelye: 'The Frequency of Heavy Rainfalls . . .', op. cit.

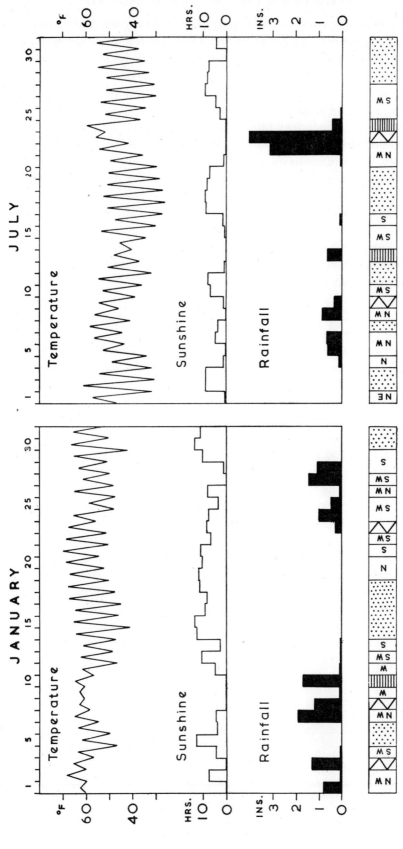

Fig. 26. Daily Temperature, Precipitation, and Sunshine during January and July, 1950, at Hokitika.

restricted even today to three routes: by rail through the Otira tunnel, and by road over the 3,000-ft. Arthur's Pass, or through the difficult Buller Gorge. There are few good harbours, and the two main ports, Westport and Greymouth, are both likely to be out of use for several days at a time, owing to treacherous sand-bars at the mouths of the Buller and Grey rivers respectively.[9] Economically the area is unique in New Zealand in that all its major lines of development have been connected with extractive industries. The gold rushes of the eighteen-sixties brought the usual influx of population and the rapid growth, and subsequent rapid decline, of 'shanty' and 'canvas' towns.[10] Later, coal and timber exploitation formed the economic mainstay. Some of the largest sawmills in the country are found there today, and the collieries of the Buller district, and at Reefton and Brunner, supply the bulk of New Zealand's domestic coal output.[11] Farming has developed slowly.[12] The region is still in the pioneer stage, and farm settlements are sporadic, and placed on convenient river flats or where the sawmillers have cleared the local 'bush' and left. Dairying is the chief farming activity, and is confined to the area from Wataroa northward. In the south, sheep and beef-cattle form the dominant livestock. Farming is by no means the principal economic activity of Western South Island, however, and agricultural landscapes are raw, ragged, and untidy compared with those of other parts. Economic development has thus altered the area only in detail. Large-scale transformation of the physical landscape, such as has occurred in many other regions of the country, has not yet been achieved. Hence, natural factors assume a large role in the total geographic make-up, and climate is important through its direct and indirect influence on soils and vegetation.

Fig. 27 shows the distribution of soil types in Western South Island. They are principally in three classes: skeletal soils, recent (azonal) soils, and mature (zonal and intrazonal) soils. The first of these are developed on the steep bounding ranges; their origins are such that they are related to relief conditions which prevent the development of proper profiles, and the influence of climate is unimportant in their character. Similarly, recent soils are too young to show any climatic relationship. Where time has given a degree of maturity to soil character, however, climatic influence is seen in the high degree of leaching and marked podzolization which has taken place. Practically all mature soils are podzolized. This process is more apparent here than elsewhere in the country, and reflects the influence of climate working in association with level, water-accumulating land, where drainage is heavily impeded. Thus, we find that mature, groundwater podzols occupy extensive areas of flat, or undulating, swampy terraces throughout Western South Island. They generally consist of a peaty topsoil, or a grey-brown, fine sandy loam, below which lies a yellow-brown, or brownish-grey subsoil. The whole complex lies over a hard pan, some two or three feet below the ground surface. The layers immediately above this pan are almost continuously waterlogged, and the pan itself consists of stones, cemented firmly together by iron and humus. Such soils are by nature infertile; acid in character (pH 4.5–5.0), with a low base-exchange capacity and less than 10 per cent base saturation, they can only be made productive first by breaking through the hard pan, and then by the continual application of lime, initially at the rate of a ton or more to the acre.[13]

Soils such as these, aided by the general wetness and warmth of the climate, support a heavy

[9]The writer recalls one occasion, early in 1940, when Westport was cut off from the rest of the country for two or three days. Slips blocked the roads, the railway connecting the town with Reefton had not then been built, the ships in port were 'bar bound', and the small local aeroplane was bogged down on the swamped airfield.

[10]In addition to standard texts on New Zealand's economic history, a popular account of this era will be found in E. I. Lord: 'Old Westland: a story of the golden west coast of the South Island of New Zealand', Christchurch, n.d. (1940?).

[11]J. Pascoe: 'Coal from the Buller', *N.Z. Geogr.*, Vol. 4, 1948, pp. 163–82.

[12]K. B. Cumberland: 'The Agricultural Regions of New Zealand', op. cit. J. R. Shepherd: 'Farming in New Zealand: Westland', *N.Z. Journ. Agric.*, Vol. 79, 1949, pp. 255–66.

[13]C. S. Harris and A. C. Harris: 'Soil Survey of the Westport District', *N.Z. Dept. Sci. and Ind. Res. Bulln.*, No. 71, 1939. H. S. Gibbs, A. D. Mercer, and J. W. Collie: 'Soils and Agriculture of Westland', *N.Z. Dept. Sci. and Ind. Res. Bulln.*, No. 2 (N.S.), 1950.

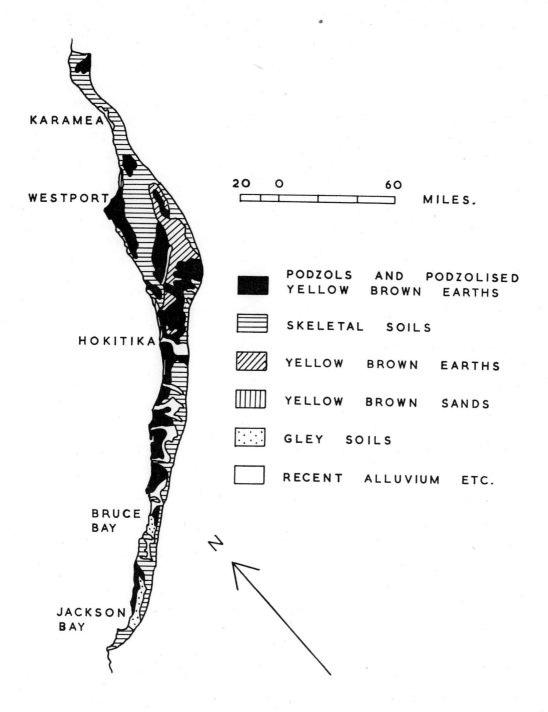

FIG. 27. The Distribution of Soil Types in Western South Island (from Soil Map of N.Z., 1948).

growth of rank, coarse vegetation. Originally all the area below 3,000 ft. of elevation was clothed in the dense, subtropical rain-forest characteristic of nearly all the country at the beginning of the last century.[14] The general make-up of this forest consisted of a complex of tall trees—totara (*Podocarpus totara*), rimu (*Dacrydium cupressinum*), tawa (*Beilschmeidia tawa*), and rata (*Metrosideros robusta*, or *M. lucida* according to locality)—matted together by a dense undergrowth, rotting logs, creepers, and lianes. This sombre, green, podocarp-dicotylous forest was specifically distinguished in Western South Island by an abundance of kahikatea (*Podocarpus dacrydiodes*) semi-swamp forest. More restricted in area, but no less significant regionally, was the prevalence of bog forest, made up of associations dominated either by silver pine (*Dacrydium Colensoi*), or yellow pine (*D. intermedium*). Sawmilling has substantially reduced the forest at low levels, and some clearing for farming has extended the destroyed area. The climatic incentive to growth in these areas, however, is everywhere apparent. Farmers wage a continual battle against a spirited invasion of weeds and returning vegetation, while areas cleared and left to themselves quickly revert to 'second growth'; native fern, bracken, manuka scrub, and young rimu, the latter eight to ten feet high already, stand as vigorous expressions of the powerful growth incentive of bright, warm sunshine after a plentiful fall of rain.

The landscapes of Western South Island, then, bear the unmistakable imprint of the region's climate. It is clearly seen in the overall picture of soils and vegetation, and is also perceived in the double impression one carries away after several months' residence on 'the Coast': on the one hand, there is a picture of a grey sky, with rolling storm clouds from which pours a drenching deluge, soaking the land and making the water pour through the street gutterings; on the other hand, there is the remembrance of sunshine and a blue sky, with scattered clouds, and everywhere a dustless atmosphere which allows long views of the forest and its clearings, and of the distant mountains beyond.

[14]L. Cockayne: 'The Vegetation of New Zealand', in *Die Vegetation der Erde* (edrs. Engler and Drude), 2nd edn., Leipzig, 1928. K. B. Cumberland: 'A Century's change . . .', op. cit.

PLATE III. *Landscapes of Middle New Zealand*
(*a*) A view of cattle-grazing country with the 'tortured slopes' of inland Wanganui and Taranaki in the background. (*b*) Mature agricultural landscapes of lowland Taranaki with cloud on Mount Egmont in light northerly conditions.

PLATE IV. *Weather conditions in Western South Island*

(*a*) Storm clouds over the Southern Alps near Jackson's Bay. (*b*) Cattle grazing after a storm as the clouds clear rapidly and the sun shines again.

7

NORTHERN NEW ZEALAND

THE climatic characteristics of the two previous regions are derived fundamentally from atmospheric influences common to the whole country. Middle New Zealand, indeed, has been shown as distinguished by 'typicality', because it combines together so many of the elements normal to the land. But in Northern New Zealand there is a somewhat different situation. Here is an area which, in addition to being influenced by the atmospheric circulations general to the country, is also subject to forces not normally experienced to such an extent elsewhere. These are in part derived directly from the tropics, and in part related to the near presence of the general belt of subtropical high pressure.

Herein lies the importance of the region's location. As its name implies, it is the most northerly of the climatic regions of the country. The southern boundary is the northern edge of the volcanic plateau, and from here the region stretches northwestwards as a long, narrow territory of rolling country and irregular relief, with a highly indented coastline. The relief conditions help to differentiate its climate in detail, but do not add significantly to its general distinguishing qualities. The latter are derived from its external relationships, particularly as expressed in three main factors: location, the proximity of the subtropical high-pressure belt, and the influence of tropical conditions, the latter consisting mainly of occasional cyclonic disturbances.

Northern New Zealand is generally warmer than the rest of the country. This is more the result of location than of any other single factor. The position is summed up in the map of mean annual temperature (*Fig.* 4) which shows that it is the only climatic region with a mean annual figure above 55°F everywhere. But during every season some aspect of temperature distribution marks it off as warmer than the rest: in winter, 21 per cent of the area averages over 50°F and none of it is below 45°F; in spring, average temperatures exceed 55°F over nearly half the region; in summer, it is not so clearly differentiated, but even so it is the only part where mean temperatures exceed 65°F in any section; finally, in autumn, north of Kaitaia, temperatures average more than 60°F and they are 55°F or more over all the territory, except in the mountains of the Coromandel peninsula (*Fig.* 28).

These statistics provide the measure of the average temperature qualities of Northern New Zealand. They imply that its separateness as a thermal unit is more apparent in winter and in autumn than at other seasons. This is illustrated further in *Table* 14. In this table, the average of the mean monthly temperatures for each season in Northern New Zealand, derived from the statistics of all the stations available, is given the index value 100, and the corresponding temperatures for other regions are indexed relatively. The table exemplifies not only that the difference in average temperature through the country is greater in winter than in summer, but also that the difference between the average temperature of Northern New Zealand and that of the next warmest region is more in winter and autumn than at other times of the year. Similar distinctions are shown in the second half of *Table* 14 and also in *Table* 15. In these cases they are not quite so clear, however. Northern New Zealand is everywhere open to the influence of the ocean, and maximum temperatures are rarely excessive. Those parts of New Zealand which lie east of the ranges, on the contrary, may experience remarkably high maximum temperatures, especially when northwesterly conditions

Table 14

RELATIONSHIP OF MEAN TEMPERATURES IN THE CLIMATIC REGIONS OF NEW ZEALAND
TO THOSE OF NORTHERN NEW ZEALAND

(Index Value of Northern N.Z. = 100 in each case.)

(a) *Index Values of Mean Monthly Temperatures:—*

Region	No. of Stations	Wi.	Sp.	Su.	Au.	Year
Northern N.Z.	24	100	100	100	100	100
Middle N.Z.	16	91	95	96	94	95
Western Sth. Is.	5	90	92	91	91	91
Southern N.Z.	11	84	90	90	86	88
Eastern Nth. Is.	14	92	96	98	94	95
Eastern Sth. Is.	16	84	92	93	89	90
Central Nth. Is.	11	83	90	92	89	89
Inland Sth. Is.	11	74	88	91	83	85
Upland Sth. Is.	7	79	89	92	86	87

(b) *Index Values of Mean Monthly Extreme Maximum Temperatures:*

Region	No. of Stations	Wi.	Sp.	Su.	Au.	Year
Northern N.Z.	10	100	100	100	100	100
Middle N.Z.	8	95	98	99	97	99
Western Sth. Is.	3	92	90	89	91	91
Southern N.Z.	3	93	102	101	97	103
Eastern Nth. Is.	10	98	102	104	100	104
Eastern Sth. Is.	11	99	105	106	102	108
Central Nth. Is.	6	92	97	98	95	100
Inland Sth. Is.	4	87	99	102	95	103
Upland Sth. Is.	5	92	99	100	96	102

Table 15

MEAN DAILY MAXIMUM TEMPERATURES (°F) FOR DIFFERENT PLACES IN NEW ZEALAND

Station	Jan.	Apr.	Jul.	Oct.
Te Paki	72.6	68.3	59.3	63.5
Auckland	72.7	67.1	56.7	63.1
Ruakura	74.5	67.5	55.9	64.0
Rotorua	74.3	64.7	53.5	62.2
Hastings	77.0	68.2	55.7	66.8
New Plymouth	69.1	64.6	54.8	60.3
Nelson	71.1	64.7	53.8	62.1
Hokitika	66.2	61.3	52.8	58.7
Christchurch	70.3	61.8	50.0	62.0
Gore	69.3	60.4	47.4	61.2

bring föhn-like winds. Thus, it is only in winter that the mean extreme and daily maximum temperatures in the north are above those of everywhere else. That these facts are widely recognized through the country is suggested by the popular phrase, 'the winterless north', which sums up well enough the region's most distinguishing temperature feature, and the principal consequence of location alone upon its climate.

A second climatic feature which may be examined in the present context, however, is atmospheric humidity. People who arrive in Auckland province from the south often complain that the atmosphere is humid and oppressive. Relative humidity tends to be a little above the average for the country, and is fairly uniform throughout the area owing to the absence of high mountains and the narrowness of the territory.[1] There is, however, a good deal of water vapour in the atmosphere owing to the region's warmth. Thus, mean vapour pressures tend to be higher in Northern New Zealand than elsewhere. During the period 1938–50 at Tauranga, for example, the mean relative humidity in January at 9.30 a.m. was 67 per cent, the mean saturation deficit 7.6 millibars, and the mean vapour pressure 15.7 millibars. These figures may be compared with those for Jackson's Bay, in Western

[1]E. Kidson: 'Climatic Notes . . .', op. cit.

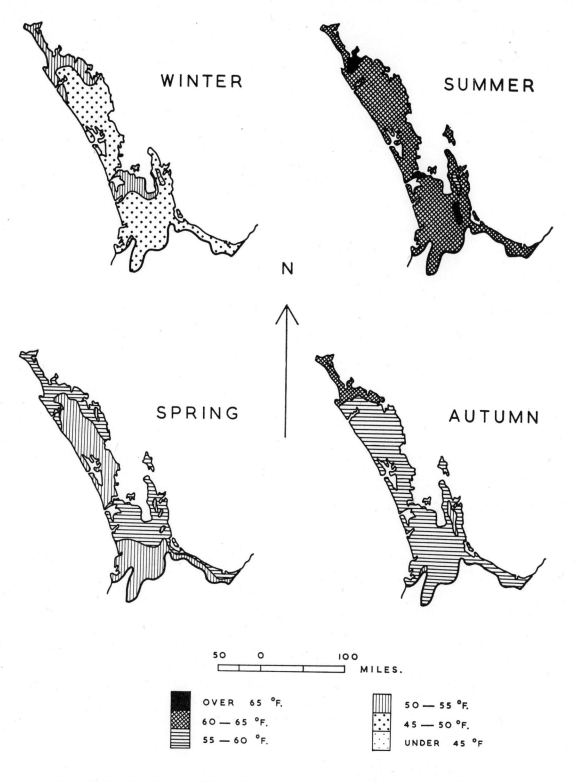

WINTER

SUMMER

N

SPRING

AUTUMN

50   0   100
MILES.

OVER 65 °F.   50 — 55 °F.
60 — 65 °F.   45 — 50 °F.
55 — 60 °F.   UNDER 45 °F

Fig. 28. The Distribution of Mean Temperatures at each of the four seasons of the year in
Northern New Zealand.

73

Table 16

ATMOSPHERIC HUMIDITY IN NORTHERN NEW ZEALAND

(a) Temperature, °F.   (b) Vapour Pressure, mbs.
(c) Saturation Deficit, mbs.   (d) Relative Humidity, per cent.

Station	Jun.	Jul.	Aug.	Sept.	Oct.	Nov.	Dec.	Jan.	Feb.	Mar.	Apr.	May	Year
Waipoua[1]													
(a)	51.4	50.2	51.5	54.7	58.4	61.7	63.8	66.2	66.5	64.0	60.0	55.0	58.6
(b)	11.5	11.1	11.3	12.0	13.0	14.1	14.8	16.9	17.2	16.3	15.2	13.3	13.9
(c)	1.5	1.3	1.7	2.6	3.7	4.7	5.4	5.1	5.0	4.1	2.5	1.5	3.3
(d)	90.0	89.0	87.0	82.0	78.0	75.0	73.0	76.0	77.0	80.0	86.0	90.0	82.0
Auckland[1]													
(a)	51.8	51.0	52.5	56.0	59.0	62.2	65.2	67.2	67.7	65.2	61.8	56.7	59.7
(b)	11.4	10.8	11.0	11.8	12.6	13.4	14.6	16.0	16.6	15.8	14.8	12.9	13.5
(c)	1.7	1.9	2.5	3.5	4.4	5.7	6.5	6.7	6.5	5.4	4.0	2.9	4.3
(d)	84.0	85.0	81.0	77.0	74.0	70.0	69.0	70.0	72.0	74.0	79.0	82.0	76.0
Auckland[2]													
(a)	57.2	56.5	56.7	59.4	61.9	65.2	67.0	71.1	71.8	69.9	65.2	61.2	63.6
(b)	11.5	11.2	10.8	11.4	12.5	13.6	14.4	15.6	16.2	16.0	14.3	13.1	13.4
(c)	4.5	4.4	4.9	5.9	6.4	7.6	8.1	10.4	10.3	9.0	7.0	5.3	7.0
(d)	72.0	72.0	69.0	66.0	66.0	64.0	64.0	60.0	61.0	64.0	67.0	71.0	66.0
Tauranga[1]													
(a)	50.9	49.5	51.5	55.5	59.4	62.6	66.0	67.9	68.3	66.0	60.8	56.1	59.5
(b)	10.3	9.8	10.2	11.0	12.2	13.5	14.8	15.7	16.1	15.6	13.9	12.5	13.0
(c)	2.4	2.3	2.8	4.0	5.1	5.9	7.0	7.6	7.4	6.2	4.3	2.9	4.8
(d)	81.0	82.0	79.0	72.0	70.0	70.0	69.0	67.0	68.0	72.0	76.0	81.0	74.0
Ruakura, Hamilton[1]													
(a)	47.0	46.0	48.6	53.0	57.3	61.1	64.4	65.3	65.7	62.6	57.6	51.9	56.7
(b)	9.6	9.2	9.9	11.2	12.2	13.4	15.3	15.6	16.3	15.2	13.7	11.6	12.8
(c)	1.4	1.4	1.8	2.5	3.8	5.0	5.3	5.7	5.2	4.2	2.5	1.6	3.4
(d)	87.0	87.0	84.0	81.0	76.0	73.0	74.0	73.0	75.0	79.0	84.0	88.0	80.0

[1]Average of observations at 9.30 a.m., 1938–50.

[2]Average of observations at 2 p.m. at Mechanics Bay, 1941–44, and 1949–50, and at Auckland Observatory, 1945–48.

South Island, which were 82 per cent, 3.0 millibars, and 14.2 millibars respectively, and with those for Waipiata, in Inland South Island, which were 64 per cent, 5.9 millibars, and 10.4 millibars. Over the same period of years at Auckland the mean relative humidity at 9.30 a.m. in July was 85 per cent, the mean saturation deficit 1.9 millibars, and the mean vapour pressure 10.8 millibars. Equivalent figures at Hokitika were 87 per cent, 1.1 millibars, and 7.7 millibars, and at Alexandra they were 87 per cent, 1.0 millibars, and 5.6 millibars. Similar contrasts, which illustrate further the higher vapour content of the atmosphere in northern parts, may be observed by comparing the statistics given in *Table* 16 with those available elsewhere in this volume.

Let us consider next how the seasonal migration of pressure belts affects the region. In summer, the subtropical high-pressure cells are farther south than at other times of the year. This movement displaces the general track of the anticyclones so that they now frequently pass over the North Island.[2] Moreover, activity within that part of the low-pressure trough between them which crosses Northern New Zealand is rather weak, and the strong contrasts in air streams necessary to precipitation and changeable weather are uncommon. In winter, on the other hand, the high-pressure cells have moved northward, and the whole arrangement of pressure belts moves with them. Migratory anticyclones accordingly follow a more northerly track and their centres no longer regularly cross the North Island. Troughs of contrasting and vigorous air take their place, and activity within these troughs is intensified by a high degree of cyclonic activity likely to be produced by periodic invasions of subtropical air in the wake of a retreating anticyclone.

This general movement of pressure belts causes differences between the precipitation of summer and winter in Northern New Zealand which are clearly expressed in average figures. More than

[2]E. Kidson: 'The Climatology of New Zealand', op. cit.

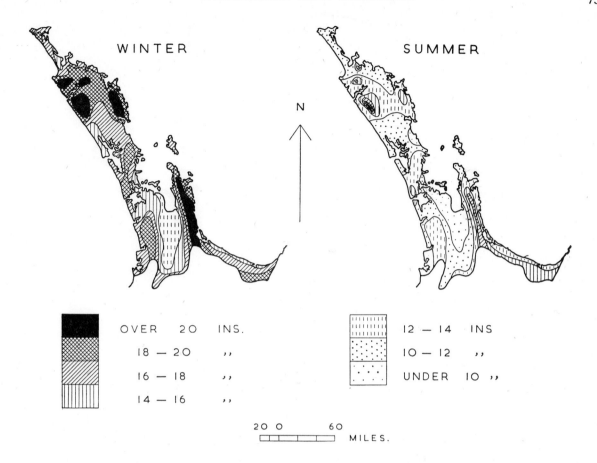

FIG. 29. The Mean Distribution of Precipitation in Northern New Zealand during winter and summer.

30 per cent of the annual fall occurs in the three winter months, when most of the area has a mean rainfall which totals over fourteen inches (*Figs.* 9 and 29). On the other hand, in the three summer months there is generally less than twelve inches, and some parts experience under 20 per cent of their annual total. Such a degree of seasonal contrast is found only in two other regions of the country: Eastern North Island and Inland South Island.[3] The former of these is similar to Northern New Zealand in that most rain comes in winter, but the season of minimum precipitation differs a little since about a third of the area has least in spring and the rest least in summer. Inland South Island, however, is entirely different, as over 30 per cent of the annual total falls in December, January, and February, and less than 20 per cent in the three winter months.

The final factor to be considered in the external relationships of Northern New Zealand is the effect of tropical invasions. These invasions are of two kinds: one is the tropical cyclone proper, which originates as a disturbance on the intertropical front; the other is an intense disturbance which results from the movement of tropical air southwards and its contact with colder, subpolar air.

Cyclonic disturbances of the first type occur with the seasonal migration southwards of the intertropical front.[4] This produces a succession of intertropical front waves and tropical convergence troughs, which move westward in the air stream on the northern side of the south Pacific high-pressure cell. If there is sufficient convergence, the frontal disturbances assume storm proportions

[3]There is almost as great a contrast between seasons in Eastern South Island where, on the average, 29 per cent of the annual precipitation falls in summer and 22 per cent in winter.
[4]M. A. Garbell: 'Tropical and Equatorial Meteorology', op. cit.

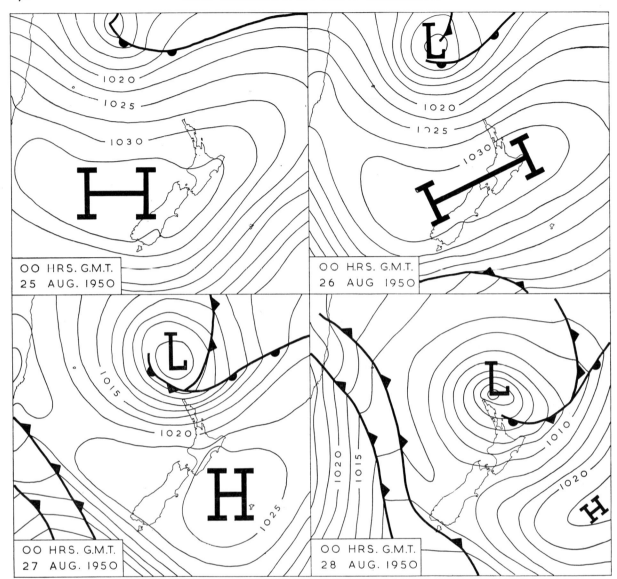

FIG. 30. Cyclonic disturbance produced by tropical air invading a cold anticyclone lying over New Zealand, August, 1950.

and are likely to recurve towards higher latitudes, following the upper air flow, or else move towards a frontal system in temperate areas. In the south Pacific recurvature commonly takes place in the region of frontogenesis east of Australia. Tropical cyclones of this kind are a summer and early autumn phenomenon. Should such a cyclone last long enough, it may well pass sufficiently close to Northern New Zealand to bring hurricane winds and torrential rain during the short time of its passage.

More common, and liable to take place at any season, are the disturbances which can be attributed more particularly to the contact between tropical and subpolar air. Here again we must distinguish between two types: the cyclonic development produced by an air stream of tropical origin invading colder air and creating a very steep pressure gradient, and a disturbance which results from the intensification of an already existing wave on a cold front.

The precursor of the former type is often an intense anticyclone with its centre south of the normal

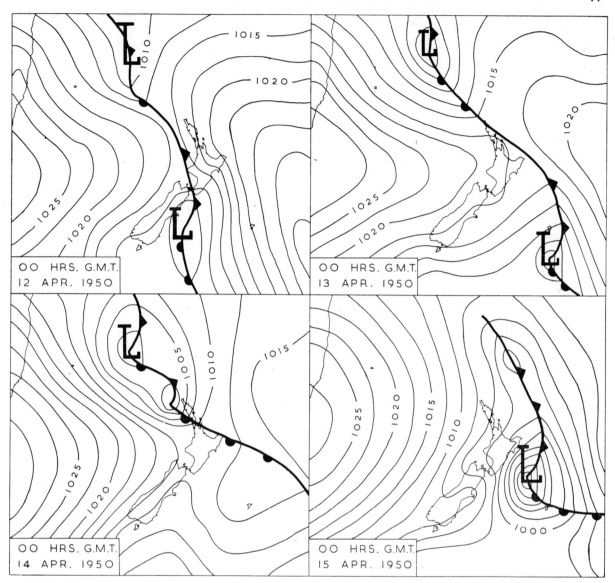

FIG. 31. Cyclonic disturbance produced by tropical air intensifying a wave on a cold front, April, 1950.

track (*Fig. 30*).[5] Against the northern side of this, invading tropical air creates a steep pressure gradient. This is likely to develop into a very deep cyclone, which is the cause of heavy rain in Northern New Zealand and also much of Eastern North Island. In the case of the second type, an intense disturbance is caused by tropical air invading and intensifying an already existing wave on a cold front (*Fig. 31*). The paths taken by these disturbances are normally from northwest to southeast, and they can traverse New Zealand like any normal wave-depression. It is, however, more common for those which maintain the intensity of a tropical disturbance to pass across the North Island, and whatever part of the country they affect, Northern New Zealand will almost certainly be included.

[5]E. Kidson: 'The Climatology of New Zealand', op. cit. Note also the following extract from B. V. Pemberton: 'Weather Forecasting in New Zealand', *N.Z. Journ. Sci. and Tech.*, Vol. 2, 1919, pp. 87–94: 'The excessive rainfall in the northern districts when the high pressure systems move in higher latitudes is brought about by the greater number of extra-tropical cyclones which are then able to approach within effective range of the northernmost portion of New Zealand.'

Table 17

DAILY TEMPERATURE AND PRECIPITATION CONDITIONS IN NORTHERN NEW ZEALAND,
(a) 11–16 APRIL, AND (b) 24–29 AUGUST 1950

	(1) Min. Temp., °F						(2) Max. Temp., °F		(3) Precipitation, in.			
Station	*April 1950*								*August 1950*			
	11	*12*	*13*	*14*	*15*	*16*	*24*	*25*	*26*	*27*	*28*	*29*
Glenbervie, Whangarei												
(1)	55.0	63.5	59.0	59.5	54.0	53.0	34.0	30.0	38.0	50.0	50.0	52.5
(2)	70.2	68.5	64.0	68.0	65.0	63.0	57.5	58.0	57.0	56.0	57.0	57.5
(3)	0.35	0.38	0.70	2.10	0.23	0.14	0.08	0.57	0.31	2.70	0.10	Nil.
Auckland												
(1)	61.5	62.1	57.2	54.2	54.7	52.2	44.2	44.9	46.3	46.8	51.1	53.3
(2)	70.2	68.4	66.8	59.8	64.8	61.8	59.3	57.1	59.3	56.9	60.7	58.9
(3)	0.13	0.75	0.54	1.80	0.05	0.36	Nil.	Tr.	Nil.	0.15	0.01	0.05
Ruakura, Hamilton												
(1)	50.8	58.3	53.8	53.7	49.6	38.3	32.8	40.4	31.3	38.9	47.3	49.9
(2)	72.7	69.5	66.7	57.4	65.5	58.6	59.1	61.0	60.5	57.3	62.7	58.9
(3)	0.11	0.57	0.10	1.34	Nil.	0.53	0.02	Nil.	Nil.	Nil.	0.93	0.01
Tauranga												
(1)	52.1	62.1	52.1	58.5	55.2	46.0	32.9	42.6	35.6	40.8	48.0	51.4
(2)	70.0	67.1	69.2	61.2	65.8	61.1	63.5	56.6	58.8	55.8	62.2	59.7
(3)	0.10	0.10	0.07	2.63	Nil.	0.33	Nil.	Nil.	Nil.	0.20	0.03	Nil.
Daily Hours of Bright Sunshine at Auckland	1.8	Nil.	0.3	Nil.	5.8	3.2	8.3	0.4	8.5	Nil.	0.2	3.9

Table 17 indicates statistically the temperature and precipitation conditions which accompanied the disturbances illustrated in *Figs.* 30 and 31. That which took place during the middle of April 1950 brought the most widespread rain to Northern New Zealand. Its onset was marked by warm conditions and low diurnal ranges of temperature, with a little rain, especially from Auckland northwards. Later, with the rapid intensification of the system into one of tropical violence on the 14th, there was heavy rain, and temperatures dropped sharply as the cold front passed. In the second example, the region at first experienced fine, anticyclonic weather, with temperatures falling from near the sixties by day to almost freezing point at night. Then came an influx of warmth from the north. The isobaric gradient steepened, and a circular disturbance developed immediately north of the country which gradually moved towards the east of the land. Its influence was particularly marked in north Auckland, where it brought heavy rain and much cloud. Temperatures, although they were by day about the same as before, were as high as 50°F at night, and diurnal ranges, which had been 20F° or more, now became less than 10F°.

At times, cyclonic disturbances of tropical origin may cause a great deal of damage to life and property. On the 2nd February, 1936, for example, an exceptionally violent storm travelled from west of Cape Maria van Diemen, to southwest of Auckland, and then southeast towards Napier.[6] It originated as a tropical disturbance which was further intensified in its character, and directed over New Zealand in its track, by coming into contact with a cold front about half-way between New Caledonia and New Zealand. The results were chaotic: in Kaitaia there were over three feet of water in the main street, and a man was drowned trying to save the contents of his house; a miner was drowned near Thames when his hut was carried into a stream by a landslide; and in the Manawatu, where rain was not excessive, a monstrous gale blew the last two carriages and van of an excursion train off the rails. Such violent visitations are fortunately rare. More typical was the storm of 26 March in the same year.[7] No place then recorded more than four inches of rainfall and the winds, though strong, reached destructive proportions in only a few places.

[6]M. A. F. Barnett: 'The Cyclonic Storms over Northern New Zealand . . .', op. cit.
[7]ibid.

There are several ways in which the climate of Northern New Zealand reflects these occasional tropical influences. One way is that they cause the heaviest rainfalls in the region to occur in northeast winds. In 1882, for example, a total of 46.68 inches of rain was recorded at Auckland.[8] About two-thirds of this was brought by winds from a westerly quarter. This total fell on about three-quarters of the year's total of rain days, which gives an average intensity of 0.22 in. per wet day. The amount which was brought by northeast winds totalled only 8.36 inches, but it fell on so few days that the average intensity was nearly half an inch per day of rain. Occasional short, heavy downpours of tropical origin, moreover, underline the region's 'normal' New Zealand characteristic of having comparatively few wet days in spite of mean annual totals of between 40 and 80 inches. Statistical evidence for the intensity of this rainfall is not lacking, while a colloquial way of expressing it was given many years ago by one William Flower who remarked in a letter, written from Auckland in 1863: 'When it does rain it does rain, and no half and half sort of showers.'[9]

This irregular occurrence of particularly heavy rain, derived mainly from northeast winds, explains the high rainfall variability here. It is especially great in eastern districts, where its mean annual value is over 14 per cent, and exceeds 18 per cent in places. The mean monthly variability in summer and early autumn in these eastern districts may be as high as 60 per cent, but in winter and spring it is in the vicinity of 40 per cent, or even as low as 30 per cent.[10]

In addition to those features developed principally from its location and tropical relationships, Northern New Zealand displays climatic characteristics widely found in New Zealand. There are several ways of illustrating this. Sunshine, for example, is plentiful and rather above the average for the country. Most places receive between 2,000 and 2,150 hours a year, and nearly a third of this total comes in the three months of summer, which is the only season to receive more than 50 per cent of the possible sunshine. Another point is that, despite the importance of northerly air streams, the prevalent wind over the area is from a westerly quarter. Southwesterlies predominate, especially north of Auckland City, and the winds generally, like those of New Zealand as a whole, are gusty rather than strong. Furthermore, a high proportion of the rainfall comes from the cold fronts which sweep the area, particularly in winter. In the unstable maritime air behind them hail is not uncommon, and relatively cold conditions can occur here in any month of the year.[11] Frosts, indeed, are not as infrequent as might be expected. The mean annual occurrence of screen frosts for all stations in the region averages 12.5, which is higher than the corresponding value for Western South Island, and only 4.4 short of the figure for Middle New Zealand. Where Northern New Zealand differs particularly from other parts is in the relatively small number of ground frosts. These are common only in special localities, like the middle Waikato basin, or the sheltered intermontane depression near Waihi. For the region as a whole, they average less than thirty-five a year, which is about twenty less than the corresponding value for any other region of the country. Late frosts are rare, but do happen: on Christmas

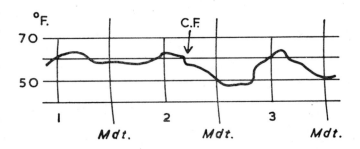

FIG. 32. Tracing from a thermograph chart to illustrate the passage of a cold front at Whenuapai, Auckland, on 2 November 1950.

[8] J. T. Meeson: 'The Rainfall of New Zealand', *Trans. N.Z. Inst.*, Vol. 23, 1890, pp. 546–69.

[9] S. Braune: 'Voices from New Zealand: being a compilation of authentic letters from emigrants who have located in New Zealand since 1863, also a series of questions answered', London, 1865.

[10] C. J. Seelye: 'Variations of Monthly Rainfall . . .', op. cit.

[11] One recalls, for example, the discomforts of camping in north Auckland during early December 1948, while being lashed by hail and a southwesterly gale.

Day 1918, for example, there was a frost at Tauranga. As a rule, however, the frost season is over by the end of August in all but the most exposed localities, and an 'unseasonal' invasion of cold air rarely produces freezing-point temperatures. The examples of frost given, however, and the fact that the mean annual extreme minimum temperature at every station in the region, except Auckland, is 30°F or less, indicate that the area is not immune to the occasional cold snap. Moreover, as in the rest of the country, temperatures may change markedly with the passage of a cold front (*Fig.* 32).[12]

The combination of all these various features in Northern New Zealand has produced a climate which can be broadly described as humid, sunny, and warm. It is one which reflects, on the one hand, the stimulating changeableness so characteristic of New Zealand, and, on the other, the warmth of the tropics, with their sultry weather and sweet earthy smells after falling rain. The lineaments of its weather are well illustrated by *Figs.* 33 and 34, which portray conditions at various stations during January 1950, and from 24 June to 31 July of the same year.

In January there was settled weather, with plenty of sunshine, large diurnal ranges of temperature, and little rainfall. Occasionally frontal activity upset the picture, as at the beginning of the month. But there was nothing like the amount of contrast which was experienced during the same month in Middle New Zealand and Western South Island, for example. High-pressure cells dominated the weather of the north to a much greater degree than farther south. This summer sequence contrasts markedly, but in a typical way, with what was experienced during the following winter. From 24 June to the end of July the region displayed a weather pattern characteristic of the passage of low-pressure troughs between successive anticyclones. Short periods of wet, changeable weather were interspersed with several days of sunshine and large diurnal temperature ranges. Such sequences produced the higher rainfall totals and lower hours of bright sunshine, together with the changes from warm to colder conditions, followed by a more settled period, which exactly fit the average qualities of the region's winter climate.

In spite of a general climatic uniformity throughout Northern New Zealand, there are some local contrasts which are mainly due to differences in relief and exposure. Physically the area is bounded in the south by the volcanic plateau of the central North Island, and by the irregular spurs of highlands inland from Kawhia Harbour. The region itself is long and narrow, with a highly indented coastline, and contains a very irregular surface which, geologically and pedologically speaking, is as diverse as anywhere in the country.[13] For the most part, however, the surface irregularities are only of microclimatological significance. From the broader climatic viewpoint, the physical diversity is not great and follows a relatively simple plan, involving two areas of highland and one basin region.

The principal highlands are those which rise to 4,000 ft. of elevation in the Coromandel peninsula. They make a well-marked physical feature which is the most continuous area of elevated land in the region. Moreover, their slopes are steep and their direction lies north to south, so that they are well placed for creating contrasts on either side of them. A lower area of high ground, sufficiently elevated nevertheless to be climatologically significant, lies across the central part of the north Auckland peninsula. The eastern part of this forms a greywacke range which is geologically an extension of the Coromandel ranges, and its western sector is a tableland of sandstone and mudstone, out of which rises a jumble of volcanic peaks and cones. The depressed block which forms the middle Waikato basin is the only basin region of note in the area. Actually a complex of two or three basins is found here, separated by ranges and hills lying generally parallel to the Coromandel ranges. The

[12]It should be noted in passing that a local feature of Northern New Zealand is the way the arrival of warm air may cause a marked rise in temperature. An increase of as much as 10F° has been noted during the passage of a warm front. See M. A. F. Barnett: 'The Cyclonic Storms over Northern New Zealand . . .', op. cit.

[13]N.Z. Geological Survey Officers: 'The Outline of the Geology of New Zealand; notes and maps on a scale of 16 miles to the inch', Wellington, 1948. There is also a large collection of Bulletins of the New Zealand Geological Survey, written by individual authors, many of which refer to Northern New Zealand.

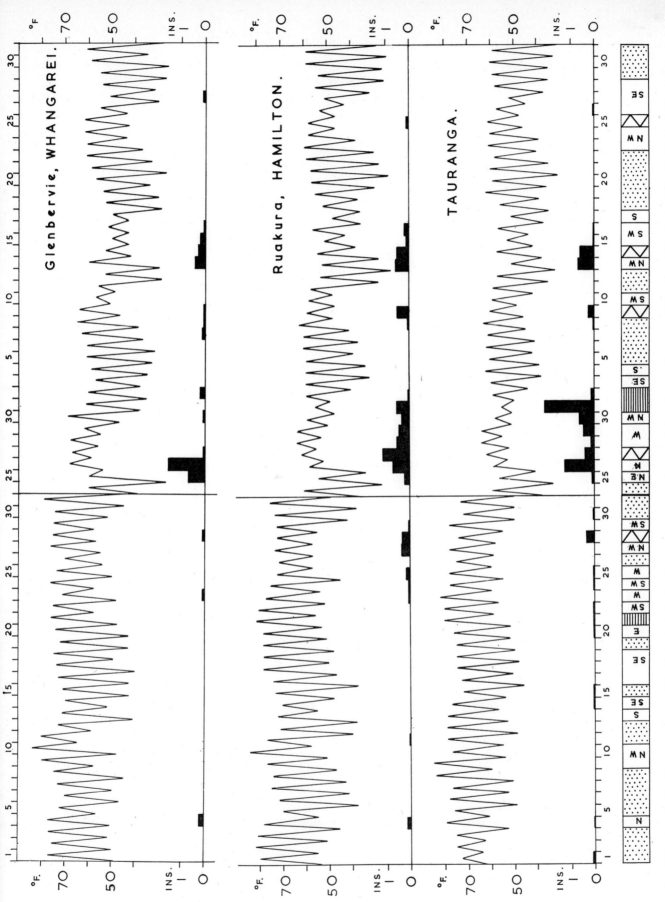

Fig. 33. Daily Temperature and Precipitation during January, 1950, and part of the winter of 1950 at Whangarei, Ruakura (Hamilton), and Tauranga.

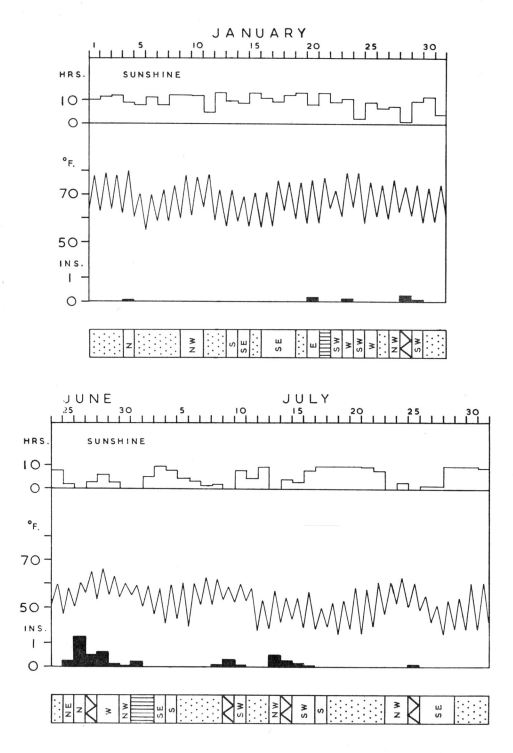

FIG. 34. Daily Sunshine, Temperature, and Precipitation at Auckland during January, 1950, and part of the winter of 1950.

depressions are flat-floored and sufficiently low, compared with neighbouring areas, to be somewhat drier than the surrounding parts and to experience slightly higher ranges of temperature.

The highlands of the area affect the climate in two ways: they increase rainfall totals, and they contribute to differences between the west and the east. The former point needs no comment, as its nature may be seen from the map of annual rainfall (*Fig.* 7). The second factor is chiefly expressed in figures of rainfall variability and rainfall intensity. The mountains are fully exposed to the influx of moist, tropical air, and to the northeasterly downpours of cyclonic depressions. Under these circumstances, rainfall is heavy, both within the mountains and on their eastern flanks. An indication of how heavy these falls can be is given in Devereux's study on Waihi:[14] he there records that 21.50 inches fell in nine days in January 1907, and that on 3 July 1909 a total of 6.50 inches fell between 8 a.m. and 4 p.m., with a maximum rate around 3 p.m., when 1.45 inches fell in half an hour. These intensities are not untypical of what is likely to happen here on quite frequent occasions. It has been estimated, for example, that a fall of over 4 inches in twenty-four hours may be expected annually throughout the Coromandel range, as well as in the ranges between Whangarei and the Bay of Islands, and that more than 6 inches over the same period is likely at least once in ten years.[15] The irregularity of these happenings, however, means that the variability of annual rainfall is high. In these eastern parts it is in the neighbourhood of 18 per cent in contrast with a figure of 14 per cent or less in those areas which derive their precipitation more particularly from westerly winds (*Fig.* 10).

Within the middle Waikato basin rainfall tends to be less than elsewhere in Northern New Zealand. It is the only part of the region where the mean rainfall of summer and early autumn falls below potential evapotranspiration in the same period. The difference is not normally sufficient to cause moisture deficiencies but it is a factor of regional significance. Similarly, one finds here rather more extreme temperature conditions than elsewhere. At Ruakura (Hamilton), for example, the mean diurnal range of temperature in July is 18.8F° and in January it is 22.9F°. These are higher figures than those for places elsewhere in the region, and express a similar relationship to that found in other temperature statistics (*Table* 18).

Table 18

STATISTICS ILLUSTRATING THE DIFFERENCES BETWEEN THE TEMPERATURE CONDITIONS OF THE MIDDLE WAIKATO BASIN AND THOSE OF OTHER PARTS OF NORTHERN NEW ZEALAND

		Ruakura	*Waipoua*	*Auckland*	*Tauranga*
Mean Diurnal Temp. Range, F°:	July	18.8	15.8	10.6	17.3
	Jan.	22.9	17.7	12.6	19.8
	Year	20.8	16.7	11.7	18.5
Mean Extreme Temp. Range, F°:	July	38.5	33.4	24.4	33.7
	Jan.	43.5	34.7	26.4	40.0
	Year	65.1	51.1	43.8	56.6
Mean Annual No. of Ground Frosts:		79.3	12.3	3.0	38.7

Northern New Zealand, therefore, is a region of only moderate climatic diversity, whose principal characteristics have been obtained from a position which has allied it both with forces affecting all New Zealand, and with influences which are less widely felt. The result is a climate distinguished more particularly on account of its comparative warmth and its winter rainfall maximum than because of its other qualities. These pecularities are expressed in other aspects of the region's geographic character, in spite of the vast transformations which both Maori and European occupance of the territory have achieved.

Although most of the original vegetation is now destroyed, it is not without significance that its relics display characteristics not found outside these territories. Cockayne, for example, points out

[14]H. B. Devereux: 'The Remarkable Rainfall and Meteorology of Waihi', *Trans. N.Z. Inst.*, Vol. 42, 1909, pp. 408–41.
[15]C. J. Seelye: 'The Frequency of Heavy Rainfalls . . .', op. cit.

that the New Zealand rain-forest is, as a whole, most catholic regarding its soil demands, and forests of much the same floristic and ecological character thrive equally well on soils of greywacke, granitic, volcanic, or calcareous origin.[16] This means that the distribution of species in the primitive forest was strongly affected by climate. Its influence is seen in the gradual dropping out of species from north to south. Latitude 38°S, which is the approximate southern boundary of Northern New Zealand, was significant in this process (*Fig. 35*). Thereabouts certain northern forest species disappeared: kauri (*Agathis australis*), taraire (*Beilschmeidia taraire*), and pohutukawa (*Metrosideros tomentosa*), are examples. Similarly, there are some differences in pasture composition between Northern New Zealand and the rest of the country. The distribution of *paspalum dilatatum* illustrates this. Its growth as a dominant is largely confined to northern parts (*Fig. 35*), and unless checked by careful management it rapidly assumes command in the paddocks.[17]

The climate is reflected perhaps more than in any other way, though, by the vigour of growth in these northern parts. The sun pours forth its energy from a rain-washed sky and the plants respond, being well-watered and never suffering extremes of either cold or heat for any great length of time. They have only a short resting period, and grass growth is continuous for all but about six weeks of the year. No other part of the country has such continuity of growth. It is illustrated by the 'grassland economy' peculiar to intensive livestock rearing here.[18] There is a striking absence of green fodder and root crops. The animals feed on grass almost throughout the year, and the little supplementary feeding that is necessary uses hay and ensilage. Farm management, therefore, aims at establishing swards of perennial ryegrass and white clover, and there are very few ploughed fields in Northern New Zealand. To a large extent this represents the New Zealand farmer's response to the region's climatic character.[19]

The general degree of climatic unity which exists in Northern New Zealand, however, is not matched by its other current geographic qualities. The only corresponding cohesion is found in the community of interest which centres upon Auckland as the largest town and the region's social and economic capital. This, like climate, gives a certain amount of 'common feeling' to the whole area. Otherwise we must recognize the differences which exist, particularly between the north Auckland and Coromandel peninsulas on the one hand, and the rest of the territory on the other. The contrast is largely derived from processes of economic development: it is a man-made difference. It consists fundamentally in a contrast between an area of highly developed farm and urban life, and one displaying the qualities of a pioneer fringe. The former occurs from just north of Auckland City southwards. Auckland itself, the biggest urban centre of New Zealand, sprawls around Waitemata Harbour and over the stumps of ancient volcanoes. Its importance depends chiefly on the wealthy countryside which supports it—a countryside won from swamp and scrub and forest by human toil and the lavish use of Pacific island phosphates. Today there are small paddocks, well-made roads, square, red-roofed houses, and hundreds of fat lambs and dairy cattle feeding on rich, green pastures.

Good-quality landscapes of this nature are found mainly in the Waikato valley and adjacent areas. Northwards, and in the Coromandel peninsula, are the pioneer fringes, land awaiting development and containing, over short distances, remarkable contrasts. Perhaps nowhere are the contrasts

[16]L. Cockayne: 'The Vegetation of New Zealand', op. cit.

[17]The occurrence of *Paspalum dilatatum* as a dominant, or as a vigorous invader, appears to be governed very largely by temperature, although there is some doubt as to whether it is the mean minimum or the mean extreme minimum which is the limiting factor. See E. A. Madden: 'The Grasslands of the North Island', op. cit.

[18]K. B. Cumberland: 'The Agricultural Regions of New Zealand', op. cit.

[19]There are certain 'warm climate' crops which are virtually confined to Northern New Zealand. For example, the region contains all the tung tree plantations of the country. It also has 90 per cent of the passion fruit, and about two-thirds of the grape vine acreages. Similarly, 90 per cent of the country's citrus fruit trees are found here. See M. M. Burns and N. H. Taylor: 'A Survey of Tung Groves in New Zealand', *N.Z. Dept. Sci. and Ind. Res. Bulln.*, No. 66, 1939; K. B. Cumberland: 'Soil Erosion in New Zealand', op. cit.; W. H. Hamilton: 'A Preliminary Survey of the Citrus Fruit Industry in New Zealand', *N.Z. Dept. Sci. Ind. Res. Bulln.*, No. 53, 1937.

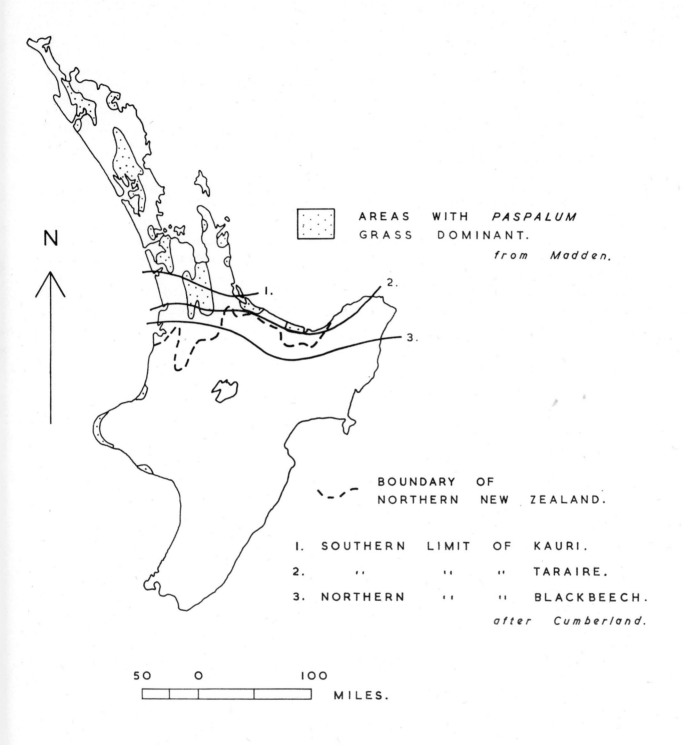

N

AREAS WITH *PASPALUM* GRASS DOMINANT.

from Madden.

BOUNDARY OF NORTHERN NEW ZEALAND.

1. SOUTHERN LIMIT OF KAURI.
2.   "   "   "   TARAIRE.
3. NORTHERN   "   "   BLACKBEECH.

after Cumberland.

50   0   100

MILES.

FIG. 35. Some Vegetation characteristics of the North Island of New Zealand.

so great as in the north Auckland peninsula, as the following paragraph from Cumberland so clearly illustrates:[20]

> There are warm, smiling, sheltered lowlands with gently sloping, low-angled scoria cones, rich red-brown soils and trim and tidy dairy farms on lush green meadowland or rye-grass and paspalum (*Paspalum* spp.) sheltered by remnant clusters of tall puriri trees. There are open, wild stretches of easy podsolic 'moorland' worked over by gum diggers and abandoned to a stunted secondary growth of manuka, prickly hakea (*Hakea acicularis*), bracken and umbrella fern (*Gleichenia microphylla*)—drab dismal wastes awaiting the arrival of mechanical equipment, artificial fertilizers and certified grass and clover seed before being converted from grey wilderness to green farm. There is dissected hilly country of greywacke, of Tertiary mudstone and of Cretaceous limestone, partially deforested, incompletely grassed and being rapidly invaded by hardfern, bracken, blackberry and gorse. . . . There are, too, high-standing, undulating andesite plateaux still carrying dense groves of giant kauri and mixed forest stands or here and there clearings with blackened stumps and isolated tree ferns amidst rank browntop (*Agrostis tenuis*) pastures.

The dominant note of this north Auckland landscape is a drab one. In time, no doubt, the differences between it and the well-developed territories to the south will disappear. There is no climatic reason why they should not. Both areas are fundamentally similar in their climates and, as the frontier of settlement moves forward, it is not unreasonable to think that north Auckland too will become a well-farmed area, making use of the moist, warm sunshine which the climate here provides.

[20]K. B. Cumberland: 'Soil Erosion in New Zealand', op. cit.

(a)   *By courtesy of The High Commissioner for New Zealand*

(b)   *By courtesy of The High Commissioner for New Zealand*

PLATE V. *Contrasting landscapes of Northern New Zealand*
(a) Herekino settlement in the north Auckland peninsula. (b) Roberts' farm in the Waikato valley.
'As the frontier of settlement moves forward it is not unreasonable to think that north Auckland too will become a well-farmed area, making use of the moist, warm sunshine which the climate here provides' (see page 86).

PLATE VI. *The grey skies of Southern New Zealand*

A view near Winton, Southland, illustrating the farming richness of this cool, well-watered area.

8

SOUTHERN NEW ZEALAND

SOUTHERN New Zealand has an impressive regional personality. It is striking from whatever direction the traveller first sees it. Along the main coast road from the north, the region is entered some miles south of Oamaru. Here the varied colourings of the south Canterbury and north Otago downlands give way to rolling hills, covered by a coarse growth of grass and patches of manuka (*Leptospermum* spp.) and broom (*Cytisus scoparius*), with better, light-green pastures in places. The air, too, has become cooler and, if it is evening, coastal mist may envelop the hill tops. The route passes through Dunedin, with its grey stone buildings and long main street, on to the multi-coloured chess-board of the Taieri plain. After that comes rough, hill country again until, after passing Balclutha, the pastures get greener and the sheep population denser. From here onwards we are reminded of the North Island's intensively-farmed livestock areas, of Waikato dairy farms and the greenness of Taranaki. But there is a difference: it arises from greyer skies, cooler air, the feel of rain, and the pattern of the fields, many of which are ploughed and cultivated for fodder crops—turnips, rape, and choumoellier.

Sharper still is the impression of contrast obtained by reaching the area from Inland South Island. The approach is via Rae's Junction, and over the Tapanui Range. Central Otago is brown, bare, and, in summer, dusty, and the road from Rae's Junction winds up through sombre, dun-coloured tussock grazing land. But over the crest of the hills there is a different world: a green world, a world of rich grass and fodder crops, in which the white dots of innumerable sheep speckle the undulating downlands that stretch towards the plains and cradle the tidy homesteads tucked among them.

These southern landscapes reflect the area's climate to a remarkable degree. As in the rest of New Zealand, of course, their major features have been created by human endeavour, by men and women working in terms of the encouragement and opportunity provided by political policies and by the economic return from sending meat, dairy produce, and wool to a distant European market. But these are stimulants universal to the economic life of New Zealand, and in reacting to them the people of Southern New Zealand have had to come to terms with their local environment, and particularly with its climate.

This climate may be distinguished from that of other parts by both its moisture and temperature characteristics.

Rainfall in Southern New Zealand is among the most reliable in the whole country. Only Western South Island compares with it in this respect. Mean annual variability is under 12 per cent, and in some parts of the coast, notably the Catlins district, it falls as low as 8 per cent, which is lower than anywhere else in the country (*Fig.* 10).[1] The time of greatest variability is in late summer and early autumn. February is the only month in which the mean variability attains as much as 50 per cent, and a figure under 40 per cent is the normal for most months (*Fig.* 36).[2] Rainfall, moreover, in addition to varying little from one year to the next, is evenly spread through the seasons. The maximum concentration averages about 28 per cent of the annual total in any one season, and

[1]C. J. Seelye: 'The Variation of Annual Rainfall . . .', op. cit.
[2]*idem*: 'Variations of monthly rainfall . . .', op. cit.

Table 19

MEAN ANNUAL RAINFALL AND MEAN ANNUAL NUMBER OF RAIN DAYS IN SOUTHERN NEW ZEALAND
COMPARED WITH THOSE OF OTHER PARTS OF NEW ZEALAND

(a) *Comparison between Regions:*

Region	No. of Stations	Mean Annual Totals Rainfall (in.)	Mean Annual Totals Rain Days	Index Values of Mean Annual Totals Rainfall (Sth. N.Z.=100)	Index Values of Mean Annual Totals Rain Days (Sth. N.Z.=100)
Southern N.Z.	23	37.54	162	100	100
Middle N.Z.	69	55.98	150	149	93
Western Sth. Is.	14	123.36	186	329	115
Northern N.Z.	71	56.68	161	151	100
Eastern Nth. Is.	113	50.05	141	133	87
Eastern Sth. Is.	59	32.28	111	86	69
Central Nth. Is.	31	60.31	156	160	96
Inland Sth. Is.	24	21.01	97	56	60
Upland Sth. Is.	24	67.19	130	179	80

(b) *Figures for Individual Stations:*

Station	Mean Annual Totals Rainfall (in.)	Mean Annual Totals Rain Days
(i) *In Southern New Zealand:*		
Dunedin	39.28	160
Owaka	37.10	160
Tapanui	40.80	163
Otautau	44.79	171
Bluff	39.61	191
Portobello	29.99	154
(ii) *Not in Southern New Zealand:*		
Raglan	52.14	164
Reefton	75.86	165
Otira	201.18	167
Morrinsville	44.52	129
Gisborne	39.85	146
Darfield	31.51	105

the minimum 22 per cent. In conformity with a general quality of the South Island, particularly from the latitude of Christchurch southwards, summer or even autumn is the season of maximum fall (*Fig.* 36). Owing to the relatively cool temperatures at these times of year here, its effectiveness is high. Other areas of summer maximum are not so favoured: in Eastern South Island, for instance, the warmth of summer so reduces precipitation effectiveness that this is the season both of maximum rainfall and of maximum moisture deficiency.[3] Nowhere do moisture deficiencies occur in Southern New Zealand to an extent detrimental to plant growth. North of Balclutha and from Gore inland, the water balance is such that there are one or two months in summer or autumn when precipitation is normally less than potential evapotranspiration, but the extent of the difference is small, being similar to that of the middle Waikato basin, or of the plains of the Manawatu (*Fig.* 37).[4]

The mean annual rainfall over most of Southern New Zealand is between 30 and 60 inches. It occurs on a relatively large number of days. On the average, more than 125 days a year are 'wet', and in about half the territory this figure rises to over 175. Having regard for the mean annual rainfall totals these are high values, as the general comparisons and individual examples given in *Table* 19 indicate. Most of the rain comes from cold fronts and from the unstable air which follows them. It arrives, however, in frequent showers rather than in a limited number of heavy falls. As a rule, more than an inch of rain in twenty-four hours occurs no more than once or twice a year, which is a low

[3] B. J. Garnier: 'The Climates of New Zealand . . .', op. cit.

[4] *idem*: 'The Application of the Concept of Potential Evapotranspiration . . .', op. cit.; and 'Thornthwaite's New System of Climate Classification . . .', op. cit.

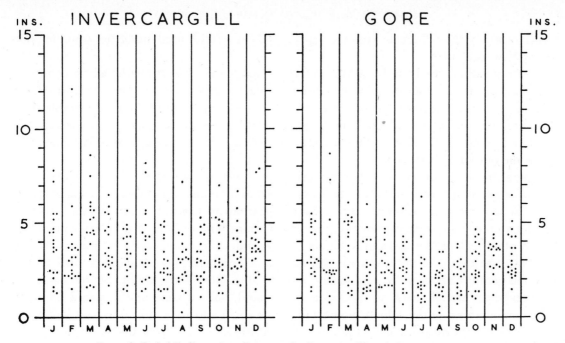

FIG. 36. Rainfall dispersion diagrams for Invercargill and Gore, 1935–54.

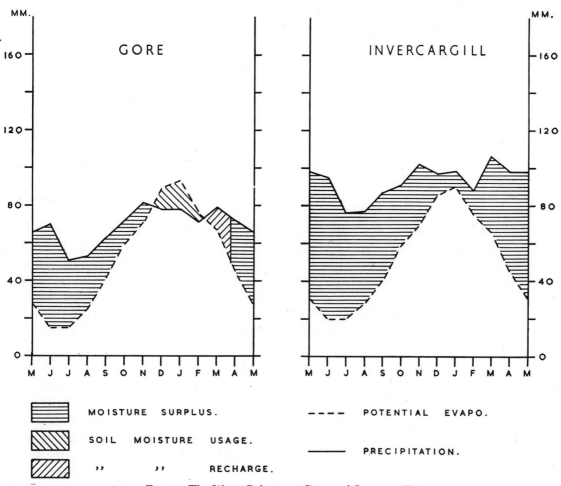

MOISTURE SURPLUS.

SOIL MOISTURE USAGE.

„   „   RECHARGE.

- - - -   POTENTIAL EVAPO.

———   PRECIPITATION.

FIG. 37. The Water Balance at Gore and Invercargill.

incidence of heavy rainfall for the country, especially in areas with total quantities equalling those of Southern New Zealand.[5]

The area is rather cloudy and sunshine values are among the lowest for the whole country. The mean annual hours of bright sunshine number less than 2,000 everywhere, and in most parts their total is under 1,750. The latter figure represents less than 40 per cent of the total possible sunshine for the year, but one aspect which should not be neglected is the frequency with which the sun shines. Long periods without it are uncommon, and there is rarely more than a day when the sun fails to come out for a short time.

Temperatures in Southern New Zealand are, on the average, lower at all seasons than in other lowland areas of the country and they are lower also than in many of the upland areas of the North Island. The average temperatures of the recording stations in Central North Island, for example, all of which exceed 1,000 ft. of elevation, are lower than those of Southern New Zealand only in spring; at other seasons they are a little higher, the greatest difference being in summer when nearly 2F° separate the means of the two areas. No station in Southern New Zealand records a monthly average temperature above 60°F,[6] and for five months of the year, from May to September inclusive, monthly averages are all below 50°F. On the other hand, only at Gore and Tapanui do the mean monthly temperatures of the coldest month fall below 40°F, and then only by about half a degree. These figures give the measure of the average temperatures here. A noteworthy feature is the region's relative coolness during summer (*Table* 20). At this season, the only areas of other regions which are,

Table 20

INDEX VALUES OF MEAN TEMPERATURES DURING WINTER AND SUMMER IN THE
CLIMATIC REGIONS OF NEW ZEALAND
(Southern N.Z. = 100)

Region	No. of Stations	Winter	Summer
Southern N.Z.	11	100	100
Middle N.Z.	16	111	107
Western Sth. Is.	5	107	102
Northern N.Z.	24	119	112
Eastern Nth. Is.	14	110	109
Eastern Sth. Is.	16	100	104
Central Nth. Is.	11	102	103
Inland Sth. Is.	11	89	102
Upland Sth. Is.	7	95	102

on the average, cooler than Southern New Zealand are those which exceed 3,000 ft. of elevation. Another way of expressing the coolness at this time is by referring to statistics for frost. Ground frosts have occurred at least once in the past five years at every recording station of the area during each of the summer months. Nor are screen frosts absent at this season. At Tapanui, for example, the screen temperature fell below freezing point on 28 December 1918, and also on New Year's Day 1948; Gore has recorded screen frosts during both December and January at different times; and even at Invercargill, where frosts are relatively absent in spite of its southerly exposure, a screen frost occurred on 3 December 1947, and a forty-five-year record gives an average incidence of ground frosts as at least once every five years for each month of summer.

Though winters are cold in Southern New Zealand, they are not as cold as one might expect after this somewhat frigid estimate of summer conditions. The temperatures of this season average between 40°F and 43°F, the values being higher on the coast than inland. Even a few miles may make an appreciable difference: for example, the average temperature at Dunedin in July is 43.2°F and at Taieri aerodrome, eight miles away behind a low range of coastal hills, it is 41.0°F. A similar

[5]C. J. Seelye: 'The Frequency of Heavy Rainfalls . . .', op. cit.
[6]The highest monthly mean temperature of any station in Southern New Zealand is 58.6°F at Dunedin in January.

contrast exists between Invercargill (40.9°F in July) and Gore (39.4°F in July), forty miles inland and with no major relief barrier intervening. These temperature figures, however, are not particularly low. Clear days are common in winter, and there is a good deal less wind and changeableness than at other seasons, owing to the frequency of cold anticyclones. From time to time cold, southerly rainstorms occur, but they do not last long, and the general impression of winter derived from several years' residence in the area is that it is, on balance, a more pleasant season to live through than the changeableness, windiness, and coolness of summer.

In general terms, then, we may sum up the climate of Southern New Zealand by saying that it is one of cold winters and cool summers, with a reliable, evenly distributed rainfall, falling frequently in comparatively short showers of moderate intensity; it is also cloudy, there being less sunshine than in any other lowland area, or in many upland districts of the country as well.[7]

Figs. 38 and 39 illustrate the kind of weather conditions which are responsible for these climatic qualities. Like the diagrams in previous chapters, they indicate the effects, at different seasons, of anticyclones preceded by southerly or westerly winds, and followed by northerlies or northwesterlies. The latter brought little rain, but were almost invariably attended by high temperatures and followed by rain, and a fall in temperature as the cold front passed. Sometimes, indeed, the temperature changes involved caused a difference of as much as 10F° behind the maxima of successive days. The southerlies or westerlies which followed the fronts generally lasted for several days. They varied in their direction according to the direction of the isobars behind each individual front,[8] and on occasions, when attached to a depression over or close to Southern New Zealand, they brought plentiful rainfall. An example of this occurred on 27 and 28 June (*Fig.* 38), when southeast winds attached to depressions passing over the South Island brought heavy rain to Dunedin. Comparatively large amounts of rain occurred between 13 and 17 July (*Fig.* 38) also, when a depression, arriving from the northeast on a wave in a major cold front, moved on eastwards, yielding cold southeast and southerly winds in its rear. On the other hand, there was less rain when the air flow was related primarily to a high-pressure system in more northern latitudes, and when the winds were southwest or west. Examples of this in *Fig.* 38 are from 21 to 23 June, and also from 25 to 28 July, after the passage of a wave-depression on 24 July. There is a good deal of cloud at these times and the wind keeps the air in motion so that diurnal ranges and daily maximum temperatures are both low. Indeed, as *Fig.* 38 shows, temperatures may vary by only a few degrees between day and night.

We have already pointed out that summer weather tends to be rather changeable in Southern New Zealand, and this is well shown in *Fig.* 39. Temperatures varied considerably during the first half of the month, for instance, and there were several days with more than half an inch of rain. In the middle of the month, however, there was a period of fine, anticyclonic weather, which culminated in especially high day temperatures at Invercargill and Gore on 20 January, in the northwesterly air which followed. After this a change set in from the southwest, and weather was rainy and variable once more. In short, the diagrams in *Figs.* 38 and 39 taken together, clearly illustrate the salient features of the area's climate. They exemplify matters particularly well when compared with those given in previous chapters for other territories: for example, the changeableness of summer conditions here compared with those of Northern New Zealand, the tendency towards frequent, small rainfalls, interspersed with sunshine, in contrast to the 'blocks' of heavy rain in Western South Island, and the possibility of big extremes and low temperatures at any season.

The best way of understanding weather sequences such as these is by thinking of them as produced

---

[7]It is interesting to note, in passing, that the climate of Southern New Zealand is, from many points of view, more like that of the British Isles than any other part of New Zealand. The comparison with southern England is especially marked. It may explain the success of English grasses here, which do remarkably well and are singularly free from native weeds. See H. J. Critchfield: 'Pastoral Murihiku', *N.Z. Geogr.*, Vol. 7, 1951, pp. 1–20.

[8]I. E. M. Watts: 'Forecasting New Zealand Weather', op. cit.

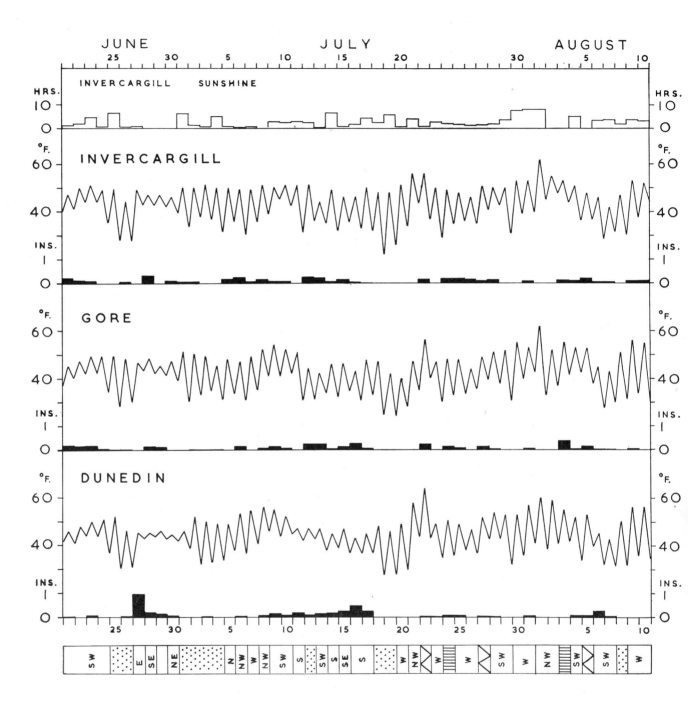

FIG. 38. Daily Temperature and Precipitation during part of the winter of 1950 at Invercargill, Gore, and Dunedin: also daily hours of bright sunshine at Invercargill.

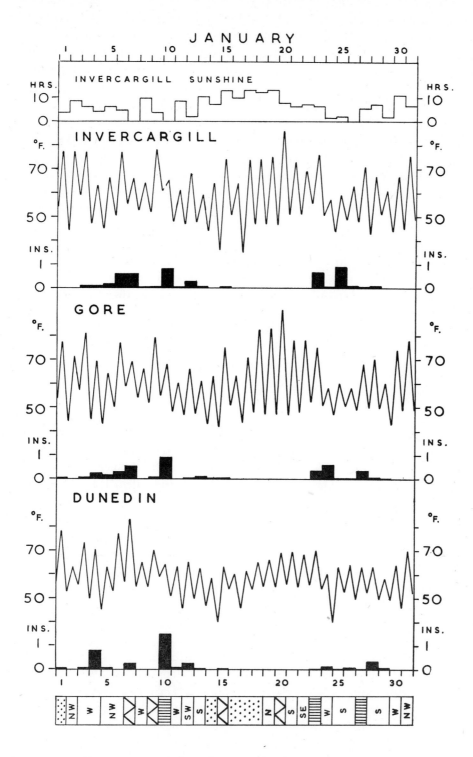

FIG. 39. Daily Temperature and Precipitation during January, 1950, at Invercargill, Gore, and Dunedin: also daily hours of bright sunshine at Invercargill.

by the frequent passage of cold fronts, followed by winds from a generally southerly or westerly quarter. The dominance of cold fronts is probably greater here than in other parts of the country. On many occasions, the traveller from Dunedin to Invercargill is met by a text-book example of a cold front cloud: it advances like a dark wall, and obliterates the sunshine with cloud, a cold wind, and pelting rain. An hour or two later the weather becomes showery and although it remains cold there are bright intervals. At other times one experiences gusty winds, with the air in continual motion from the west or southwest.

Such prevailing conditions are the result of the area's southerly location. When migratory anti-cyclones pass across the north of the land, they normally create southwest or west winds over Southern New Zealand. When wave-depressions affect New Zealand, whichever track they take, it is generally only their cold fronts which influence Southern New Zealand, or else it is the cold air which follows in their wake. The only time when warm-front conditions are felt is in the special instance when a wave-depression passes from northwest to southeast across or near Fiordland and Stewart Island. This is not a common route. Finally, should frontolysis take place on a major cold front as it lies across the Tasman Sea, then Southern New Zealand is often the only part of the country to experience a frontal passage, and once again it is a cold one.

The particular effects of the country's common weather controls, therefore, explain the character of much of Southern New Zealand's climate. In addition, however, one should realize that, like Northern New Zealand, it is also affected by its 'external relationships'. The relationships in this case, however, are antarctic and not tropical. From time to time there are invasions of cold, maritime subpolar air. They may come either in advance of an anticyclone which is lying over the south Tasman Sea, or when there is a high-pressure ridge, oriented north to south, lying west of the country.[9] An example of such a ridge is shown in *Fig. 40*. On this occasion, temperatures at Dunedin and Gore rose to 70°F and 71°F respectively, before the cold front which preceded the high-pressure ridge passed over on the evening of 16 December 1949. That night temperatures fell to 48°F at Gore and Invercargill, and to 46°F at Dunedin. For three days thereafter no station recorded a temperature above 60°F and minima remained at 45°F or less. By the beginning of Christmas week, however, conditions were 'seasonable' again, and daytime maxima of 70°F and over were experienced once more.

A further external influence which affects the region is the generally cloudy belt in the storm tracks of subpolar areas. An indication of the cloudiness of these is given by figures from Campbell Island. In a ten-year period, from 1941 to 1950, sunshine averaged only 684 hours a year, and clouds covered, on the average, seven-tenths of the sky each month. In July 1949 there were fifteen consecutive days without sunshine, and in every month of the year a fifth of the days normally lack sun, while the proportion rises to 50 per cent in winter months. This belt of cloudiness, which is associated with frequent rather than heavy rains,[10] tends to move with the seasons, and the coast of Southern New Zealand in particular may be influenced by it from time to time.

On the whole, Southern New Zealand lacks major internal climatic contrasts. This is to be expected in a region of comparatively low relief. The area consists mainly of a series of river-built plains, interspersed with rolling hills, carved from the soft Tertiary sediments which composed the overmass of the original New Zealand geanticline.[11] Among these hills and plainlands there are a few high areas: the Longwood, Takitimu, and Hokonui ranges are all over 3,000 ft. above sea level, and in the southeast the Catlins provide a rugged massif, rather more than 2,000 ft. above the sea.

[9] The latter phenomenon, if it lies east of the country, is responsible for the nearest approach to an invasion of tropical air experienced in Southern New Zealand.

[10] Rainfall at Campbell Island averages 57 in. a year, falling on 328 days.

[11] C. A. Cotton: 'Otago's Physiography', in 'The Face of Otago' (edr. B. J. Garnier), *Otago Cent. Hist. Pubn.*, Dunedin, 1948. W. N. Benson: 'Some Landforms in Southern New Zealand', *Austr. Geogr.*, Vol. 2, No. 7, 1935, pp. 3–22.

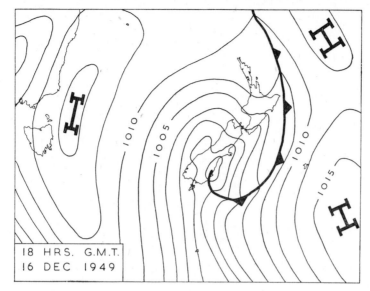

18 HRS. G.M.T.
16 DEC 1949

Fig. 40. A high pressure ridge over the Tasman Sea during December, 1949.

These highlands stand out prominently as superhumid localities within the uniformity of the surrounding humid climatic province. Otago peninsula, also, a basaltic, hilly promontory, is sufficiently high to experience a local climate, and also to create a rain-shadow in southeasterly winds over the neighbouring Taieri plains.

The climatic differences due to relief, however, are slight, and the principal contrasts which exist are derived from the different degree to which areas are exposed to the controlling climatic influences. Southwest and west winds, for example, which are particularly strong along the coast from Invercargill to Nugget Point, decrease in strength and rainfall effectiveness towards Dunedin. Under their influence, therefore, conditions are wetter west of Nugget Point than north of it. On the other hand, south and southeast winds produce more rain along the coast from Nugget Point northwards than on the plains of Southland. Both groups of wind systems are less effective inland, so that inland areas have less rain and more sunshine than the coast, and experience greater temperature extremes as well.

The foregoing remarks have emphasized that Southern New Zealand derives its climatic character partly from its position with respect to the chief influences controlling New Zealand's weather, and partly from its susceptibility to invasions of cold, subpolar air. These have produced distinctive elements and given it a unique climatic personality. The expression of these in landscape is particularly strong, in spite of the fact that it is an area with, for New Zealand, a long history of occupance.

Although it was gold that first attracted large numbers of people to Southern New Zealand, economic prosperity here has always been based upon agriculture.[12] To begin with the land was held in large blocks for extensive livestock rearing. This was followed by grain growing, but with the advent of refrigeration the economic advantages of meat production and then dairy farming became apparent. The most spectacular developments of the twentieth century in this respect have taken place in the North Island, but in the South Island, too, the changeover from grain growing and livestock ranching to more intensive animal production occurred wherever possible, and no South

[12]In addition to the standard books on New Zealand's history, a considerable amount of material on Southern New Zealand will be found in the series of publications of the Otago Centennial Historical Committee from 1948 onwards. In particular reference should be made to A. H. Maclintock: 'The History of Otago', Dunedin, 1949.

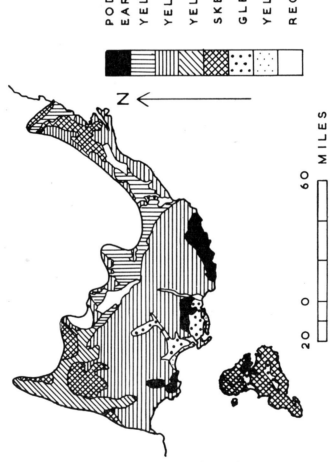

PODZOLISED YELLOW BROWN EARTHS AND PODZOLS.

YELLOW GREY EARTHS.

YELLOW BROWN EARTHS.

YELLOW BROWN LOAMS.

SKELETAL SOILS.

GLEY AND ORGANIC SOILS.

YELLOW BROWN SANDS.

RECENT ALLUVIUM.

N

20   0   60   MILES

FIG. 41. The Soil Types of Southern New Zealand (from Soil Map of N.Z., 1948).

96

Island area was more suited for this than Southern New Zealand. Today, therefore, the region is dominated by fat-lamb production and dairy farming, but it retains some of its original character in the relatively large amount of grain growing and livestock ranching which takes place, especially in the 'back country' where the region impinges upon Inland South Island, and where the climate is a little drier, with more sun and greater extremes of temperature.

The incentive for this development was economic: the particular form it has taken and its resulting character are largely due to the combined effect of advantageous and disadvantageous climatic factors. An evenly distributed rainfall, which comes in frequent and relatively light falls, is the most favourable climatic asset here. It has facilitated the production of high-quality pastures which carry a dense livestock population.[13] For the region as a whole the ratio of livestock units to land occupied is two to the acre. This is higher than any other South Island region and is about half that of the intensively farmed North Island dairy areas.[14] Actually, allowing for the lightly stocked 'run country' on the periphery, the carrying capacity of the core of the region is probably as great as that of much of Middle and Northern New Zealand. Moreover, the reliability of rainfall here means that there is little danger of drought. It is a boon to farmers, not only in Southern New Zealand, but also in neighbouring areas, who are able to sell off their lambs for fattening in 'rainy Southland' when there are moisture deficiencies in their own territories.[15]

High production has, however, only been achieved in the face of climatic difficulties which are chiefly the result of low temperatures. These have acted both directly and indirectly. In a direct sense, the cold of winter limits the period of grass growth to eight months of the year. This is a shorter time than that of other areas of intensive livestock farming. The result is that farmers have found it necessary to use supplementary feed, especially green fodder and root crops; 33 per cent of the total New Zealand acreage of these is found in Southern New Zealand, and their density, 82 acres per 1,000 acres of occupied land, is matched only in Eastern South Island on the plains and downlands of Canterbury and north Otago.[16] Indirectly, cool temperatures, in association with plentiful rain, have produced strongly leached and, in places, podzolized soils (*Fig.* 41).[17] In their natural state, therefore, the soils are acid and infertile—a local characteristic which unites the area with Western South Island, although there is not in this case the extreme development of the groundwater podzol. To overcome this condition liberal top-dressing, especially with lime, has been necessary, which has given rise to the local saying that 'lime has made Southland'.

The landscapes of Southern New Zealand, then, are dominated by the imprint of intensive livestock farming, against a remnant background of large-scale ranching and extensive grain growing. There is also, however, a good deal of cropping. The result is the creation of a farming landscape which in many ways is reminiscent of the British Isles, with its widespread use of rotation agriculture. In this respect Southern New Zealand differs from the intensive livestock areas of other parts of the country, where continuous pasture production, with hay as supplementary winter feed is the keynote. This local difference is largely climatically derived and is the principal way in which present-day landscapes express the region's particular climatic qualities.

[13]It is worth noting here that the relatively light falls of rain mean that the area, even on steeper slopes, is not liable to excessive soil erosion. Flooding, however, due to heavy rain in the 'back country', is not uncommon in the lower reaches of the rivers which wander over wide gravel beds.

[14]K. B. Cumberland: 'The Agricultural Regions of New Zealand', op. cit.

[15]H. J. Critchfield: 'Pastoral Murihiku', op. cit.

[16]K. B. Cumberland: 'The Agricultural Regions of New Zealand', op. cit.

[17]J. T. Holloway: 'The Vegetation and Soils of Otago', in 'The Face of Otago', op. cit.

9

EASTERN NORTH ISLAND

THE first four regions discussed have a certain degree of climatic unity, in spite of the distinctions between them. It is derived from the fact that westerly influences are both the prevalent and dominant climatic controls, and are responsible throughout for maintaining equable temperatures and plentiful, reliable rainfall. Differences arise from three causes: firstly, the degree to which westerly influences are active at different times; secondly, the effect of relief in modifying westerly weather; and thirdly, the extent to which 'external' relationships alter the picture. In a sense, therefore, we can regard Middle New Zealand, Western South Island, Northern New Zealand, and Southern New Zealand as subdivisions of a major climatic unit, which obtains its unity from the dominance of the country's 'normal' weather controls.

In the east of the country, however, instead of maintaining thermal equability and rainfall reliability, westerly influences produce, on the leeward side of mountain ranges, moisture deficiencies and extreme conditions of temperature. As causes of rain they act as the fundamental origins of the cold fronts which are responsible for nearly all the rainfall in eastern parts. The actual air streams which bring the rain, however, are commonly from the south and southeast, and the dominant weather factor is, therefore, an easterly or a southerly one. Such weather is irregular, and produces a high variability of rainfall, sharp, sudden temperature changes, and big diurnal and monthly temperature extremes. These are, accordingly, the common factors distinguishing all eastern New Zealand from western parts, and provide the bond uniting the two 'eastern' regions of the country, Eastern North Island and Eastern South Island, as a climatic entity. In detail, however, the climates of these two areas are so different that they must be treated separately, and only that of the former area will be considered in this chapter.

'Eastern North Island' occupies all the territory on the eastern side of the North Island mountains, from East Cape to Cape Palliser, and also includes the hills and plains of northeast Marlborough in the South Island. It is convenient to deal with its climate under three heads: firstly, the qualities due to its eastern location, secondly, those due to its association with North Island conditions generally, and thirdly, those due to its physiographic form.

The differences which exist between the climate of the east and of the west in New Zealand are the result of the extent to which the intervening mountain ranges form a climatic barrier. In the North Island the chief mountain ranges lie along its eastern side, east of the central volcanic plateau. The main divide consists of four ranges—the Tararua, the Ruahine, the Kaimanawa, and the Raukumara mountains. They consist of a massive ridge of Trias-Jura (greywacke) rocks, exposed for almost the entire length of the mountain system. The ranges are steepest and most individual in character south of the Manawatu Gorge. Here the Tararua range rises to over 5,000 ft. above sea-level and slopes steeply on both sides, on the west to the coastplain of Wellington and the lower Manawatu valley, and on the east to the fault-angle depression made by the Wairarapa valley. North of the Manawatu Gorge the mountain system broadens, and the main ranges are flanked on the east by ridge and valley country, created from the erosion of the late Cretaceous and Tertiary overmass of limestone, mudstone, and sandstone. The result is a series of ridges with steep scarps to the west and long undulating dip-slopes to the east. The average height of the main divide here is between 4,000

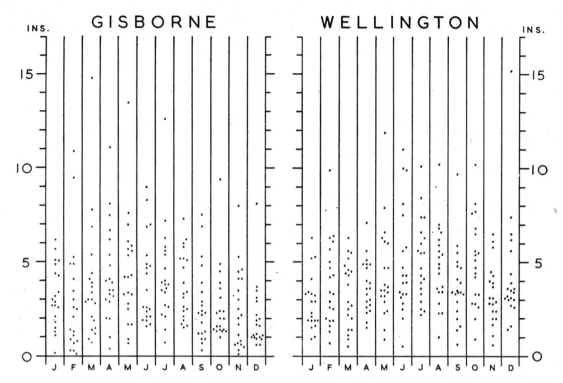

FIG. 42. Rainfall dispersion diagrams for Wellington and Gisborne, 1935–54.

and 5,000 ft. above sea-level, but on the western side its relative height is reduced by some 1,500 ft., because of the volcanic plateau. North of the Manawatu Gorge, therefore, the actual westward-facing scarp is only some 3,000 ft. above the level of the neighbouring land. Although by South Island standards the physical barrier is not very high, it is sufficient to cause climatic contrasts between the west and the east.

Broadly speaking, there tends to be less rain in Eastern North Island than there is to the west of the region. Average figures express this by the low mean annual totals of such restricted localities as the plains near Gisborne, Hastings, and Blenheim, and in the Wairarapa valley. There is not, however, the complete contrast in rainfall totals that there is in the South Island. Indeed, where the mountains broaden north of the Manawatu Gorge, the average annual rainfall is as much as in the greater part of Taranaki. South of this area, however, between the Tararua mountains and the Pacific Ocean, the mean annual rainfall is generally under 50 inches and compares with the annual totals of the 'rain-shadow' area of the lower Manawatu.

A clearer view of the region's moisture character may be obtained by regarding the variability, incidence, and origins of rainfall. The mean annual value of the first of these is more than 14 per cent everywhere. North of Dannevirke it is over 16 per cent, and it exceeds 20 per cent in mid-Hawke's Bay, where the highest figure of mean annual variability for the whole of New Zealand (24 per cent) is found at Sherenden.[1] These figures are consistently higher than those for Middle New Zealand, for example, with which we can conveniently contrast Eastern North Island, and the same kind of contrast appears when we regard the monthly values. Even in winter and spring, when the rainfall is generally more reliable than it is at other seasons, the mean monthly variability is in the vicinity of 40 per cent, and during the rest of the year it rises to over 60 per cent in parts. *Fig.* 42 illustrates the kind of variation which can occur over a relatively short time. In the twenty years

[1]C. J. Seelye: 'The Variation of Annual Rainfall . . .', op. cit.

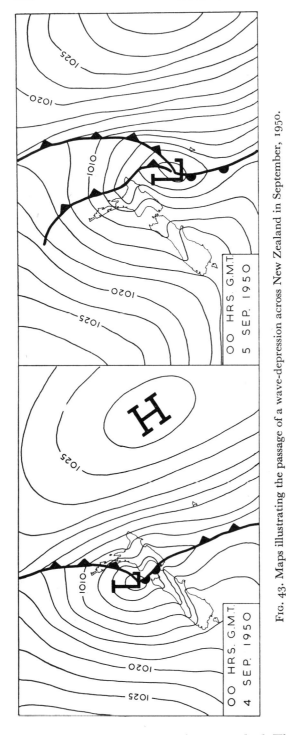

FIG. 43. Maps illustrating the passage of a wave-depression across New Zealand in September, 1950.

between 1935 and 1954 the rainfall at both Gisborne and Wellington varied from almost nothing to over 10 inches in several months. Moreover, even in months of relatively reliable rainfall, such as August at Gisborne or November at Wellington, the range of rainfall totals was in the vicinity of 6 or 7 inches.

When westerly winds predominate over the North Island rainfall is low in Eastern North Island. This fact is reflected in a tendency towards a rainfall minimum in spring, when westerlies are strongest and most persistent. This is particularly true of the area from the Manawatu Gorge northwards, where a large number of stations average less than 20 per cent of their mean annual total at this time. The contrast between the west and east during westerly weather, however, is better illustrated by specific examples. *Fig.* 43, for instance, depicts the passage of a wave-depression through the middle of the country on 4 and 5 September 1950. As it approached, moist north-west winds deluged the west coast with rain and over 4 inches were recorded at New Plymouth during the twenty-four hours ending 9.30 a.m. on the 4th. There was no rain in the east until later in the day, by which time the depression was over Cook Strait. The rain ceased on the afternoon of the 4th at New Plymouth, but continued until the following midday in the east, where in the twenty-four hours preceding 9.30 a.m. on the 5th it totalled over an inch at Onepoto (Lake Waikaremoana), and between a quarter of an inch and half an inch at Blenheim and Hastings. A further example of the same kind of phenomenon in the last week of June 1950 is provided by comparing *Fig.* 44 with *Fig.* 24.[2] During this period a series of disturbances travelled across the country bringing general rain to the North Island (*Fig.* 45). Rain fell, however, at different times and in different quantities at New Plymouth and Hastings, the heavy rain at the latter station occurring after the passage of a cold front, whereas at the former there was rain both from this source and from the warm sector as it approached. The daily rainfall at the two stations is given in *Table* 21.

Somewhat different is the situation when a depression moves southwards off the coast of the North Island. Then, there is likely to be rain in the east but not in the west. An instance of this

[2]It is not proposed to offer any comments on the general conditions shown in *Fig.* 44. It has been included to illustrate characteristic summer and winter conditions in Eastern North Island in the same way as the various diagrams given in this book do for other parts.

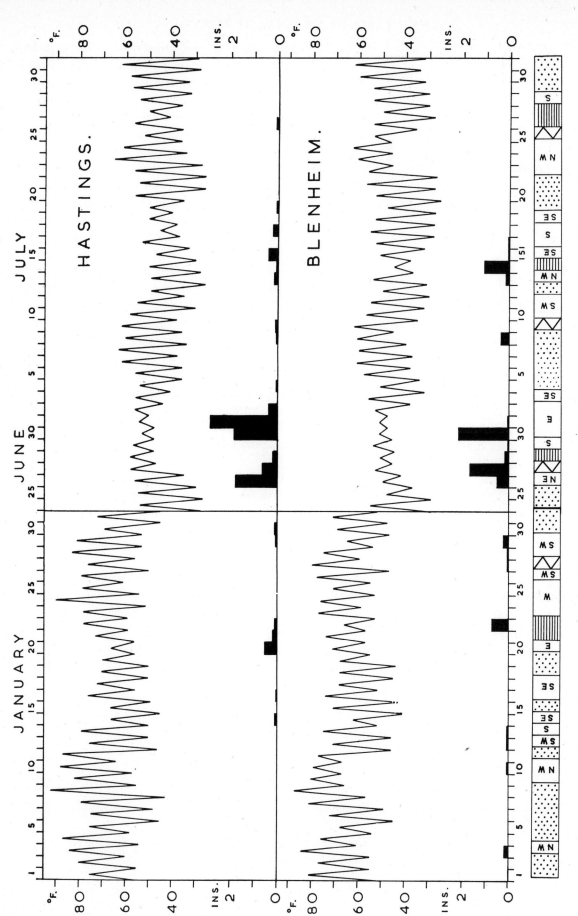

FIG. 44. Daily Temperature and Precipitation during January, 1950, and part of the winter of 1950 at Hastings and Blenheim.

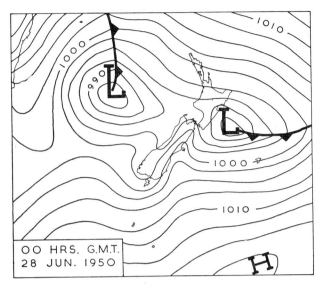

FIG. 45. Map illustrating depressions over New Zealand during the last week of June, 1950.

occurred in mid-January 1950 (*Figs.* 44 and 23). A depression moved slowly southwards while an anticyclone lay near the Chatham Islands, and in two days, 20 and 21 January, nearly 3 inches of rain fell on the eastern flanks of the ranges, and two-thirds of an inch at Hastings. None fell in the west: no rain was recorded those days at New Plymouth, and only traces in the Manawatu.

Since so much of the rainfall of Eastern North Island occurs in showers of relatively short duration, it is not surprising that the number of days with rain is comparatively few and that there is plenty of sunshine. The latter is augmented by the region's position in the lee of mountain ranges. The prevalent westerly winds clear the skies east of these and since the ranges lie close to the shore, in places indeed rising abruptly from it, coastal cloud is comparatively absent.[3] Napier (mean annual hours of sunshine 2,406), Blenheim (2,449 hours), and Gisborne (2,284 hours) stand out as sunny spots in a land of plentiful sunshine. The only station in Eastern North Island where the average annual sunshine is under 2,000 hours is Wallaceville (1,974 hours) in the upper Hutt valley. Out of eight New Zealand stations averaging over 2,250 hours of sunshine a year, five are in Eastern North Island.

Table 21

DAILY RAINFALL AT NEW PLYMOUTH AND HASTINGS, 25 JUNE–1 JULY 1950
(Figures in inches)

Station	25	26	27	28	29	30	1
New Plymouth	0.07	0.60	1.37	1.15	Tr.	1.72	0.02
Hastings	Nil.	1.79	0.65	0.18	0.02	1.85	2.88

The generally clear skies and plentiful sunshine are reasons for the comparatively high diurnal ranges of temperature found in Eastern North Island. Whereas in Middle New Zealand the mean diurnal range of temperature is in the neighbourhood of 15F° in winter, and of 17F° in summer, in Eastern North Island for the same seasons it is in the vicinity of 17F° and 20F° respectively. These are not among the highest figures for the country: they are exceeded in the interior and east of the South Island, and even over much of Central North Island. They are, however, greater than those for all regions of westerly exposure and, comparatively speaking, reflect the influence of easterly location in the climate of the area. A further temperature contrast between east and west lies in the greater extreme maximum temperatures of the former area as revealed in the statistics given in *Table 22*. This difference is chiefly due to the influence of föhn-like winds along the east coast, which will be discussed in more detail in the next chapter, since they are most fully developed over the Canterbury plains.

Let us now consider how the region's location as a part of the North Island influences its climate. This manifests itself in three ways: by the seasonal distribution of rainfall, by the region's 'external' relationships, and by the warmth of the winter.

[3]This is a point of contrast with Eastern South Island where the wide, level plains of Canterbury are sunniest some distance from the sea owing to the frequent cloud belt along the coast.

Table 22

MEAN EXTREME MAXIMUM TEMPERATURES IN EASTERN NORTH ISLAND AND
MIDDLE NEW ZEALAND
(°F)

Station	Jan.	Apr.	July	Oct.	Year
(a) Eastern Nth. Is.					
Gisborne	89.6	78.2	64.8	75.2	90.2
Hastings	88.7	80.5	64.4	78.4	89.8
Masterton	86.8	77.2	62.0	73.1	88.8
Blenheim	88.5	78.4	61.8	74.5	90.0
(b) Middle N.Z.					
New Plymouth	76.9	71.1	60.2	66.5	79.3
Wanganui	80.6	76.4	61.4	70.6	82.1
Palmerston North	79.6	73.1	59.4	68.4	81.6
Nelson	79.3	72.1	60.0	70.2	81.7

Over 30 per cent of the annual rainfall normally arrives during the three winter months of June, July, and August. By contrast, 20 per cent or less occurs in the season of least rainfall, which is spring from mid-Hawke's Bay northwards but is summer elsewhere. Thus, except for the region of spring minimum, the area displays the common North Island tendency to have most rain in winter and least in summer, which is related to variations in the occurrence and vigour of cold fronts. Since the region depends so heavily upon them for its rainfall, variations in their arrival and activity are particularly significant here. These variations explain the greater part of the seasonal rainfall pattern. In the case of the spring minimum from mid-Hawke's Bay northwards, however, an additional factor is the prevalence of westerlies at this season. They act both directly and indirectly: directly by creating drier conditions in the area concerned, and indirectly by helping to maintain the rainfall farther south, since northwesterly rains may penetrate through the Manawatu Gorge and Cook Strait, and so reach the Wairarapa Valley and lowlands near Blenheim, so that the region of spring minimum is thereby confined to the northern part of Eastern South Island.

The region's 'external relationships' are like those of Northern New Zealand in causing it to experience the effects of occasional tropical disturbances. Their rainbearing sectors may be responsible for heavy rainfall which is concentrated and intensified by the mountains, especially from mid-Hawke's Bay northwards. Kidson, for example, has reported on the dire effects in mid-Hawke's Bay of a tropical cyclone which passed over the north Auckland peninsula and then east of New Zealand on the 9th, 10th, and 11th of March 1924.[4] In Hawke's Bay the greatest amount of rain fell between 4 a.m. and 6 p.m. on the 11th. At Rissington, for example, there were 20.14 inches between 7.30 a.m. and 5.30 p.m., and at 11.15 a.m. that day the Mangaone river, 34 ft. above its ordinary level, took away the Rissington bridge. Even on the coast rainfall was heavy. At Napier 3.3 inches fell between 2.30 p.m. and 5 p.m. and a 3-knot current of water flowed down the main street of Port Ahuriri, the old port for the town.[5]

Although the whole region may be affected by disturbances of tropical origin, they more commonly influence the north than the south. As a rule, they are not so violent as that described by Kidson, and a more usual experience is illustrated in *Fig.* 46. It shows how a circular disturbance, after forming north of New Zealand while a ridge of high pressure lay to the south, moved across East Cape and then eastwards between the 23rd and 26th of April 1950. It deepened as it went, and brought rain throughout Eastern North Island. As *Fig.* 47 shows, however, the quantity decreased from north to

---

[4] E. Kidson: 'The Flood Rains of the 11th of March, 1924, in Hawke's Bay', *N.Z. Journ. Sci. and Tech.*, Vol. 12, 1930, pp. 53–59.

[5] The particularly heavy falls of rain on this occasion were probably caused by warm air, associated with the forward part of the cyclone, being cut off between the mountains and the sea by the rapid advance of cold, southerly air along the coast. Such movement illustrates the rapidity with which conditions can change in this part of New Zealand.

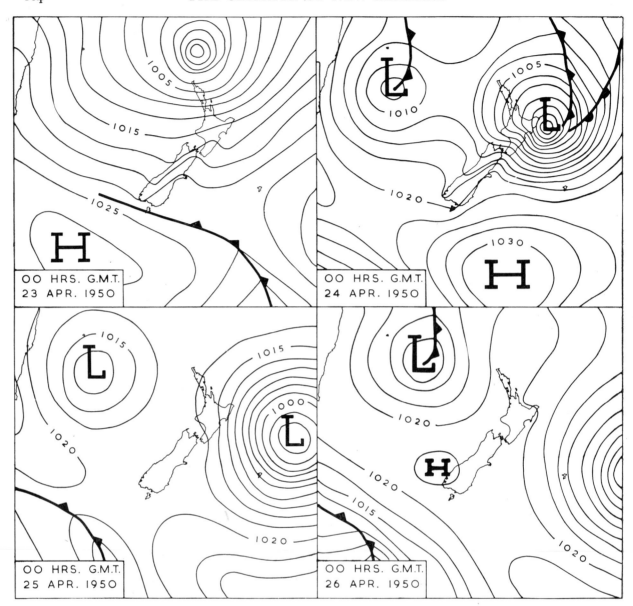

FIG. 46. Maps illustrating the passage of a circular disturbance which affected Eastern North Island during April, 1950.

south. In two days over 5 inches of rain fell at Onepoto (Lake Waikaremoana) and over 2 at Hastings. At Pahiatua, on the contrary, there was only a little over half an inch during the same time, and at Blenheim there was barely one-tenth of an inch. This distribution is typical of that normal to this kind of atmospheric situation.[6]

Finally, we may note that, as in other parts of the North Island outside the central highlands, winters are relatively mild in Eastern North Island. After a summer which is, on the average, nearly as hot as that of Northern New Zealand, mean temperatures fall gradually through March to early April, but drop more rapidly at the end of the month so that, as in other parts of New Zealand, the

[6] Fig. 47 also shows temperature and rainfall conditions in Eastern North Island earlier in the month when tropical air intensified a wave on a cold front as illustrated in Fig. 31 and discussed in Chapter 7. On this occasion, also, rainfall decreased from north to south.

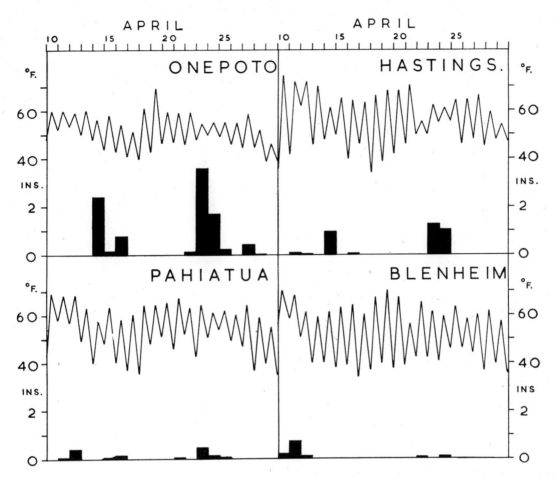

FIG. 47. Daily Temperature and Precipitation from 10–29 April, 1950, at Onepoto (Lake Waikaremoana). Hastings, Pahiatua, and Blenheim.

largest differences between the mean temperatures of successive months occur between April and May. Mean winter temperatures, however, are not really low. They average about 46°F, which is similar to conditions in Middle New Zealand, but there is a greater likelihood of cold nights and frost in Eastern South Island. The average number of screen frosts is about twenty-five a year, while rather more than sixty ground frosts can be expected annually in most places, although this figure rises considerably in specific instances. The mean annual number of ground frosts at Blenheim, for example, is 104, and at Masterton it is 93. There is thus a greater tendency towards frost here than elsewhere in the North Island, outside the highlands of the interior.

The third main group of climatic features to be considered arises particularly from the area's physiography. The relief here is more diverse than in any other region of the North Island. The main ranges stand out prominently as a continuous, rugged area bounding the western side. From southern Hawke's Bay northwards, normal erosion has carved the soft Tertiary strata which lie to the east of them into a ridge and valley pattern in which scarp-slopes face west and long dip-slopes fall gently east. In the south is the Wairarapa Valley—an extensive lowland, level in its southern part, which is set between the steep slopes of the Tararua mountains to the west and irregular hills, more than 1,000 ft. high, to the east. River-carved valleys and river-built plains have further diversified the physiography nearly everywhere. The latter are most apparent near Gisborne, Hastings, and Blenheim. Each of these is a flat area, embedded in a crescent of mountains which slope steeply and abruptly join the flat floors across which the rivers meander. In these instances, therefore, the contrasts in relief are strong, and typical of the scenic changes over short distances which the New Zealand landscape provides.

These differences in relief within Eastern North Island are large enough to create climatic contrasts. Their most noticeable effects are on precipitation, in which respect they operate in two directions: on the one hand they promote remarkably heavy rainfalls, and on the other they create rain-shadows which produce the North Island's driest climates. Over most of the region a fall of 2 or 3 inches in twenty-four hours may be expected at least once a year.[7] These are not unusual values in New Zealand. Where Eastern North Island is peculiar, especially from Dannevirke northwards, is in the rainfalls of phenomenal intensity which may occur. Indeed, as Cumberland has suggested:[8]

> It seems likely that when automatic gauges are more numerous it will be demonstrated that Hawke's Bay and adjacent hill tracts experience rains of greater intensity than the remainder of New Zealand—and greater than all but a few areas beyond New Zealand.

Certainly some of the heaviest falls in the country have been recorded here, of which some examples are given in *Table* 23. These heavy falls occur where the mountains rise abruptly from the coast, and they exemplify, therefore, the effects of orographic uplift. It is noteworthy, however, that the examples quoted in *Table* 23 have all taken place in autumn or summer, and had the list been ex-

Table 23

SOME EXAMPLES OF HEAVY RAINFALL IN EASTERN NORTH ISLAND

Station	Date	Amount (in.)	Duration
Rissington	11/3/24	20.14	10 hrs.
Tokomaru Bay	21/1/17	19.00	21 hrs.
Baring Head	26/12/39	15.25	10½ hrs.
Eskdale	24/4/34	0.97	20 min.
Cape Runaway	22/3/33	1.55	30 min.
Tutira	11/3/24	8.00	3 hrs.
Puketitiri	23–25/4/38	39.40	3 days

tended the same fact would have been further illustrated. At these seasons temperature differences between the air over the land and that of the invading cold front are at a maximum and so thermal contrasts, as well as orographic causes, are operative. Seelye has pointed out, for instance, that cold-front rains at Wellington City may be rarer in summer but they are also heavier.[9] This is equally true of Eastern North Island in general. It is especially marked when an invasion of tropical air precedes a cold front which moves rapidly along the coast, after having been temporarily retarded by the Southern Alps. An invasion of warm air, rapid frontal movement, and the surging up-currents of unstable air forced against the mountain sides, all combine to produce the remarkable falls that occur in the area from time to time. Heavy rain may occur anywhere in the region in this way, but it is more common from mid-Hawke's Bay northwards, where the orographic features and contrasting temperatures are more favourable for its formation than farther south.[10]

But if the region's physiography causes the intensification of precipitation in certain localities, it is equally active as an agent promoting the dryness of particular areas. These are the lowland tracts, small coastal areas for the most part, embedded in the mountains. They display rain-shadow conditions and are the driest parts of the North Island, while in the South Island part of our region, near

[7]C. J. Seelye: 'The Frequency of Heavy Rainfalls . . .', op. cit.

[8]K. B. Cumberland: 'Soil Erosion in New Zealand', op. cit.

[9]C. J. Seelye: 'Wellington City Rainfall', *N.Z. Journ. Sci. and Tech.*, Vol. 26, Sec. B, 1944, pp. 36–46.

[10]An example of heavy rainfall elsewhere will be found in E. Kidson: 'The Wairarapa Floods of August, 1932', *N.Z. Journ. Sci. and Tech.*, Vol. 14, 1933, pp. 220–6.

Blenheim, there is a subhumid climate not greatly dissimilar from that of the south Canterbury district. On the whole, however, the moisture deficiencies are not extreme, and in only two areas are they serious. These are near Blenheim, and on the Heretaunga plains, among the fruit-growing and mixed-farming lands near Hastings and Napier. These two areas are subhumid according to Thornthwaite's classification, and during the latter half of summer and the first part of autumn a moisture deficiency is likely.[11] Rainfall is so low that plants need to depend heavily on soil moisture reserves from about the end of November to the middle of autumn. As a result the water balance shows a moisture deficiency from mid-December onwards, which reaches a maximum at the end of January, and attains a total of nearly 2 inches at Blenheim by the end of March. On the lowlands elsewhere, in the Wairarapa Valley (*Fig.* 48) and near Gisborne, rainfall is not normally so little that soil moisture reserves are unable to supply sufficient moisture for maximum growth. However, they are being utilized all the summer and, in view of the high rainfall variability, especially of the Gisborne area, maximum crop and pasture production requires a controlled irrigation system.

Altogether about a fifth of Eastern North Island can be regarded as having a measurable if slight moisture deficiency. The areas so classed, moreover, are scattered and separated from each other by intervening humid parts, so that they help to diversify the climate here very considerably. In addition, it is possible to recognize subdivisions which arise from the region's extent through latitude. From Dannevirke northwards, for example, the climate is allied in many ways to that of Northern New Zealand, with its warm winters and subtropical influences. Southwards from Dannevirke, on the other hand, the climate has features which link it with Middle New Zealand in some respects and with Eastern South Island in others. It is like the former area in being liable to rain from westerly winds, via the Manawatu Gorge and Cook Strait; it resembles the latter, however, in its liability to frost.[12] These subdivisions, combined with the varied moisture conditions, provide the region with a greater degree of climatic diversity than any other in the North Island.

The overall climatic picture of Eastern North Island, therefore, is one in which some diversity is held together in a framework of common distinguishing elements, derived from the region's location in the east of the country. A remarkable quality of the area as a geographic entity is the way this pattern is repeated by other features. The area's physiography, for example, conforms to the general plan: there is the common bond of the major mountain ranges; there is the subdivision of the region into a northern part dominated by a ridge and valley pattern, and a southern sector composed of a lowland trough between a mountain range and coastal hills; and, finally, there is the detailed diversity created by several river-built plains. The area displays a similar arrangement as an economic unit. It derives its economic cohesion from being one of the four livestock-ranching regions of the country.[13] There is a relatively dense animal population, mainly of sheep, with two livestock units for every acre of occupied land, and wherever one goes one is conscious of the dominance of sheep farming. From roads which twist among the hills covered with danthonia pasture, for example, there are views of woolsheds and stockyards, set beside a homestead surrounded by exotic and native trees. On the roads themselves flocks of sheep are commonly encountered, and the shepherd with his horse and pack of dogs is a familiar sight. The northern part differs from the southern part, however, in being a sheep-rearing area which has been created out of bush, scrub, and bracken. The landscapes are badly eroded and disorderly in appearance, with much land reverting to 'second growth' and covered by fern, bracken, and grey manuka. Northern grasses appear in the swards, Maori shearing gangs operate in the sheds, and the people's outlook is to Auckland. In the south, on

[11]B. J. Garnier: 'The Application of the Concept of Potential Evapotranspiration . . .', op. cit.; *idem*: 'The Climates of New Zealand . . .', op. cit.; *idem*: 'Thornthwaite's New System of Climate Classification . . .', op. cit.

[12]The mean annual number of frosts at Masterton and Blenheim, for example, is comparable with that in north Canterbury or at Christchurch.

[13]K. B. Cumberland: 'The Agricultural Regions of New Zealand', op. cit.

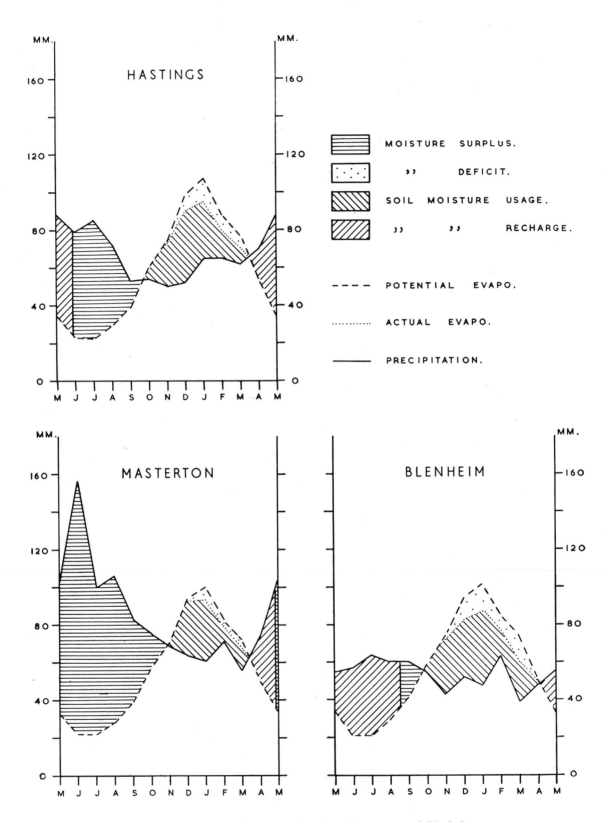

FIG. 48. The Water Balance at Hastings, Masterton, and Blenheim.

the contrary, social and economic contacts are with Wellington. It is an area with more open spaces and longer views. The landscapes of the Blenheim area are clearly South Island in character, with eroded hillsides, sparsely covered with dun-coloured tussocks, but in the Wairarapa Valley the features of large-scale sheep farming are interspersed with scenes typical of North Island dairy farming—dairy cattle feeding on lush green meadows, and a dairy factory at the crossroads.

Pocketed within the major region are the flats of drier climate, where cropping, orcharding, market-gardening, and haymaking occur and where rural settlement is close, and centred upon towns such as Blenheim, Masterton, Hastings, Napier, and Gisborne. These small areas greatly diversify the landscape, just as their distinctive qualities diversify the climate. They are not, however, alien outposts in the geographic complex. On the contrary, they fit neatly into the picture like bright pieces in a jig-saw puzzle. Economically, they are areas of lamb-fattening and intensive farming, drawing much of their nourishment from the stock reservoirs of the surrounding hill stations; socially, they provide focal points for the scattered population of the wider region; physically, they are built from the sediments of the neighbouring mountains; and climatically, they derive their distinguishing qualities from the protective influences of these same massifs.

10

EASTERN SOUTH ISLAND

THE general climatic qualities of Eastern South Island are similar in kind, if not in degree, to those of Eastern North Island. There are, however, also notable differences between the climates of the two areas, and in order to bring out these contrasts the method of treatment in this chapter will be similar to that followed in the previous one. We shall, accordingly, consider the climate of Eastern South Island initially from three points of view: firstly, the characteristics due to its eastern location, secondly, those due to its being a part of the South Island, and thirdly, those due to its physiographic form.

Eastern South Island extends from Gore Bay to south of Oamaru. It is a generally level area within which only the downlands of the north and south, and the volcanic hills of Banks Peninsula, display appreciable relief. To the west are the Southern Alps and to the east the south Pacific Ocean. The former create a barrier which is far more formidable than that which in the North Island separates eastern from western parts. The Southern Alps are highest where they form the western boundary of Eastern South Island, having there an average elevation of over 8,000 ft., with many peaks more than 10,000 ft. above sea-level. This towering line of snow-capped peaks, arêtes, and knife-edge ridges falls steeply away on both sides—on the west as the gigantic escarpments bounding Western South Island, and on the east as the steep slopes which end abruptly where the plains of Canterbury, seemingly flat, but in reality evenly-sloping, stretch onwards to the shore of the Pacific. Deep valleys gash the mountains on the east. Flat-floored and narrow, they contain fast-flowing streams racing between echoing rock walls. The valleys may be a mile or more wide, sloping with an almost imperceptible grade from the foot of the precipices which mark their head and reach upwards to cols between neighbouring peaks. Over these cols and down these valleys come the winds and weather of the west which, though modified in transit, significantly affect the climatic picture of the region we are considering. The long valleys, therefore, are an essential element in the physical picture of the area's western boundary, forming important lines of climatic communication.

The effect of this western barrier on the climate of Eastern South Island is similar to that of the ranges in the North Island upon Eastern North Island. The results in the South Island are more extreme, however, in view of the great size of the Southern Alps. The difference is particularly apparent in the precipitation of the two areas. Whereas over all of Eastern North Island mean annual rainfall exceeds 30 inches, the equivalent area of the South Island experiences nearly everywhere less than this figure. Higher values than this are only found in Banks Peninsula, owing to local orographic uplift, and also in discontinuous areas opposite the valleys down which westerly conditions pass.

The low rainfall of the area is due to the prevalence of westerly winds which may deluge Western South Island and the mountains with rain, but which are dry over the eastern lowlands. Individual instances, particularly of northwesterly air streams, show this contrast to be absolute. A case in point occurred during early October 1949, when a moist, northwesterly air stream approached the west coast as part of the warm sector of a depression centred towards the south (*Fig.* 49). The result was heavy rain on the west coast: Hokitika, Bruce Bay, and Haast, for example, received totals of 6.30, 9.47, and 3.69 inches respectively on the two days in question, 5 and 6 October, but there was no rain recorded at Darfield, Timaru, or Waimate. On the other hand, near the ranges,

PLATE VII. *The diversity of Eastern North Island*

(a) A view near Waipukurau in Hawke's Bay. Sunshine and rain promote rich pastures and vigorous growth on the lowlands, but in the background the hills are scarred by accelerated soil erosion. (b) Near Blenheim: a 'pocket of drier climate' with rain clouds mantling the surrounding hills.

(a)   *By courtesy of The High Commissioner for New Zealand*

(b)   *By courtesy of The High Commissioner for New Zealand*

PLATE VIII. *The subhumid lowlands of Eastern South Island*
(*a*) A general view across the subhumid lowlands of Eastern South Island from Banks Peninsula towards the Southern Alps. (*b*) A close-up of mixed farmlands near Ashburton showing the shelter belts which give protection from northwesterly gales.

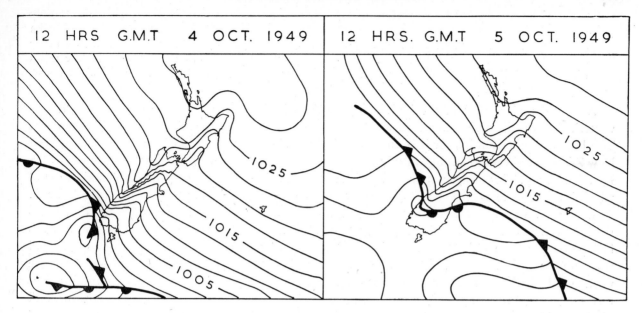

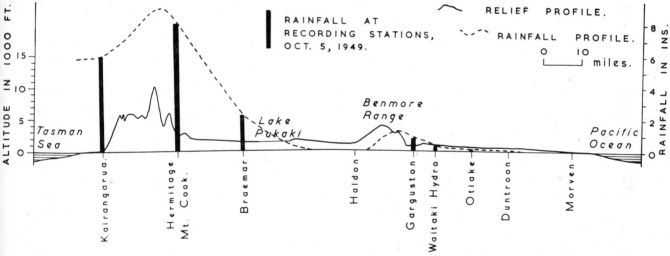

FIG. 49. An atmospheric situation leading to the passage of northwesterly air across the South Island and a cross-section illustrating the resulting distribution of precipitation.

especially opposite the cols, rainfall was considerable but fell off rapidly in the space of a few miles. For instance, Horwell Downs, situated east of a comparatively low col (the Tekapo Saddle), received 2.19 inches in the two days, nearly all on the 5th in actual fact. Ten miles farther east, at Fairlie, only 0.28 inches was recorded, and a few miles farther on there was none at all.

The cumulative effect of individual cases like this is especially marked during periods of prolonged westerly weather. Kidson describes such an example during the summer of 1930–31:[1]

In the summer of 1930–31, there was a protracted period of westerly weather, and a journey from Hokitika to Christchurch during this period was most instructive. The Taramakau and Otira valleys would be ascended in pouring rain, the sky dark with ragged nimbus, but on coming through the Otira tunnel to Arthur's Pass, signs of clearing would be seen ahead, and within

[1] E. Kidson: 'The Elements of New Zealand's Climate', op. cit.

a few miles one would be travelling under clear skies and in warm weather through country that was almost drought stricken. In January and February 1931 the total rainfall at Hokitika on the west coast was 23.24 inches; at Otira, thirty miles further east, and on the western side of the divide, 65.16 inches; at Arthur's Pass, on the eastern side of the divide and five miles distant from Otira, 64.58 inches; at Mount White Station, forty miles from the west coast, 9.56 inches; and at Christchurch, near the east coast, 3.01 inches.

A second major effect of the high Southern Alps is the existence of the Canterbury 'north-wester'.[2] It normally arrives in advance of a low-pressure trough approaching from the Tasman Sea. The best synoptic situation for it is an inverted V attached to a depression, passing over southern New Zealand or in subantarctic latitudes, with high pressure lying north, or northeast, of the South Island (*Fig.* 50). This brings a stream of moist, northwesterly air towards the South Island, some of which is deflected along the coast to Puysegur Point and some of which passes through Cook Strait. At the same time some of it rises over the crests and cols of the Southern Alps and passes down into the long valleys of the eastern sides.[3] Latent heat is liberated through the condensation that leads to heavy precipitation in the west and in the mountains, so that the wind in the east is hot and dry and typically 'föhn-like'. It sets in across Eastern South Island after a characteristic build-up from the west, in which clouds roll over the crests and tower against the summits of the mountains. Immediately east of the ranges it is clear, however, and these clouds—alto-stratus, nimbo-stratus, and nimbus, with high cirrus above them—form the well-known northwester arch. The warm wind arrives suddenly in the east. It comes down the valleys after a few preliminary puffs of alternating cold and warm air, due to turbulent mixing east of the ranges. A little later the full force of the northwester is experienced as warm, dry air blows over the land, parching the skin and raising clouds of dust from river-beds and newly ploughed fields. Often it is powerful and in extreme cases destructive gales occur. As a general rule it reaches, at the surface, to within about twenty miles of the east coast, where there is likely to be a north-east wind curving in towards the region of lowest pressure in the lee of the ranges. This wind has come through Cook Strait and is cooler than the northwester which climbs over it on its way towards the sea.[4]

Of itself the northwester has two main consequences for the climate of Eastern South Island: it brings occasionally very high temperatures and it is responsible for low humidities. The first of these is seen in the high mean annual extreme maximum temperatures which are characteristic of Eastern South Island. Their average, derived from statistics of all stations in the area, is 88.7°F, which is greater than the corresponding figure for any other region. Moreover, the area is similarly outstanding at all seasons except winter. The average of the mean extreme monthly maximum temperatures at all stations in the region amounts to 74.8°F for the three months of spring, to 85.0°F for those of summer, and to 75.6°F for those of autumn. These figures are some four to five degrees higher than the corresponding ones for other regions.[5] Such high temperatures are nearly always related to northwest winds. For example, at Darfield, in mid-Canterbury, the thermometer reached 80°F or

[2]E. Kidson: 'The Canterbury "Northwester"', *N.Z. Journ. Sci. and Tech.*, Vol. 14, 1932, pp. 65–75.

[3]Kidson (ibid.) points out that the warm air which passes over the mountains rises initially over cooler air lying at their base, which has been derived from conditions preceding the arrival of the northwesterly air stream.

[4]The contrast in temperature between the interior and the coast is illustrated by the following statistics for the 'north-wester' period shown in *Fig.* 50.

	Altitude ft.	5TH MAR. Min. °F	5TH MAR. Max. °F	6TH MAR. Min. °F	6TH MAR. Max. °F	7TH MAR. Min. °F	7TH MAR. Max. °F
DARFIELD	640	45.5	79.3	55.4	82.5	63.3	69.7
TIMARU	56	46.5	75.8	46.2	78.8	53.0	77.4

Note: Darfield is some twenty-five to thirty miles inland, and Timaru is on the coast.

[5]The equivalent figure for the three winter months in Eastern South Island is 62.4°F. This is 1.6F° lower than that for Northern New Zealand, and 0.3F° lower than that for Eastern North Island. Otherwise, the figure for Eastern South Island exceeds that of other regions, in spite of its low average winter temperature.

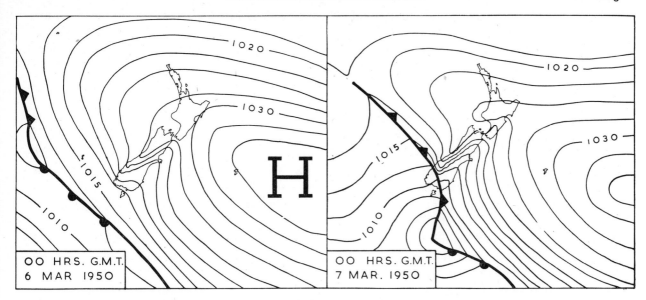

FIG. 50. Atmospheric conditions for a 'Northwester' across Eastern South Island in March, 1950.

more (once it exceeded 90°F) on fifteen occasions between 1 October 1949 and 31 March of the following year: on all but two occasions the wind direction at 9.30 a.m. was from the northwest.

The influence of northwester conditions on relative humidities can be seen in the occasional low value of individual days. At Wigram Aerodrome, for example, relative humidity fell as low as 15 per cent four times between January 1939 and December 1948, and on another seven occasions in the same period it was below 20 per cent. The average relative humidity in Eastern South Island at 9.30 a.m. is below 70 per cent during spring and summer, and this comparatively low value is in large part due to northwesterly influence.

Warm dry northwester conditions are commonly followed by an invasion of cold air due to the arrival of a front along the eastern side of the ranges. The resulting rapid change contributes to the large diurnal and extreme ranges of temperature found here. Their magnitude is similar to that of Eastern North Island. Mean diurnal ranges of temperature in most parts exceed 17F° in winter and 20F° in summer, and the mean annual extreme range of temperature is in the neighbourhood of 65F°. These are common tendencies in the east of the country, but are particularly noticeable in the South Island in view of the speed with which cold fronts travel through the east of the island, after having been initially retarded by the mountains to the west. Their advance is easily perceived. In a car drive southwards from Christchurch, for example, the first part of the journey may be made in warm morning sunshine through mixed farmlands, with their small, square, wooden, bright-roofed farmhouses. Near Ashburton, however, a dark band of cloud may be seen ahead—the perfect arc formed by an approaching cold front. Soon it is encountered. There is a sudden whistle of wind, the lash of driving rain, and the sun becomes blotted out, turning the sky grey. All these can occur in the space of minutes as the front passes over on its way northwards, to reach Christchurch by lunchtime and Wellington during the night.

Eastern South Island, like its northern counterpart, derives the greater part of its precipitation from these cold fronts, particularly if they are followed by southerly or easterly winds. As a result, and for reasons already given, the mean annual variability of rainfall is high, especially in comparison with that in the west, and the average number of wet days is low. This is similar to conditions in the north. There are, however, two ways in which Eastern South Island differs from Eastern North Island: in the former area variability decreases from the coast inland, whereas in the latter it tends to increase in this direction, and the remarkably heavy rainfalls which are common to the north are less likely in the south.

The first of these differences arises from the fact that the interior of Eastern South Island obtains 'westerly' rain by way of the valleys of the Southern Alps, and is thus less dependent on easterly conditions for its precipitation. Indeed, there is a tendency for rainfall from the latter direction to decrease away from the coast. Consequently, mean annual variability of precipitation near the coast is higher than inland, averaging about 16 per cent as compared with 12 per cent at the foot of the mountains (*Fig.* 10). The second point of contrast with Eastern North Island arises from the fact that rainfall in Eastern South Island is not intensified orographically. Thus, stupendous falls of the kind which occur from time to time in mid-Hawke's Bay, for example, are absent here. For the most part the heavy rains of Eastern South Island are produced by cold southerly or easterly air undercutting warmer air, which is not then forced up farther by high ground. The rain which results is soaking rather than violent. It falls steadily from a leaden sky, and is frequently accompanied by a cold wind which drives it against buildings and people in a way which searches out, with remarkable success, any chinks in structural or sartorial defences against the weather. Such rain may continue for twenty-four hours or more, and its duration, rather than its rate per hour, is responsible for high totals from time to time. An extreme example of such precipitation occurred during February 1945.[6] It took place on the 20th and 21st of the month (*Fig.* 51) when a cold, easterly air stream along the northern side of a high-pressure ridge, undercut the warm air lying north of a stationary front. Later there was a change to strong southerlies, and then the weather rapidly cleared. During these two days more than 10 inches of rain fell in a lowland belt from Waimate to Ashburton, a few miles in from the coast and for the most part well to the east of the mountains. The rain was soaking, and pitilessly lashed down at first by a keen, steady, easterly wind, and then by a southerly. Heavy flooding took place and for weeks afterwards the countryside bore evidence of the disaster: wrecked sheds, abandoned machinery, and destroyed crops and hay lay scattered about or piled against the hedgerows.[7]

Although flooding from easterly or southerly rainfall seems almost an annual event in Eastern South Island, especially if the volume of water in the rivers is further augmented by heavy rain in the mountains, the case of February 1945 was extreme. More common is the kind of rainfall which took place on 23 and 24 June 1949 (*Figs.* 51 and 52). In a sense these two days epitomize the character and origins of the heavier rainfalls found here. On the first day south and southeast winds brought rain from the rear of a depression which had passed to the east, and this was followed by northeast and east winds which again brought rain, but this time as a deep depression approached from the Tasman Sea. The result was that most of Eastern South Island, from Ashburton southwards, received more than two inches of rain in a period of forty-eight hours.

Broadly speaking, Eastern South Island may be likened to Eastern North Island in those climatic qualities which have been derived particularly from its 'eastern' location. Such differences as exist are differences in degree and not in kind. When, however, we examine those characteristics which arise from the region's position as a part of the South Island, all resemblance between the two areas disappears. Whereas Eastern North Island obtains from its particular milieu winter warmth, occasional invasions of subtropical air, and a winter rainfall maximum, Eastern South Island derives from its especial environment winter cold, occasional invasions of subantarctic air, and a winter rainfall minimum.

[6]E. G. Edie, C. J. Seelye, and J. D. Raeside: 'Notes on the Canterbury floods of February, 1945', *N.Z. Journ. Sci. and Tech.*, Vol. 27, Sec. B, 1946, pp. 406–20.

[7]The writer, who was travelling in Canterbury on both these days, recalls crossing the Ashburton river, the railway bridge almost washed by flood waters, and seeing a bungalow near the submerged banks with water above the window sills: two months later he passed the same spot and saw the same house bearing the laconic notice—'To Let'.

RAINFALL OF
FEBRUARY 20 & 21, 1945.

RAINFALL OF
JUNE 23 & 24, 1949.

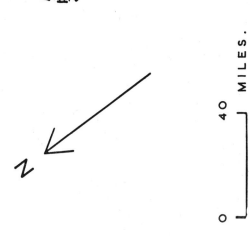

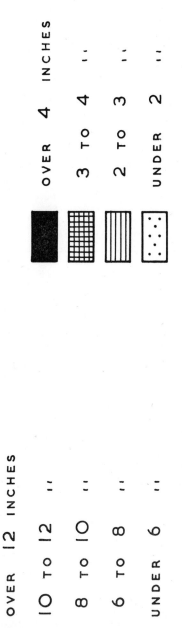

N

40   0
MILES.

OVER 12 INCHES
10 TO 12   "
8 TO 10   "
6 TO 8   "
UNDER 6   "

OVER 4 INCHES
3 TO 4   "
2 TO 3   "
UNDER 2   "

FIG. 51. Maps illustrating two heavy rainfalls in Eastern South Island. (Rainfall of February after Seelye, Edie, and Raeside.)
Towns indicated: G = Geraldine; T = Timaru; O = Oamaru; F = Fairlie; A = Ashburton; W = Waimate; D = Duntroon

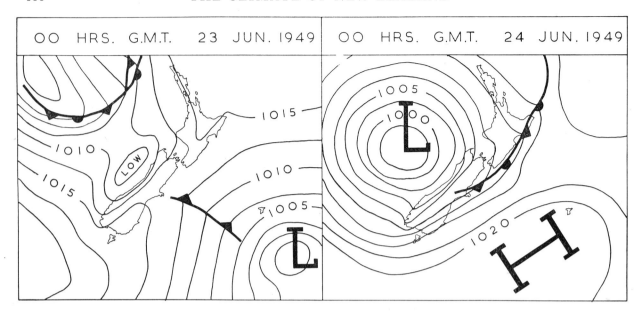

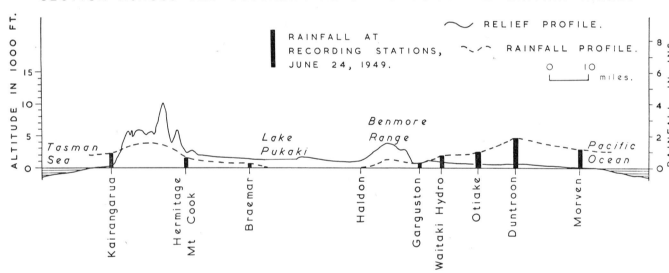

Fig. 52. Map illustrating atmospheric conditions leading to 'easterly' weather in Eastern South Island and a cross-section to show the resulting distribution of precipitation.

The fact that there are bigger contrasts in temperature between places in the North and South Islands in winter than in summer, reflects the general coldness of the latter area during the winter season, due in part to the difference in latitude, but also related to the great area of ice and snow in the mountains. The winter snow-line is at about 4,000 ft. of elevation, and air from this frigid reservoir drains down to the lowlands of the east and the interior. This movement is at all seasons a factor favouring the low minimum temperatures common to Eastern South Island, but it is especially noticeable in winter during the periods of cold, stable weather which may last for several days at this time of year.[8] This situation, therefore, combines with the periodic invasion of air from the south in creating the low winter temperatures experienced in the region. At this season, the average of the mean temperatures of all stations located here is 42.1°F, while that of mean daily minimum tem-

[8]See, for example, conditions during the last week of July, 1950, as shown in *Fig.* 53.

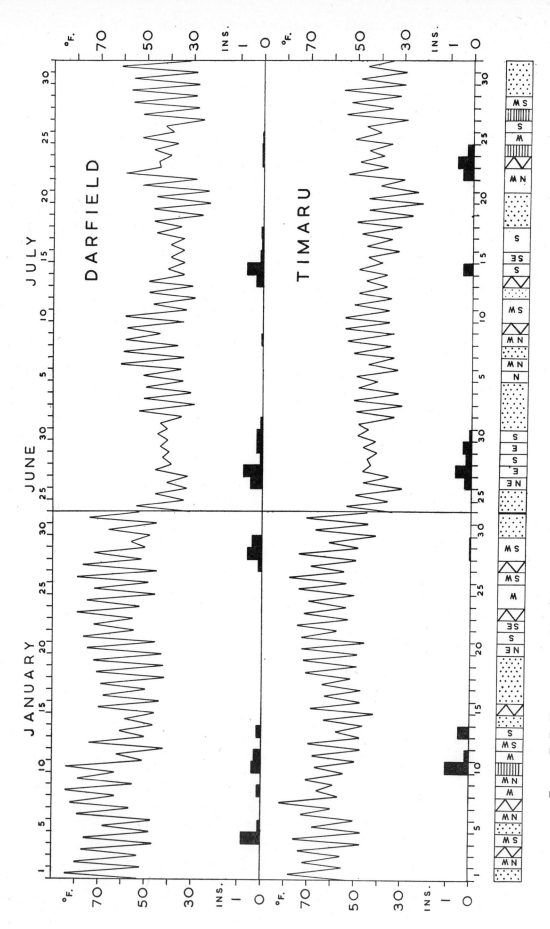

Fig. 53. Daily Temperature and Precipitation during January, 1950, and part of the winter of 1950 at Darfield and Timaru.

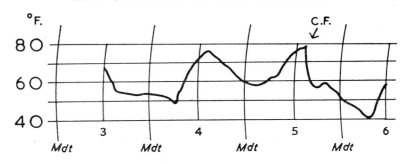

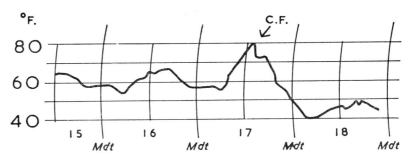

FIG. 54. Tracings from thermograph charts illustrating the passage of cold fronts at Wigram, Christchurch, on 5 and 17 February, 1950.

Table 24

TEMPERATURE CHANGES BEFORE AND AFTER THE PASSAGE OF A COLD FRONT
OVER EASTERN SOUTH ISLAND ON 17 FEBRUARY 1950
(°F.)

Station		15	16	17	18	19	20
Darfield	Min.	38.7	43.5	45.9	37.0	39.8	41.3
(640 ft.)	Max.	68.0	71.3	78.2	50.2	63.3	80.9
Timaru	Min.	48.8	49.2	46.2	41.6	43.0	40.2
(56 ft.)	Max.	68.2	70.2	68.2	52.2	63.2	66.2
Waimate	Min.	48.0	49.5	45.0	40.5	43.0	39.0
(200 ft.)	Max.	65.5	67.0	74.5	54.5	70.5	68.0
Fairlie	Min.	48.0	43.0	42.0	32.5	34.0	33.5
(1,004 ft.)	Max.	64.0	73.0	61.0	51.0	67.0	78.0

peratures is only one or two degrees above freezing point. The mean extreme minimum temperatures of winter months are all below 30°F, and for many stations they lie below 25°F. These conditions are further illustrated by the large number of ground frosts. There are more than a hundred a year, which is a higher figure than that for any other region except Inland South Island and Upland South Island. Even on the coast the incidence of frost is high during winter. At Christchurch in July there is an average of 18.8, and at Timaru, in the same month, the average is 20.8. As a rule more than 60 per cent of winter nights are frosty throughout the area, except where the continual motion of air opposite gaps in the mountains reduces its incidence.

The influxes of cold air from the south, which contribute to the low temperatures of winter, are not confined to this season. They form an integral part of the region's climate at any time of year, and illustrate an important aspect of its 'external relationships'. Their arrival is always noticeable, but if it occurs in the afternoon, especially in summer, it is particularly marked. How two cold fronts in February 1950 affected temperatures at Christchurch, for example, is shown in *Fig.* 54. On the first occasion, on 5 February, there was a drop in temperature of about 20F° between 2 p.m. and 4 p.m., and then a further fall of about the same amount during the night. The rate at which the temperature fell during the second frontal passage, on 17 February, was equally rapid, being

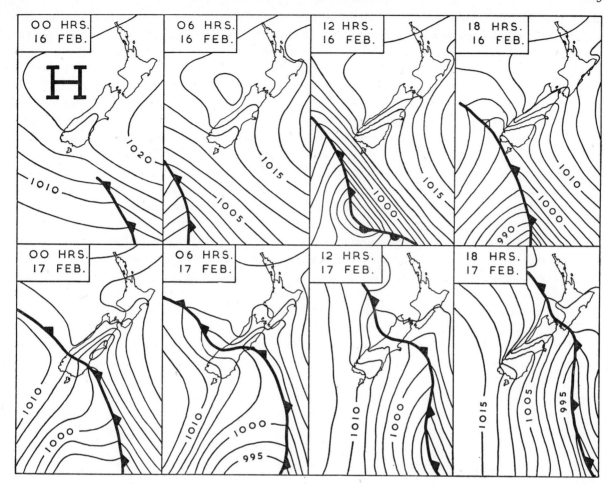

FIG. 55. Maps illustrating the movement of a cold front across the South Island during mid-February, 1950. Times shown on the map are all G.M.T.

about 8F° in half an hour. This was followed by a steady fall in temperature during the night in the icy air which followed the front, since the isobars behind it carried a north to south trend. The passage of this cold front across the country is illustrated in *Fig.* 55, and its general temperature effects in Eastern South Island are given in *Table* 24. Its approach could be well seen from the southern end of the Hunters Hills, near Waimate. Black cloud appeared beyond the Waitaki River, like a dark cloak spread across the sky, and as it got nearer the air grew deathly still and sultry. Then came heavy rain, which reached Waimate and Timaru by early afternoon. The wind changed from northwest to southwest, and later it went due south. Temperatures fell to low levels during the night, and the next day people on the coast awoke to a fine but cold day. Looking towards the mountains from Timaru one was surprised to see that they were covered with snow, right down to the 2,000-ft. level. Here, in the middle of one of the area's warmest summer months, was a scene reminiscent of the depth of a hard winter. The snow cleared quickly at lower levels, but remained for several days down to a height of 4,000 feet in the period of cold air which followed the visitation.[9]

Finally we may consider the influence of the region's location upon its precipitation. This is principally revealed by the seasonal distribution of precipitation, which follows a general South Island characteristic for there to be least rain in winter and most in summer. There is, however,

[9]While this is an extreme example, it is typical of the kind of effect cold, subantarctic air can have in Eastern South Island. Other examples may be seen in *Fig.* 53, e.g. 22–24 July, and 10–11 January.

also a tendency towards a secondary maximum in spring (*Fig. 57*) which is also a season when the variation of rainfall from year to year is less than at most other times (*Fig. 56*). Both these characteristics are related to the influence of north-westerlies in springtime. The influence of northwest rains which come through the Raikaia Gorge at Methven, for example, is seen in the secondary rainfall maximum which occurs there in September (*Fig. 57*). On Banks Peninsula, on the other hand, 'North Island' tendencies are apparent in a winter maximum of rainfall and a summer minimum, as exemplified at Akaroa, while Christchurch combines 'North Island' and 'South Island' characteristics by having a primary maximum in winter and a secondary maximum in summer.

The third major factor influencing the climate of Eastern South Island is its physiographic form. In this respect the region may be summed up as one without appreciable relief. Although in reality the plains of Canterbury slope gently from sea-level to over 1,000 ft. above it near the edge of the Southern Alps, the gradient is hardly perceptible to the eye. This apparently level terrain occupies the greater part of the area, but at the northern and southern ends of the plains there are a series of downlands, whose inconsiderable elevation and diverse relief have microclimatic importance. Otherwise it is only on Banks Peninsula that relief causes notable climatic differences. The volcanic hills here, over 3,000 ft. above sea-level, are high enough to promote orographic lifting, so that the peninsula is much wetter than the surrounding parts and has, indeed, some climatic attributes which link it more with the North Island than with Eastern South Island.

The lack of local relief has two major consequences for the region's climate, both of which serve to differentiate it still further from the corresponding part of the North Island. Firstly, it is rather cloudy for an area of eastern location. Most sunshine is experienced immediately east of the ranges in mid-Canterbury where turbulent mixing helps to maintain clearer skies, in the same way as along the coast of Eastern North Island. Elsewhere the area is frequently subject to a belt of coastal cloud, about twenty miles wide, which in the south builds up quite heavily against the seaward slopes of the Hunters Hills. This happens not only in easterly and southerly weather, but also when the country is under anticyclonic or relatively stable influences. At this time, light, locally-derived easterly or northeasterly winds move in across the plains and commonly maintain a cloud belt for a considerable part of the day. In the morning it disperses about ten o'clock, by which time the ground has heated and turbulence occurs; the cloud forms again in the middle of the afternoon, however, as the ground cools and the air begins to settle. Thus factors promoting cloudiness in this area occur frequently and the percentage of possible sunshine is rather low, being less than the average for the country, without a great deal of difference between seasons (*Table 25*).

Table 25

MEAN HOURS OF BRIGHT SUNSHINE IN EASTERN SOUTH ISLAND
(a) Mean hours received.
(b) Percentage of the possible total for the season.

Station	Winter		Spring		Summer		Autumn		Year	
	(a)	(b)	(a)	(b)	(a)	(b)	(a)	(b)	(a)	(b)
Christchurch	375	41	563	46	605	45	445	43	1,988	45
Rudstone, Methven	396	45	579	47	628	47	474	46	2,077	47
Ashburton	354	40	509	42	553	41	413	40	1,829	41
Waimate	376	43	466	38	444	33	411	40	1,697	38
Oamaru	384	44	514	42	516	38	425	42	1,839	41

Secondly, the lack of local relief means that there is a corresponding absence of climatic diversity within the region. Such differences as occur are comparatively insignificant and related to the different degree of exposure to prevailing influences. Thus, to give two examples, mid-Canterbury immediately east of the ranges is sunnier and more liable to rains from the west than elsewhere, and the southern part of the area tends to experience less northwesterly weather than the rest, since cold fronts often reach it before the northwester is fully established.

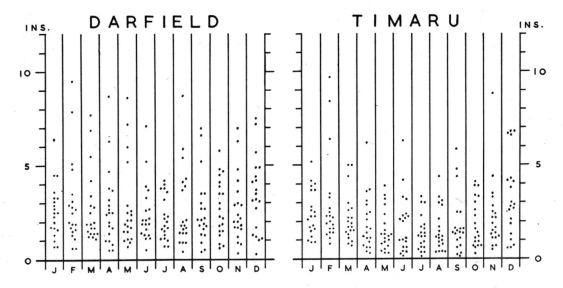

FIG. 56. Rainfall dispersion diagrams for Darfield and Timaru, 1935–54.

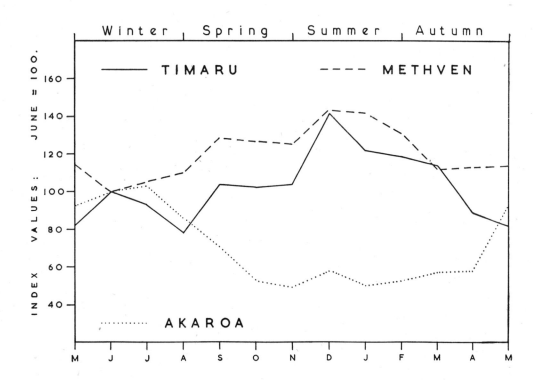

FIG. 57. Graphs illustrating the seasonal régime of precipitation in Eastern South Island.

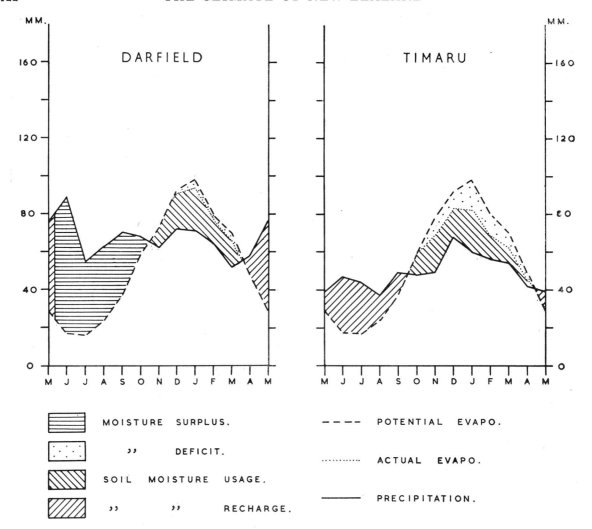

FIG. 58. The Water Balance at Darfield and Timaru.

Remembering always the particular qualities of Banks Peninsula, therefore, we can describe Eastern South Island as a homogeneous climatic unit. It is predominantly microthermal and its low, unreliable rainfall creates the likelihood of moisture deficiencies in many parts (*Fig.* 58).[10] This is, in itself, an aspect of the region's distinctive climatic qualities, since there is no other subhumid area of comparable size in the country. An equally distinctive feature of the climate here, however, is the way it can alter from year to year. These alterations are largely due to variations in rainfall. A mean annual variability of rainfall of about 16 per cent for most of the region links it with such areas as Northern New Zealand, Eastern North Island, and Inland South Island. Eastern South Island, however, is different from these, and all other regions, because its mean annual rainfall is such that a relatively small variation in it has more significant climatic consequences than has a similar variation in the totals normal to other regions. The point is illustrated in *Fig.* 59 and *Table* 26.[11] These

[10]B. J. Garnier: 'The Climates of New Zealand . . .', op. cit.; *idem*: 'The Application of the Concept of Potential Evapotranspiration . . .' op. cit.

[11]The classification of climates in this table has been made by using a modification of Thornthwaite's 1931 formula, the validity of which for New Zealand conditions is set out in B. J. Garnier: 'The Climates of New Zealand . . .', op. cit. The diagram used in *Fig.* 59 was devised by C. J. Seelye in a review of Garnier's paper. See *N.Z. Geogr.*, Vol. 3, 1947, pp. 204–6.

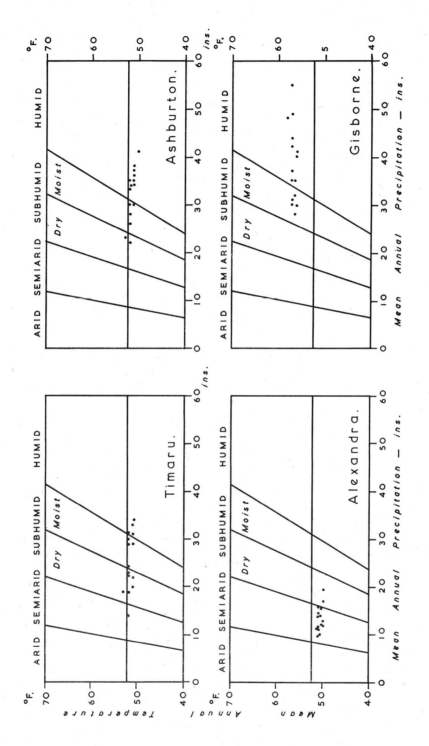

Fig. 59. The spread of 'Climatic Years' at four places in New Zealand during the period 1939–53.

Table 26

SPREAD OF 'CLIMATIC YEARS' AT DIFFERENT PLACES IN NEW ZEALAND
DURING THE PERIOD 1939–53

Station	No. of Occasions for Diff. Climatic Types*					Total No. of Years	Mean Ann. Precipita-tion† (in.)	Mean Ann. % Varia-bility†
	(1)	(2)	(3)	(4)	(5)			
(a) Stations in Eastern South Island:								
Balmoral		6	8	1	..	15	28.79	13.9
Darfield		11	3	1	..	15	32.78	14.2
Christchurch		5	7	3	..	15	28.80	17.3
Ashburton		9	4	2	..	15	32.18	14.4
Timaru		2	6	6	1	15	24.33	17.4
Waimate		3	10	2	..	15	26.52	13.1
(b) Stations elsewhere:								
Waipoua	11	4	..	..	..	15	65.23	10.3
Ruakura, Hamilton		15	..	..	..	15	45.30	9.7
Gisborne		10	5	..	..	15	38.57	17.3
Hastings		4	9	2	..	15	30.38	15.0
Nelson		14	1	..	..	15	38.85	11.4
Alexandra		..	..	2	13	15	13.52	16.9
Gore		12	3	..	..	15	32.42	11.6

*The different types of climate referred to by the numbered columns in the table are: (1) Superhumid; (2) Humid; (3) 'Moist' Subhumid; (4) 'Dry' Subhumid; (5) Semi-arid. No distinction has been made between thermal conditions since these vary little from year to year.

†The means referred to here are those of the period 1939–53.

show the spread of 'climatic years' in a fifteen-year period at different places through the country. The last column of the table gives the mean annual percentage variability of rainfall at each place during the period in question. Every station in Eastern South Island experienced a spread through at least three climatic types. Elsewhere there was a similar spread only at Hastings. Yet the mean annual percentage variability of rainfall at stations in Eastern South Island was similar to that elsewhere. In other words, this region is more likely than other parts of the country to experience different types of climate from year to year, and accordingly its mean rainfall variability tends to be of more climatic significance than that of other parts, even though it has a similar numerical value.[12]

The variation in climate from year to year is particularly apparent in the landscapes of Canterbury. A difference of a few inches in the rainfall between one agricultural season and another, for example, has significant results. In one year conditions may be 'drier' subhumid or even semi-arid, and unless irrigation is applied, pastures dry out, crops are poor, and lamb-fattening is reduced to a minimum. In a humid year, on the other hand, the picture is quite different: the population of lambs, 'exported' from the back country for fattening on the lowlands, is dense, and everywhere small white dots of feeding lambs are seen against a background of green pasture, beside ripening fields of wheat or pastures closed for hay. The realization of these potential contrasts from year to year is seen in ancient stock-watering races bringing water from the mountains, and in the modern irrigation schemes of the mid-Canterbury plains.[13] A sensitivity to climate, however, is also apparent in other ways. For instance, shelter belts have been planted to afford protection for both stock and

[12]The same kind of phenomenon probably explains the noticeable effects of long-term climatic changes in Eastern South Island. They are shown by recent changes in vegetation, and discrepancies in soil-climate relationships since the soils have developed under a former wetter climate and are not yet adjusted to present-day conditions. See J. D. Raeside: 'Some Post-Glacial Climatic Changes in Canterbury and their effect on soil formation', *Trans. Proc. Roy. Soc. N.Z.*, Vol. 77, 1948, pp. 153–71. It should be noted, however, that vegetation changes due to long-term climatic change have been observed in the forests of the southwest of the South Island. See J. T. Holloway: 'Ecological Investigations in the *Nothofagus* forest in New Zealand', *N.Z. Journ. Forestry*, Vol. 5, 1948, pp. 1–10; *idem*: 'Forests and Climates in the South Island of New Zealand', *Trans. Proc. Roy. Soc. N.Z.*, Vol. 82, 1954, pp. 329–410.

[13]N.Z. Public Works Department: 'Water Put to Work', Wellington, 1945.

crops against northwesterly gales and, in mid-Canterbury especially, long lines of *Pinus radiata* and *Cuppressus macrocarpa* are a familiar sight on the north and northwest sides of the fields. Again, the winter cold, as in Southern New Zealand, is reflected in the growing of root-crops and green fodder as well as hay, in order to feed the sheep through winter months.[14]

Broadly speaking, this climatic region coincides with an area which has distinctive geographic traits. Physiographically, it consists mainly of plainland and pedologically, it is made up of an extensive area of yellow-grey earths.[15] As an economic unit, it is mixed-farming territory which contains two-thirds of the country's grain crops, including over four-fifths of the wheat.[16] The amount of grain which is grown here is a relic of a nineteenth-century development which took place after the passing of extensive pastoralism. During that 'bonanza' wheat period, the indigenous tussock was ploughed up for grain production on huge estates. The extent of these developments in Eastern South Island is a tribute to the suitability of the climate for grain-growing as well as to the ease with which the open, indigenous grassland could be converted to grain-producing territory. As in the rest of New Zealand, however, recent progress has been towards increasing livestock-farming, and sheep and lambs now form the economic mainstay, and the chief 'crop' is grass.[17] The effects of climate here, therefore, are to be seen principally in the details of its landscapes and in the peculiarities of local farming practice, while in a broader sense climate constitutes one of several elements contributing to the complex of phenomena which distinguish the area as a geographic unit.

[14]K. B. Cumberland: 'The Agricultural Regions of New Zealand', op. cit.
[15]Soil Map of New Zealand, 1948: compiled by officers of the N.Z. Soil Bureau, N.Z. Dept. Sci. and Ind. Res.
[16]K. B. Cumberland: 'The Agricultural Regions of New Zealand', op. cit.
[17]ibid.

11

CENTRAL NORTH ISLAND

CENTRAL North Island is one of the two 'interior' climatic regions of New Zealand. The other is Inland South Island. These two are the only ones which do not reach the sea and both reflect, in their climatic characteristics, the effects of this peculiarity. Apart from this they have little in common: whereas Central North Island is superhumid, Inland South Island is predominantly subhumid or semi-arid; whereas the former contains little climatic diversity, the latter displays considerable contrasts over short distances; whereas the one is open to prevalent westerly winds, the other is sheltered from almost every rain-bearing wind over the country. So we could go on, contrasting the two areas at almost every point of their climatic character.

For the moment, however, let us concentrate on Central North Island. It is physically an area of upland, with mountains exceeding its own height only on the east. These ranges form the boundary of Eastern North Island and their position means that the region we are now considering is open to the prevailing westerly influences which cross the country. Its local climate, therefore, depends to a large extent upon how its physical form reacts to these influences.

Broadly speaking, the result of this interaction is to provide the North Island with its only major area of cool, superhumid climate. The region averages about 1,500 ft. above sea-level, and south and west of Lake Taupo it greatly exceeds this height. South of the lake lies an area of high ground from which rises Mount Ruapehu (9,175 ft.), the highest peak of the North Island, and Mount Ngaruhoe (7,515 ft.). Farther east, towards the Kaimanawa mountains, there is more alpine country. In these two districts cold climate prevails, with conditions of permanent frost and snow upon the summits of the higher peaks. West of Lake Taupo there is a ridge, 40 miles long, with a series of summits which reach elevations above 3,000 ft. The ridge is not high enough to produce cold climate conditions, but it is significant in helping to create a rain-shadow northeast of the lake. In the vicinity of Rotorua and west of the ridge of high ground west of Lake Taupo, the land is lower and the climate is warm enough to be classified as mesothermal. Except for these comparatively small areas of cold and warm climate respectively, however, the climate of the area is cool (microthermal) and this clearly distinguishes it from the rest of the North Island.

The second major distinguishing feature of the region's climate is its wetness, much of it being superhumid. To some extent this is due to large rainfall totals, but even regions of comparatively little rain are superhumid, or nearly so, because of low evaporation in the cool, damp atmosphere. Indeed, Central North Island, although wet, cannot be regarded as a region of outstandingly heavy precipitation. It experiences neither the heaviest individual falls nor the greatest mean annual totals even of the North Island, let alone New Zealand. More than three-quarters of the area has a mean annual rainfall of under 80 inches, and 40 per cent has less than 60. This is distributed on between 150 and 200 days, which is an average figure for New Zealand, and of twenty-nine recording stations only five have an average of over half an inch per rainy day. Again, the likelihood of heavy rain in twenty-four hours is not remarkable: it varies from 2 to 3 inches according to locality, which is much the same as that for most of the North Island.[1] Thus, while occasional deluges may be expected in the limited area of mountain, over the region as a whole the high moisture values are not so much

[1]C. J. Seelye: 'The Frequency of Heavy Rainfalls . . .', op. cit.

the consequence of plentiful precipitation as of low evaporation related to cool temperatures and a comparatively still atmosphere—itself a product of relatively cool air and distance from the sea.

The details of this somewhat generalized picture may be filled in by regarding the climate from the viewpoint of conditions at different seasons, rather than by looking at specific elements as we have tended to do before. Winter, in addition to being the coldest time of the year, is also the wettest. At this season cold, raw, damp weather characterizes the region for much of the time. As in the rest of the North Island, it is the period of maximum precipitation, and most stations of Central North Island average between 25 per cent and 30 per cent of their annual total at this time. Little of this comes as snow, however. The number of snowfalls averages barely ten a year, though locally, on the highlands above 4,500 ft., snow lies through the winter. Hailstorms, occurring in the cold, unstable

Table 27

STATISTICS OF TEMPERATURE AND FROST DURING WINTER AND SUMMER IN CENTRAL NORTH ISLAND

(1) Mean daily maximum temp., °F.　　(2) Mean daily minimum temp., °F.
(3) Mean extreme maximum temp., °F.　(4) Mean extreme minimum temp., °F.
(5) Mean number of screen frosts.　　 (6) Mean number of ground frosts.

Station		Winter			Summer		
		June	*July*	*Aug.*	*Dec.*	*Jan.*	*Feb.*
Rotorua	(1)	54.4	53.6	55.2	70.3	74.3	73.6
(931 ft.)	(2)	38.4	36.9	37.9	49.7	51.3	52.2
	(3)	62.3	60.7	63.1	82.4	84.8	82.9
	(4)	27.0	26.5	27.7	39.6	41.1	41.2
	(5)	5.4	8.0	6.3	Nil.	Nil.	Nil.
	(6)	14.6	17.1	16.1	0.6	0.3	0.4
Château Tongariro	(1)	43.4	42.0	43.5	58.7	61.2	62.0
(3,670 ft.)	(2)	31.1	30.0	30.7	41.0	43.3	44.3
	(3)	51.0	50.8	52.0	72.0	69.2	67.4
	(4)	22.3	18.5	21.5	33.8	33.6	30.4
	(5)	16.7	17.1	16.2	1.2	0.7	0.4
	(6)	17.8	20.3	19.7	4.1	2.2	1.2
Karioi	(1)	49.9	48.7	51.1	66.3	68.7	68.9
(2,125 ft.)	(2)	33.1	32.0	33.0	44.0	45.3	46.4
	(3)	59.7	56.4	60.2	75.2	77.4	75.7
	(4)	20.6	18.9	20.3	33.2	32.8	29.0
	(5)	14.2	14.5	14.5	0.9	0.4	0.5
	(6)	16.9	17.4	17.2	1.9	1.7	2.4

air behind a cold front, are more common, however, and form a distinguishing winter feature, particularly in the southern half of the region.[2] Winter is also a cloudy time. The average number of hours of bright sunshine at this season is only about 120 a month north of Lake Taupo, and is less than 100 south of the lake. These figures represent an average of between 35 per cent and 40 per cent of the sunshine which is possible in winter, whereas at every other season the equivalent percentage is over 40 per cent. Such relatively low values are partly due to the increased rainfall of this period, and partly due to the frequent occurrence of stratus cloud which is promoted by relatively still, cold air, and which day temperatures are not always high enough to disperse for any great length of time.[3] Nevertheless, midday temperatures can on occasions rise surprisingly high. Even at the Château Tongariro, 3,670 ft. above the sea, the mean extreme maximum temperature recorded each month of winter is over 50°F; at Karioi (2,125 ft.) and Rotorua (969 ft.) the equivalent figures are over 55°F and 60°F respectively. Mean daily maxima, however, are a good deal lower than this and nights are cold. The extreme minimum temperatures of winter are below 20°F everywhere, except

---

[2]E. Kidson: 'The Frequency of Frost, Snow, and Hail . . .', op. cit.

[3]Heavier air and interior location both reduce turbulence at this time, and the number of calms observed during the winter is considerably above that observed at other seasons (see *Table 29*).

in the Rotorua district, and mean daily minimum temperatures are likewise near or below freezing point (*Table* 27).

Since the climate of spring displays characteristics which are largely transitional between those of winter and summer, it is best to deal next with the latter season. Its most noteworthy feature is the comparatively high average percentage of the mean annual rainfall which occurs at this time. Whereas in most parts of the North Island less rain comes in summer than in other seasons, in Central North Island some stations actually receive their maximum fall during December, January, and February (*Table* 28). This feature reflects the normal tendency for places in the interior to receive more of their precipitation during the high sun period of convective turbulence than at other seasons. Such turbulence is revealed in Central North Island by the fewer calms of summer as compared with the number during spring, autumn, or winter (*Table* 29), and also by figures for the incidence of sunshine. The motion of the air dissipates cloud to such an extent that more than 50 per cent of the possible sunshine for the season is found nearly everywhere. The latter feature, taken in conjunction with the relatively low sunshine values in winter, adds further to the area's distinguishing qualities since it produces a bigger range between the proportion of possible sunshine received in summer and that of winter than in any other region of the country.

Table 28

PERCENTAGE SEASONAL DISTRIBUTION OF PRECIPITATION IN CENTRAL NORTH ISLAND

Station	Wi.	Sp.	Su.	Au.	Mean Annual Total (in.)
Rotorua	27.9	25.4	22.3	24.4	55.42
Waiotapu	27.8	24.2	23.8	24.2	52.12
Rotokawa	27.6	23.2	28.1	21.1	47.35
Taupo	28.6	25.2	23.0	23.2	43.32
Château Tongariro	23.2	25.8	27.6	23.4	108.21
Karioi	27.2	25.8	25.9	21.1	47.80
Taihape	24.5	26.6	25.7	23.2	36.91

Table 29

NUMBERS OF CALMS OBSERVED AT DIFFERENT SEASONS IN CENTRAL NORTH ISLAND EXPRESSED AS A PERCENTAGE OF THE TOTAL OBSERVATIONS AT EACH SEASON

Station	Period of Observations	Percentage of Calms at Diff. Seasons				Total of all Observations during period
		Wi.	Sp.	Su.	Au.	
Rotorua	1936–48	27.3	11.8	13.8	24.6	11,850
Taupo	1938–48	35.4	22.2	21.2	25.9	8,897
Karioi	1934–48	29.9	24.4	20.7	22.6	8,296

Clearer skies, however, mean considerable radiation-cooling at night at these elevations. Hence high mean values of diurnal temperature range are found. They amount on the average to over 20F°, which is a figure matched only in the South Island east of the ranges and away from the sea. Summer nights are consequently quite cold.[4] Extreme minimum temperatures are everywhere below 40°F in summer, and are close to freezing point at such stations as the Château Tongariro and Karioi.

The remaining two seasons, spring and autumn, display qualities which are characteristic of their transitional place in the annual cycle. In comparison with each other, spring is colder than autumn by an average of 2F° on the basis of mean monthly temperatures. Temperatures rise comparatively slowly in the former period, being retarded by the presence of snow in the mountains and by the amount of wind and changeable weather normal to the season. To begin with, average temperatures fall slowly in autumn, but from the beginning of April onwards they tend to change more rapidly.

[4] It is these cold nights which give the high diurnal range of temperature here, rather than especially high daytime temperatures.

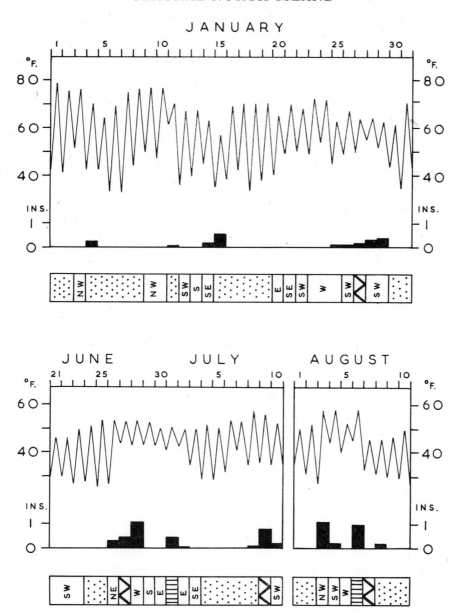

FIG. 60. Daily temperature and precipitation in January, 1950, and part of the winter of 1950 at Karioi.

A further point about the climate of autumn is that many places experience their minimum precipitation at this time. It is brought about by the fact that the land is now cooling as winter comes on so that the turbulence responsible for adding to the summer rainfall no longer operates, while frontal activity has not yet increased to any great extent.

The climatic qualities just outlined show the influence of four main factors acting in interrelation: firstly, the region's position as a part of the North Island, secondly, its exposure to westerly influences, thirdly, its interior location, and fourthly, its elevation. The first of these provides it with an essentially 'North Island' stamp to its climate, which is expressed particularly in a winter maximum of precipitation. The second factor results from the absence of an appreciable mountain barrier to the west, and produces a rhythm of weather which is like that of Middle New Zealand, for example.

This rhythm is displayed in *Fig.* 60, particularly in the graphs for January, where the action of anti-cyclones and intervening low pressure troughs is apparent in the daily changes of temperature and in the incidence of precipitation. In considering the third factor, its interior location, it is important to realize that, although the region is near the sea in the direction of the Bay of Plenty, few weather influences arrive from there, whereas it is nearly 100 miles from the ocean to the west, from which the dominant weather influences come, and its distance from the sea in the east is made effectively greater by the presence of mountain ranges. The climate of Central North Island, therefore, displays some of the characteristics associated with inland régimes. They are expressed, for example, in the seasonal distribution of calms and of rainfall, which we have already noted, and they are seen also in the diurnal ranges of temperature, which are much larger than is common to regions of westerly exposure. The final factor, its elevation, promotes the general coolness of the area. In particular, it fosters night radiation and the accumulation of relatively dense air at the surface, which tends to reduce turbulence, especially in winter and autumn.[5] Thus it acts in sympathy with the previous factor in helping to develop still further the region's 'continental' qualities.

The result of these complex forces, then, is the creation of the cool, superhumid climates which characterize Central North Island within the framework of which there exists the variety mentioned at the start of this chapter. As a geographic entity its character is controlled by the fact that it is still in a comparatively 'primitive' state. Along with Western South Island, therefore, it can be regarded as a pioneer region, in which natural factors such as climate, primitive vegetation, and soil still dominate the geographic landscape.

In view of the general qualities of the vegetation of New Zealand and the particular climatic features of Central North Island, it might be thought that rain-forest would be widespread in the area. In fact this is not the case. Rain-forest exists only south and west of Lake Taupo, northwest of Rotorua, and on the mountains which mark the eastern borders of the region. It flanks the ranges to about 4,500 ft. of elevation, and clothes the valleys with its luxuriant growth.[6] The effect of local climatic conditions may be seen in its particular floristic composition. For example, the coolness of the area is reflected by the general podocarp-dicotylous forest being liberally sprinkled with different kinds of beech (*Nothofagus* spp.) which is dominant at higher elevations. Near Rotorua, on the other hand, kauri (*Agathis australis*) and taraire (*Beilschmeidia taraire*) are found, which reflects the district's affinities with warmer parts.

A great deal of Central North Island, however, is devoid of forest growth and has been so for many centuries. Instead, there are extensive areas of scrubland, dominated by manuka (*Leptospermum* spp.) and much bracken (*Pteridium esculentum*), the whole forming a dull, monotonous wilderness. In places, too, there are extensive areas of tussock grasslands (*Poa caespitosa*, *Festuca Novae Zealandiae*). They are particularly well formed on the Waimarino Plains, which lie west of Mount Ruapehu, and on the open, windswept plains near Waioru. Such vegetative forms as these coincide closely with the areas of volcanic ash showers. Contemporary and ancient volcanic eruptions have contributed their quota of pumice dust, which the prevailing winds have spread over a wide area (*Fig.* 61). The porous nature of the resulting soils has produced a stunted vegetation, almost arid in appearance, in spite of the region having a climate which elsewhere supported a tangled growth of forest and dense undergrowth.

Until recently it was thought that soil infertility and cobalt deficiency would prevent livestock development in the area, and much of the pumice-land was planted with exotic trees, generally

[5]These effects are because it is a plateau and not a mountainous area, except in limited localities. Where mountains occur, as near Mount Ruapehu, instability and precipitation are developed rather than the more 'stable' consequences mentioned in the text.

[6]The forest is not as widespread today as it was at the turn of the present century, but considerable areas still exist in spite of large-scale clearing for farming and of accidental forest fires. See L. Cockayne: 'The Vegetation of New Zealand', op. cit.; K. B. Cumberland: 'A Century's Change . . .', op. cit.

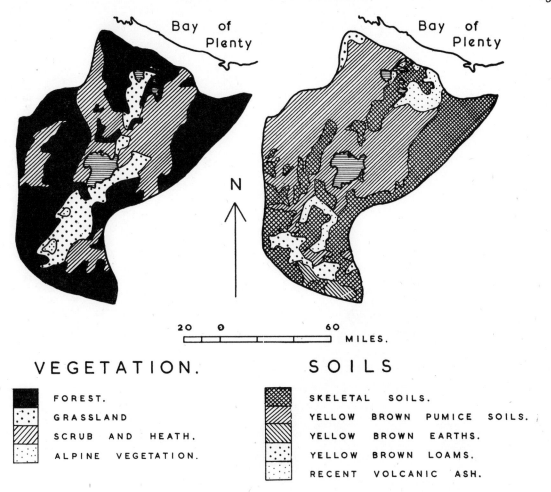

FIG. 61. Primitive Vegetation and Soil Types of Central North Island. (Vegetation from Cumberland: soils from Soil Map of N.Z., 1948.)

Pinus radiata. Clearing for livestock in the early years of the twentieth century was confined mainly to the forest areas of the southwest, where the region merges with Middle New Zealand. Recently, however, improved knowledge and the practical example of courageous pioneers have shown the potentialities of the plateau lands for farming.[7] In the warmer parts of the area pasture development is like that of the Waikato valley and consists mainly of ryegrass and white clover supporting herds of dairy cattle. On the plateau proper, however, the cool summers and liability to frost at almost any time of year have led to the use of Hereford cattle for beef, grazing cocksfoot and red clover swards (*Fig.* 62).[8]

In spite of recent changes, however, Central North Island still retains much of its primitive character. In this, climate takes its place alongside other elements, and inevitably an appreciation of the region's geography is not complete without reference to it. Its significance must not be overstressed, however. There are several aspects of the area which vary independently of climate, since soil conditions, in particular, play a dominant role in this locality. Thus, although it is a region of generally uniform climate, as a geographic entity it displays noticeable internal contrasts through the influence of other natural factors.

[7]See, for example, the account given by E. E. Vaile: 'Pioneering the Pumice', Christchurch, 1940.
[8]K. B. Cumberland: 'The Agricultural Regions of New Zealand', op. cit.

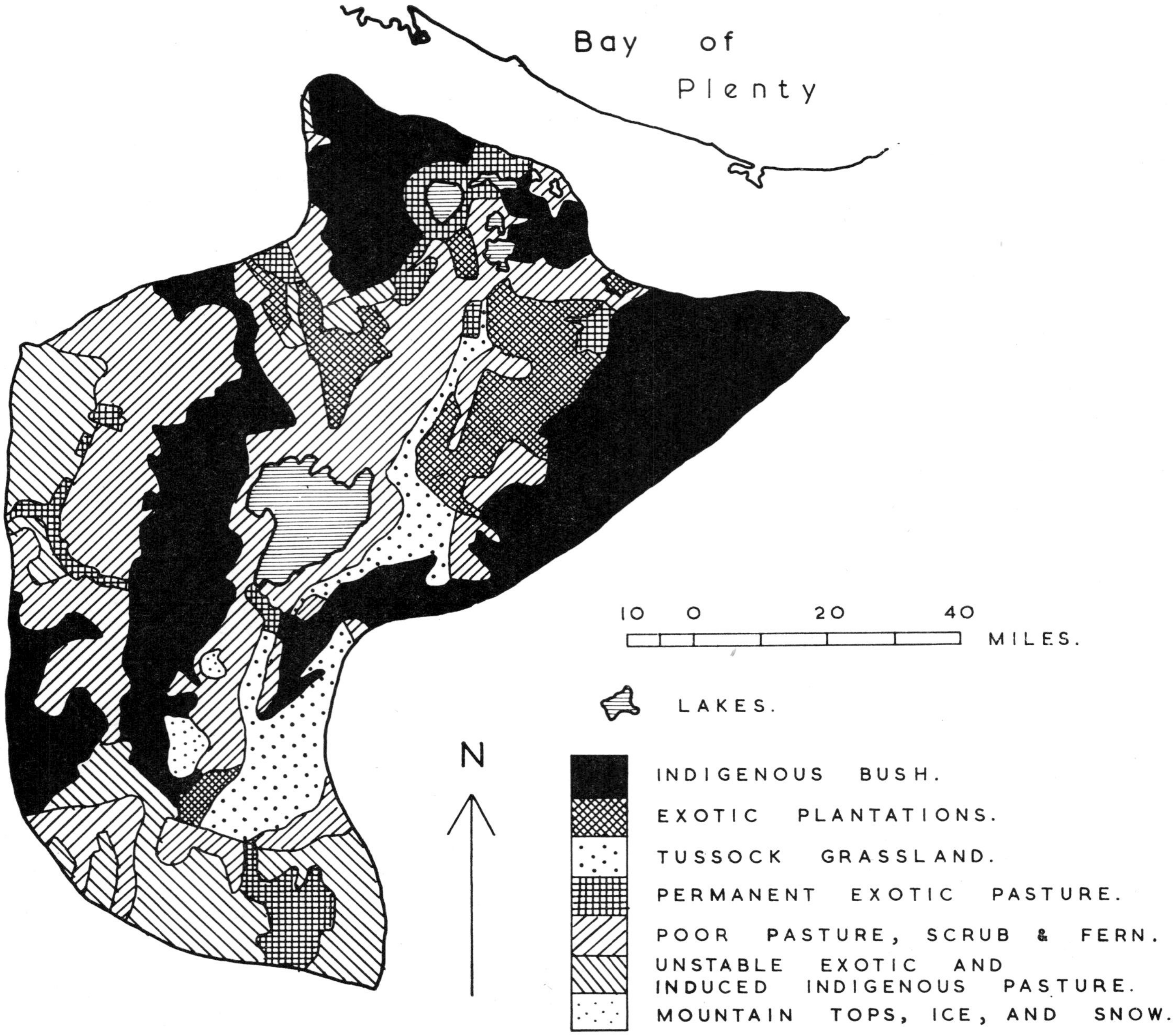

Bay of Plenty

LAKES.

INDIGENOUS BUSH.

EXOTIC PLANTATIONS.

TUSSOCK GRASSLAND.

PERMANENT EXOTIC PASTURE.

POOR PASTURE, SCRUB & FERN.

UNSTABLE EXOTIC AND INDUCED INDIGENOUS PASTURE.

MOUNTAIN TOPS, ICE, AND SNOW.

10 0 20 40 MILES.

N

FIG. 62. Cultural Vegetation and Land Use, 1940, in Central North Island. (From Cumberland.)

(a)

(b)

PLATE IX. *The North Island's cool climate*
(a) Clear skies and snow-covered mountains of Central North Island during anticyclonic weather in winter. (b) Developing the pumice plateau. Sheep pastures and exotic tree plantations in a cool, superhumid climate.

(a)

By courtesy of The High Commissioner for New Zealand

By courtesy of The High Commissioner for New Zealand

(b)

(c)

PLATE X. *Inland South Island and its climate*

(a) A general view in central Otago where 'irrigated orchards and pastures make patches of vivid green against a tawny-coloured background of badly eroded native tussock grassland' (see page 133). (b) Sunshine over lake Ohau while beyond the ranges clouds tower in a northwesterly air stream. (c) Cool, easterly mist streams through Burke's pass on an anticyclonic summer morning.

INLAND SOUTH ISLAND

MANY people would probably agree that Inland South Island displays the most remarkable climatic characteristics of the whole of New Zealand. The area comprises what is commonly referred to as central Otago, or simply 'Central', and the Mackenzie country, and, like the region we have just examined, it is interior in location. But here the qualities of its position are heightened by gigantic bounding ranges which effectively increase 'distance' from the sea to truly continental proportions. Protected on all sides from rain-bearing winds, the area displays climatic features which we normally associate with the interior of much larger land masses, and which are unexpected in such a small country.

It is, indeed, this unexpectedness, brought about particularly by the sudden transition from surrounding regions, which underlines the noticeably different qualities of the climate here. At Burke's Pass, for example, there is a remarkably abrupt change from the mixed farmlands of south Canterbury to the treeless landscape and extensive ranching country of the Mackenzie Basin; while in the south, there is an equally sharp transition between green, cool, humid Southern New Zealand and the semi-arid landscape of central Otago, where irrigated orchards and pastures make patches of vivid green against a tawny-coloured background of badly eroded native tussock grasslands.

These contrasts in landscape symbolize equally abrupt climatic differences which are often expressed in daily weather conditions. There may be heavy rain from northwest winds in the mountains, while over 'Central' and 'the Mackenzie' the sun is shining brightly; or light, cool easterlies, bringing cloud and perhaps drizzle along the coast, are not experienced over the ranges where, in winter, cold settling air brings frost and long-remaining morning mists, or where, in summer, the land is scorched by a burning sun in a cloudless sky; or there may be cold, rain-bearing southerlies sweeping across the Southland plains, only to be cut off by the mountains beyond which drier weather prevails. Daily weather differences such as these in sum create the main climatic contrasts between Inland South Island and its neighbours—contrasts which may be summarized by saying that here is to be found New Zealand's 'continental interior'. Such qualities are expressed primarily by conditions of temperature and moisture, and we shall consider them in turn.

The particular temperature qualities of Inland South Island are best observed from the ranges of temperature found there. These are higher than elsewhere. This is true whatever 'class' of temperature range we are considering: annual, diurnal, and extreme ranges are here all greater than those of other parts. For example, the mean annual range of temperature at both Ophir and Alexandra is 25.4F°. The average of the corresponding values for all stations in the region is 23.8F°, which is three degrees higher than the equivalent for any other region, and by averaging mean diurnal and extreme ranges similar distinctions are revealed. In addition to being large at all times, temperature ranges show clearly defined contrasts between summer and winter, the salient features of which may be perceived from the figures for Lake Tekapo and Alexandra given in *Table* 30. These figures show that temperature ranges are several degrees larger in summer than in winter, and that low temperatures may be expected in Inland South Island at any time of the year. Indeed, at Alexandra the mean extreme minimum of every month is below 40°F and for seven months it is below freezing point; at Ophir the corresponding value is under 36°F in every month, and for nine months it is below freezing point; at Lake Tekapo temperatures near or below freezing point may be

Table 30

ASPECTS OF TEMPERATURE CONDITIONS IN INLAND SOUTH ISLAND
(°F)

	Lake Tekapo (2,350 ft.)		Alexandra (520 ft.)	
	July	Jan.	July	Jan.
Mean Daily Maximum Temp.	42.1	69.3	44.6	72.6
Mean Daily Minimum Temp.	26.4	45.3	28.0	50.8
Mean Diurnal Range of Temp.	15.7	24.0	16.6	21.8
Mean Extreme Maximum Temp.	52.6	81.1	57.4	86.2
Mean Extreme Minimum Temp.	16.3	33.7	18.2	39.8
Mean Extreme Range of Temp.	36.3	47.4	39.2	46.4

expected at least once every month of the year. Figures such as these emphasize the likelihood of cold night temperatures. They reflect a double process: the nocturnal radiation-cooling normal to intermontane basins, which is the siting of most of the recording stations, and the influx of cold air by night-drainage from the neighbouring snow-covered mountains. It is no wonder, therefore, that screen temperatures are low at night and that frosts are frequent. No region of New Zealand, outside the areas of perpetual frost and snow, has a greater incidence of frost than this one. Screen frosts average 115 a year for the region as a whole, and the number of ground frosts is correspondingly large. At several stations the latter occur every night in winter and throughout the area at least one ground frost in summer is an annual event.[1]

Inland South Island is as unique in its moisture qualities as in its temperature characteristics. It is drier than other areas in the country, and its moisture régime and character are typically 'continental'. Throughout the greater part of the region mean annual rainfall is less than 25 inches. It rises above this value only on the mountains, which circumscribe and diversify the area, and it falls well below this figure on the floors of the basins which are so characteristic of this territory. Thus, at Alexandra, in the Manuherikia Basin, mean annual rainfall is 13.22 inches and similarly low totals are probably found in the Mackenzie Basin towards the south, and in the central Waitaki valley near Garguston, although long-term records are absent for these parts. On the average more than 30 per cent of the rain comes during summer, and less than 20 per cent arrives in winter. There is more variability in spring and summer, however, than at other times of the year (*Fig.* 63).[2] This factor, together with the seasonal régime of precipitation, accentuates the dryness of the area, since much of the rain comes during the period of high temperature when insolation is great and when evaporation is large. As a result there are considerable moisture deficiencies which are emphasized by the unreliability of the rainfall from year to year (*Fig.* 64).[3]

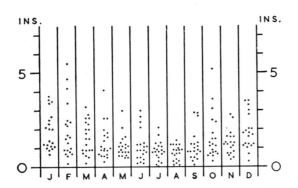

FIG. 63. Rainfall dispersion diagram for Ophir, Central Otago, 1935–54. (The totals for September and October, 1951, were interpolated since records for Ophir in those months were incomplete.)

The quantity, incidence, and régime of precipitation can thus be seen as typical of that occurring in continental interiors. A corresponding similarity is found when we consider humidity of the atmo-

---

[1] The average number of ground frosts in January at Alexandra is 1.2, at Waipiata 2.3, and at Lake Tekapo 8.3. They are a perennial cause of anxiety to the many orchardists of central Otago, where systems of frost warning and prevention are operative.

[2] C. J. Seelye: 'Variations of Monthly Rainfall . . .', op. cit.

[3] B. J. Garnier: 'The Application of the Concept of Potential Evapotranspiration . . .', op. cit.

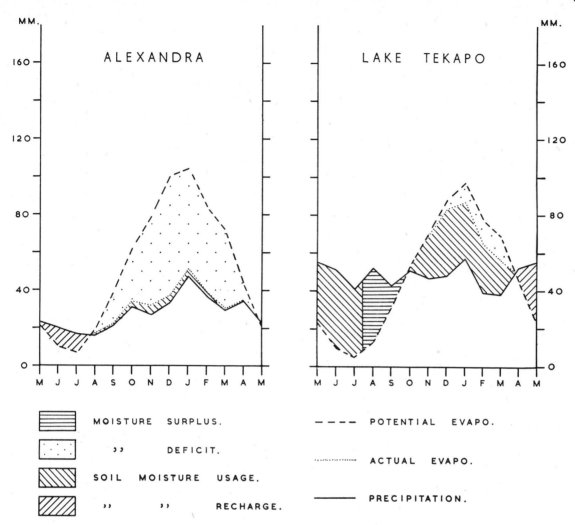

FIG. 64. The Water Balance at Alexandra and Lake Tekapo.

sphere. Speaking broadly, relative humidity is low and the saturation deficit high. This statement, however, masks the seasonal régime which illustrates the point of continentality better than the general average. In winter, cold sinking air collects over the basins of the region and maintains comparatively high relative humidities and low saturation deficits. Indeed, at this time of year these values are like those of the recognizably humid parts of the country.[4] The air becomes much drier from August onwards, however, and mean values of relative humidity fall markedly during spring. At the stations given in *Table* 31, for instance, there is a bigger difference between the mean relative humidity at 9.30 a.m. in August and September than there is between that of any other consecutive months, except in the case of Alexandra, where the difference between July and August is 1 per cent greater than that between August and September.

[4]This can be observed by comparing the figures given in *Table* 31 with those of *Table* 16. It is unfortunate that the only published figures of atmospheric humidity in Inland South Island are those for 9.30 a.m. It would be interesting to know the mean relative humidity and mean saturation deficit during the middle of the day in the area. However, Prescott has suggested that morning observations of wet and dry bulb temperatures in South Australia give a reasonably good measure of the mean for the day, and perhaps this is the case in New Zealand also. See J. A. Prescott: 'Single Value Climatic Factors', *Trans. Roy. Soc. Sth. Austr.*, Vol. 58, 1934, pp. 48–61.

Although Inland South Island is distinguishable from other parts of the country mainly on account of its temperature and moisture characteristics, some differences in other climatic elements are also observable. Like the rest of the country it is a sunny region, and mean annual totals here exceed 2,000 hours. These values are somewhat above the average for the country and their seasonal distribution is also a little different from that of other parts. For example, autumn receives approximately 50 per cent of its possible sunshine, which is about the same as the equivalent percentage

Table 31

ATMOSPHERIC HUMIDITY IN INLAND SOUTH ISLAND

		(a) Temperature, °F.					(b) Vapour Pressure, mbs.							
		(c) Saturation Deficit, mbs.					(d) Relative Humidity, per cent.							
Station	June	July	Aug.	Sept.	Oct.	Nov.	Dec.	Jan.	Feb.	Mar.	Apr.	May	Year
Lake Tekapo[1]													
(a)	36.2	32.4	36.4	44.7	48.7	53.6	57.5	59.6	58.4	54.6	49.2	42.1	47.9
(b)	6.0	5.3	5.8	7.2	7.7	8.5	10.0	10.8	11.2	10.3	9.2	6.9	7.9
(c)	1.3	0.9	1.5	2.9	3.9	5.4	6.2	6.6	5.5	4.2	2.7	2.2	3.4
(d)	82.0	85.0	79.0	71.0	66.0	61.0	62.0	62.0	66.0	71.0	77.0	76.0	70.0
Waipiata[2]													
(a)	35.8	34.5	37.9	43.7	48.5	53.0	55.3	57.8	57.1	53.3	47.0	40.8	47.1
(b)	5.6	5.4	5.7	6.6	7.3	8.1	8.9	10.4	10.7	9.8	8.5	6.6	7.8
(c)	1.5	1.4	2.0	3.1	4.3	4.9	6.0	5.9	5.3	4.0	2.5	2.1	3.7
(d)	79.0	81.0	76.0	68.0	63.0	60.0	59.0	64.0	67.0	73.0	76.0	77.0	70.0
Alexandra[3]													
(a)	34.6	33.9	37.7	46.1	52.7	57.8	60.1	62.2	60.9	56.3	48.1	39.7	49.2
(b)	5.8	5.6	6.0	7.2	8.1	9.2	10.0	11.0	11.4	10.7	8.9	6.4	8.4
(c)	1.0	1.0	1.7	3.4	5.5	7.2	7.8	8.0	6.8	4.7	2.5	1.9	4.3
(d)	87.0	87.0	77.0	68.0	60.0	56.0	56.0	58.0	62.0	69.0	78.0	83.0	70.0

[1]Average of observations at 9.30 a.m., 1938–46; observations for July and August, 1944, missing.
[2]Average of observations at 9.30 a.m., 1938–50; observations of vapour pressure, saturation deficit, and relative humidity for March 1950, missing.
[3]Average of observations at 9.30 a.m., 1938–50.

received in summer (*Table* 32). This is not a usual relationship in New Zealand and while it is found at times elsewhere, for instance in Western South Island, it is not such a noteworthy regional feature in other parts as it is in Inland South Island. Winter, on the other hand, tends to be a relatively sunless period, with its morning fogs and cold, settling air. A further locally differentiating feature is the comparatively large number of calms experienced. In this the region is like Central North Island and unlike the rest of the country. Between 1939 and 1948, for example, about 10,000 observations of wind direction and force were made at both Ranfurly and Alexandra, and at each place calms were reported on nearly half these occasions, there being, however, well-marked contrasts between their occurrence at different seasons (*Table* 33).

The particular qualities of the climate of Inland South Island are epitomized in the weather régimes and carried into popular parlance by the phrase 'sunny Central'. This is not mere tourist publicity. It expresses a widely acknowledged feeling that the weather commonly experienced here is exhilarating. Cold, crisp days in winter, with morning frost 'crackling' under one's foot, or summer days of blue skies, brilliant sunshine and a buoyant atmosphere combine to give the area weather characteristics rarely experienced elsewhere. Although such characteristics are hard to express statistically some idea of them may be obtained from *Fig.* 65.[5] This indicates the daily temperature and incidence of precipitation at Tara Hills, and the daily hours of bright sunshine at Alexandra, during part of the summer and winter of 1950. At Tara Hills in January that year the greater part of the rainfall (86 per cent) came in two days. Otherwise there were only

[5]It is interesting to compare this chart with that for Hokitika (*Fig.* 26) so as to observe the contrasts which can occur between the Mackenzie Basin and upper Waitaki valley, on the one hand, and the west coast of the South Island, fifty miles distant beyond the ranges, on the other.

light falls, and the month had fine weather with big diurnal ranges of temperature, interrupted occasionally by the passage of a cold front. In the winter sequence, the effect of cold dense air is reflected in the lower ranges of temperature, and ranges comparable with those of summer days were only experienced once or twice under the influence of northwest conditions. As in the month of summer illustrated, the greater part of the rain came in a few falls of short duration, and during both the summer and winter periods at Alexandra sunshine was plentiful.

Table 32

MEAN HOURS OF BRIGHT SUNSHINE IN INLAND SOUTH ISLAND

(a) Mean hours received.
(b) Percentage of possible total for the season.

Station	Winter		Spring		Summer		Autumn		Year	
	(a)	(b)	(a)	(b)	(a)	(b)	(a)	(b)	(a)	(b)
Lake Tekapo	406	46	624	51	731	55	547	57	2,308	52
Waipiata	399	46	577	47	648	48	503	49	2,127	48
Alexandra	396	46	612	50	670	50	492	49	2,170	49
mean:	400	46	604	49	683	51	514	52	2,202	50

Table 33

NUMBER OF CALMS RECORDED AT EACH SEASON EXPRESSED AS A PERCENTAGE OF THE TOTAL OBSERVATIONS MADE AT EACH SEASON AT ALEXANDRA AND RANFURLY

Station	Period of the Observations	Percentage of Calms				Total No. of Observations
		Wi.	Sp.	Su.	Au.	
Alexandra	1939–48	63.5	36.4	34.6	55.6	9,907
Ranfurly	1939–48	66.9	37.3	33.1	55.8	10,158

Inland South Island derives its particular climatic qualities mainly from its location and its physiography. It is farther from the sea than any other region of the country, and its actual linear distance is enhanced from the climatic point of view by the massive mountain ranges which surround it (*Fig.* 66). Moreover, their orientation is such that in every case they present a barrier lying athwart the tracks of prevailing rain-bearing winds. Weather from the northwest has to cross the formidable barrier of the Southern Alps, and that from the southwest or southeast has to pass over a whole series of high mountains in order to penetrate the region. The ranges of the latter series all reach 4,000 ft. of elevation, and most of them exceed this figure. Moreover, they share a common characteristic in having either a sharply accentuated crest, bounded on both sides by steep slopes, or else a comparatively gentle slope outwards, towards the direction of the oncoming weather, with a scarp-slope facing the interior of the region.[6] Mountain barriers of this nature effectively separate Inland South Island from the sea, so that on entering the area one loses any sense of being in a maritime country.

Inland South Island, however, does not consist solely of a huge subhumid or semi-arid basin, characterized by temperature extremes and surrounded by mountain walls. It is a region of diverse physiography consisting of a series of horsts and grabens, which themselves produce local climatic contrasts within the general framework we have just described.[7] Each uplifted block forming a mountain range has its physical individuality. Thus the Dunstan mountains are steep-sided and have a remarkably level surface. The Kirkliston ranges, by contrast, have steep sides, but irregular upper surfaces which make a saw-tooth pattern against the sky, while the Hawkduns present an even sky-line at the top of an abrupt slope when viewed from the Manuherikia Basin, though when viewed from the Waitaki side they appear more irregularly surfaced. But whatever the differences between

[6]C. A. Cotton: 'Block Mountains in New Zealand', *Am. Journ. Sci.*, Vol. 44 (4th ser.), 1917, pp. 249–93; W. N. Benson: 'Some Landforms in Southern New Zealand', op. cit.

[7]B. J. Garnier: 'Central Otago', in 'The Face of Otago', op. cit.

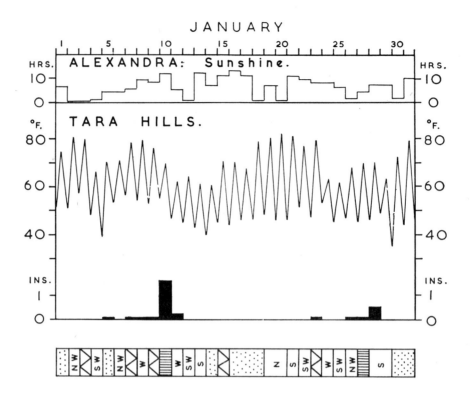

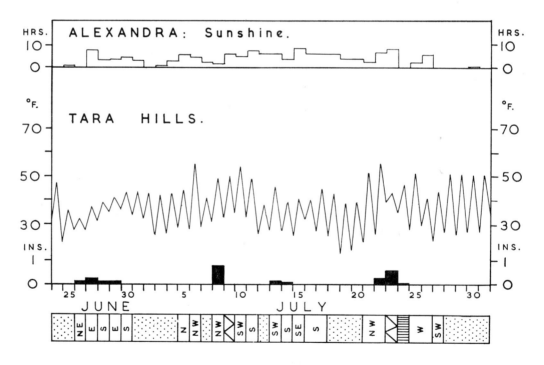

FIG. 65. Daily Temperature and Precipitation for January, 1950, and part of the winter of 1950 at Tara Hills: also daily hours of bright sunshine at Alexandra during the same period.

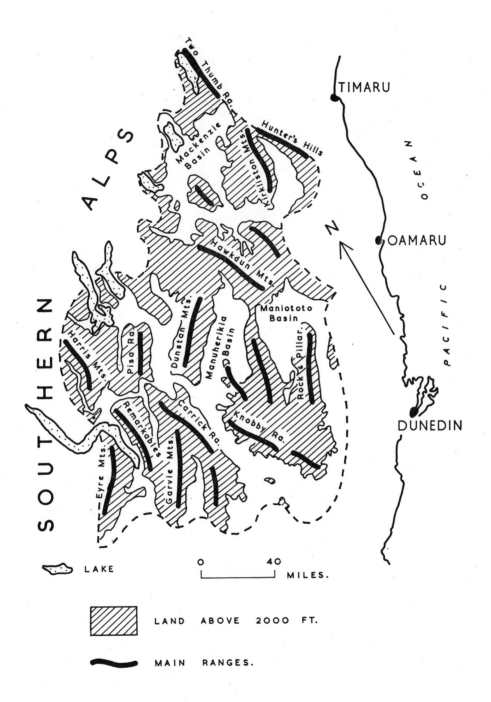

Fig. 66. Sketch-map illustrating the arrangement of the main ranges and basins of Inland South Island.

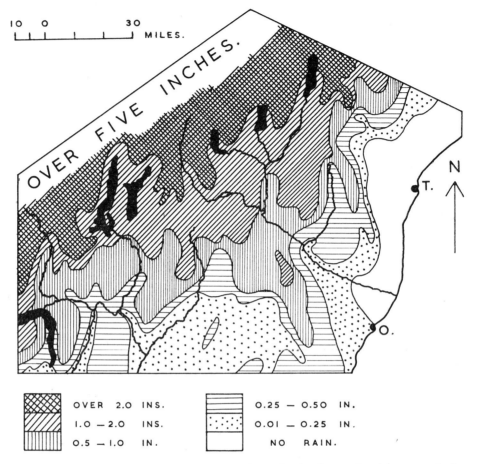

FIG. 67. Distribution of rainfall in part of Inland South Island on 5 October, 1949, during 'northwesterly' conditions. (The towns shown are: T = Timaru; O = Oamaru.)

individual blocks or ranges may be, their function in the climatic picture is the same: they break up the area into a series of basins of varying sizes, and in this way cause climatic contrasts between one part and another.

These intervening basins differ somewhat in shape and size. The Manuherikia Basin and the Cromwell Basin are rectangular and flat-floored, with steep sides; the Maniototo and the Mackenzie Basins, on the other hand, are squarer and more open in general appearance. In the Waitaki valley there is the large Omarama Basin in the upper portion, and between it and the junction of Inland South Island and Eastern South Island at Kurow, there are two small basins, the Otomatapaio Basin and the Waitangi Basin. Finally, we should note the Hakataramea valley, occupying the trench between the Hunters Hills and the Kirkliston block.

On the flat floors of these basins exist the greatest temperature extremes and the driest moisture conditions in the whole of New Zealand. It happens that each one of them has a general slope from north towards south. This means that the most extreme conditions, both of temperature and precipitation, are found in the southern portions. The Mackenzie Basin may be used to illustrate this point. Its general slope is from Lake Pukaki and Lake Tekapo towards the gorge where the Waitaki river joins the Ahuriri river at Black Jack's Point. Rainfall in this area is brought either by northwest winds or by southerly winds. It is least in the southeast edge of the basin, since rain from the former decreases steadily in quantity towards the southeast, while rain from the latter tends to keep

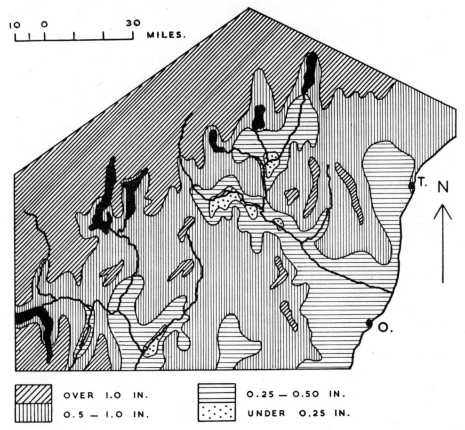

FIG. 68. Distribution of rainfall in part of Inland South Island on 4 and 5 August, 1949, during 'southwesterly' conditions. (Towns indicated: T = Timaru; O = Oamaru.)

along the ranges and so avoids the floor of the basin, and especially its southeast sector. This kind of contrast between the distribution of rainfall in northwesterly and southerly conditions may be observed by comparing *Fig.* 67 with *Fig.* 68. In the former case there is a general decrease of rainfall from the northwest towards the southeast, whereas in the latter case the rainfall distribution follows the pattern of the ranges more closely so that basins such as the Mackenzie Basin, the Omarama Basin, and the Manuherikia Basin stand out as drier areas. As regards temperature there is a tendency for extremes to be greater in the southern part of the Mackenzie Basin than in the north. This is particularly occasioned by the drainage of cold air at night, so that minimum temperatures are low. In winter fog may lie over the lower part of the Mackenzie Basin and in the upper Waitaki valley for a considerable time, perhaps all day, while the sun is shining at Lake Tekapo.

A pattern of this kind is also found in the other main basins of Inland South Island. In the Manuherikia Basin, for example, the driest region is in the southern part in the vicinity of Clyde, Earnscleugh, and Alexandra. Similarly, the least rainfall and most extreme temperatures of the Maniototo Basin are in the southern part, towards Patearoa. Even in the relatively small Hakataramea valley a similar arrangement is found, so that the driest conditions are found in a tiny triangle near Glen Cary in the lower part of the valley, where also the greatest temperature extremes are experienced.

The intervening ranges are universally wetter and cooler on the average than the valleys, and at elevations of about 3,000 ft. what may be described as 'inland mountain climate' is reached. This is often marked by a change of vegetation from the normal *Festuca Novae Zealandiae* grassland association to that of tall tussock grassland, dominated by *Danthonia raoulia*, var. *flavescens*, commonly known as 'snowgrass' (*Fig.* 69*a*). It is dangerous to rely too much on this as a climatic indicator, since a variety of other factors—edaphic, biotic, and human—complicate the picture. But if such qualifying elements do not vary over a given area, then it is reasonable to conclude that a change of vegetation also represents a difference in climate. There are several places in Inland South Island where such a conclusion seems valid. A good example is along the Benmore Range, on the side facing Benmore station. Here, farm management, economic history, the degree of slope, and the type of soil are similar throughout, and the line of 'snowgrass' coincides remarkably well with the incidence of certain climatic features: the altitude of frequent mists, the region where snow lies throughout the winter, and the areas where sunshine hours are reduced, either through the frequency of mist or the effect of shady slopes.

Such observations enable us to suggest that there is in Inland South Island a change to cooler and wetter conditions at an elevation of between 3,000 and 3,500 ft. above the sea. Here subhumid conditions merge into those of a humid region where snow lies commonly in winter. These local differences create the diversity displayed by the map showing the distribution of climatic types (*Fig.* 69*b*). It is a diversity which is as great as that of any other region of the country and which is, indeed, probably matched only by the contrasts which exist in Upland South Island, but which are difficult to map because adequate information is lacking.

In places the climate of the area is particularly affected by its 'external' contacts. These are felt here and there where gaps in the general mountain barriers permit the frequent influx of influences from outside the region. In the west, for example, are the passageways for the 'westerly' rainfall which penetrates over the cols and low passes, and moves down the long valleys. As a result bulges of the isohyets occur at the mouths of these valleys, and humid conditions may in places extend a little way into 'subhumid' Inland South Island. Such influences affect the precipitation at Braemar station, for instance, where the seasonal distribution of rainfall displays the tendency to a spring maximum typical of an area exposed to rain-bearing northwesterly winds. On the east, the more noticeable external contact is with the easterly air which commonly causes cloud to pile up against the Hunters Hills. This frequently makes mist pour over the hills or through gaps such as Burke's Pass and the Mackenzie Pass. It brings cool, humid conditions to relatively low levels, but for only a short way beyond the ranges and its effects are frequently marked by the distribution of 'snowgrass'.

Enough has now been said for us to perceive the major climatic lineaments of Inland South Island: it is an area which is essentially microthermal and either semi-arid or subhumid; it contains the driest climates and the most extreme temperatures recorded in New Zealand; and it contains such variations over short distances that a map of its climatic types displays a mosaic of contrasting conditions. Climatic individuality of this nature has contributed to a geographic personality which is equally outstanding. To understand this contribution it is necessary to refer briefly to the region's natural and economic history.

When the first white settlers reached Inland South Island in the mid-nineteenth century they found it an area well covered with native grasses.[8] The association dominated by *Festuca Novae Zealandiae* and *Poa caespitosa*, was liberally sprinkled with palatable *Agropyron scabrum*. At higher levels and in exposed positions *Danthonia raoulia* var. *flavescens* was the dominant type of grass. Into this fertile-looking area came the pastoralists who released thousands of sheep to feed upon its grasses and to trample down its soil. Young grass growth, deemed more palatable for the sheep, was encouraged by burning the pasture annually in spring, and the smoke of grassland fires became a common sight at the close of the winter months. The attack on the vegetation by sheep and man was further accentuated by the rabbit invasion which assumed large proportions by the last quarter of the nineteenth

[8] A. Bathgate: 'Some Changes in the Fauna and Flora of Otago in the last sixty years', *N.Z. Journ. Sci. and Tech.*, Vol. 4, 1922, pp. 273–83; K. B. Cumberland: 'Soil Erosion in New Zealand', op. cit.

century.[9] Millions moved in from the south and the vegetation was rapidly eaten out, especially on sunny slopes. Today rabbits are the most prolific form of livestock in the area. At sundown they come out and overrun the hillsides: a shout and a stamp sets them moving in a mass, and one can speak without exaggeration of whole hillsides 'moving' with rabbits. Trapping, shooting, and poisoning have had their effects, and rows of rabbit carcasses hung out along the fences, and the regular arrival of the 'rabbit cart' are essential characteristics of the region.

Under the stress of these invasions the delicate adjustment of vegetation and soil to their habitat has been rudely shattered. Where once native tussocks grew knee and waist high there is now a scanty covering of poor, depleted grassland interspersed with generous amounts of rubbery 'scab-weed' (*Raoulia lutescens*). Soil, too, has gone, having been washed or blown away in the absence of its protective armour of vegetation. In short, a 'man-made desert', to use Cockayne's telling phrase, has come into existence.[10]

Although the impetus to vegetation and soil loss has come about through human agency, the actual spoliation represents a climatic consequence of destroying the natural balance. The more violent of the climatic features have made themselves felt: extremes of temperature, dry föhn-like northwesterlies, and occasional deluges from a convectional storm, have all played their part in the process of destruction.[11] The significant aspect of temperature is the frequency with which freezing point is crossed. It happens here more often than in other parts. At Alexandra, for example, screen temperatures crossed this key value 158 times in 1949, and in the following year at Tara Hills crossed it 232 times. At ground level such changes must have been far more frequent. Under such influences soil, unprotected by vegetation, becomes broken up. Melting water by day encourages soil creep, and much is also blown away by northwest gales. These pulverize the soil and raise clouds of dust. Topsoil is thus removed and the more compacted lower horizons become exposed to rainfall which, instead of sinking in, tends to run straight off, thus adding to soil-wash and soil-wastage. From time to time, especially during summer in the unstable air following a cold front, sudden deluges of rain may occur. These are highly localized and last only a short time. Their effects on the unprotected soils are devastating. Deep gullies develop and rivers of mud and shingle belch forth from the hillsides on to the valleys below. The combined result of these violent climatic phenomena is to produce in Inland South Island a series of erosion forms peculiar to the locality. Their intensity, however, varies according to the basic rock structure. It is greater on the mica-schists of central Otago than on the more resistant greywackes outside that locality. The degree of erosion in the different parts of Inland South Island, therefore, is not entirely climatically controlled; a 'similar' climate will not have the same erosion effects on greywacke as it does on mica-schist, although in both cases the essential form will be climatically derived.

The successful human occupance of Inland South Island depends upon recognizing its climatic qualities and working with them. There is abundant evidence of what happens when this necessity is disregarded. There is, on the other hand, equally abundant evidence of the great possibilities of economic development, in particular of agricultural production, if climatic conditions are properly regarded. The use of irrigation demonstrates this. A Frenchman named Ferand is credited with being the first to use water for this purpose in central Otago, when he began irrigating his farm in 1865.[12] Government schemes were developed from 1916 onwards and today there is a considerable network of channels bringing water to soils naturally well supplied with phosphate and lime and

[9]K. A. Wodzicki: 'Introduced Mammals of New Zealand: an ecological and economic survey', *N.Z. Dept. Sci. and Ind. Res. Bulln.*, No. 98, 1950.

[10]L. Cockayne: 'The Vegetation of New Zealand', op. cit.

[11]K. B. Cumberland: 'Soil Erosion in New Zealand', op. cit.; H. S. Gibbs, J. D. Raeside, *et al.*: 'Soil Erosion in the High Country of the South Island', *N.Z. Dept. Sci. and Ind. Res. Bulln.*, No. 92, 1945; K. B. Cumberland: 'Contrasting Regional Morphology of Soil Erosion . . .', op. cit.

[12]B. J. Garnier: 'Central Otago', op. cit.

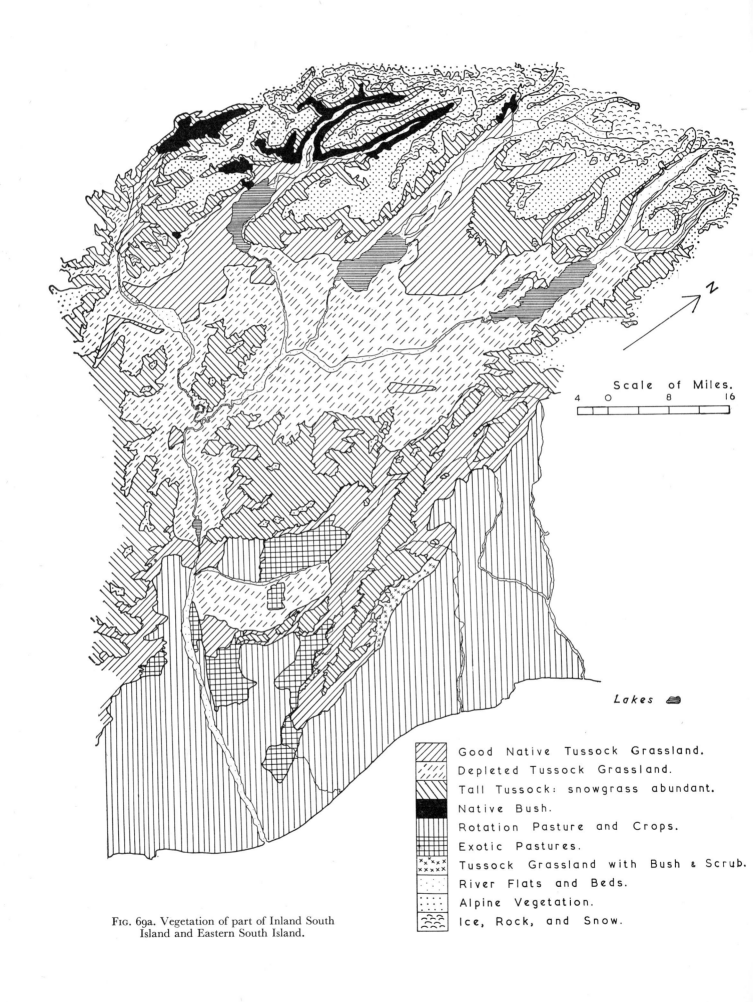

Scale of Miles.
4 0 8 16

Lakes

Good Native Tussock Grassland.
Depleted Tussock Grassland.
Tall Tussock: snowgrass abundant.
Native Bush.
Rotation Pasture and Crops.
Exotic Pastures.
Tussock Grassland with Bush & Scrub.
River Flats and Beds.
Alpine Vegetation.
Ice, Rock, and Snow.

FIG. 69a. Vegetation of part of Inland South Island and Eastern South Island.

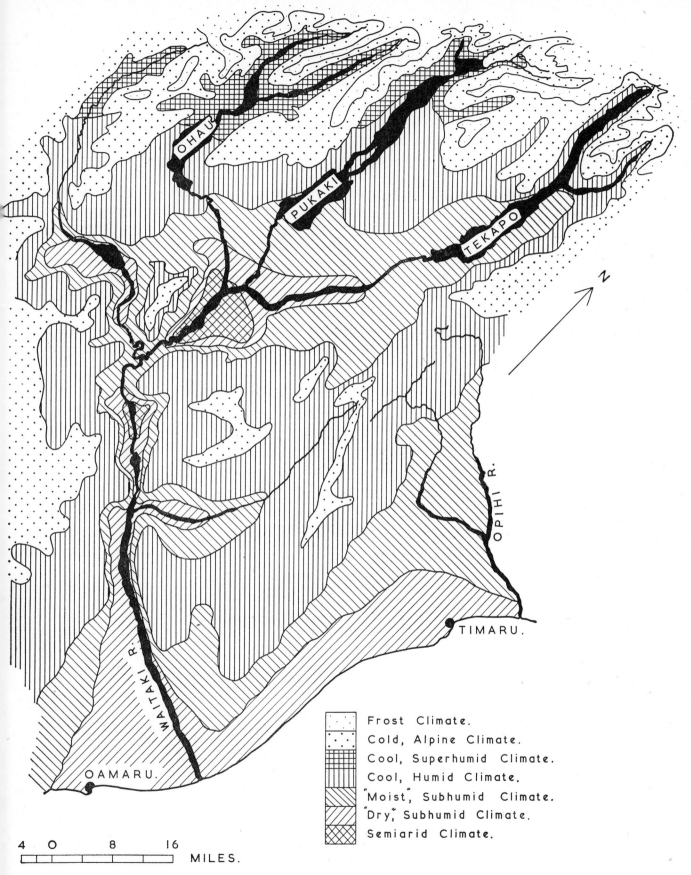

OHAU

PUKAKI

TEKAPO

OPIHI R.

N

TIMARU.

WAITAKI R.

OAMARU.

Frost Climate.
Cold, Alpine Climate.
Cool, Superhumid Climate.
Cool, Humid Climate.
"Moist", Subhumid Climate.
"Dry", Subhumid Climate.
Semiarid Climate.

4 O   8   16
MILES.

FIG. 69b. Climatic types of part of Inland South Island and Eastern South Island.

responsive to controlled irrigation.[13] By this means considerable transformation of the landscape has been effected over a limited part of Inland South Island. Good quality pastures have been created which are used for fat-lamb rearing and dairying. In localities where the frost hazard is not too great, fruit growing has been developed, and central Otago is one of the main New Zealand sources for stone and pip fruit. The success of these limited schemes shows what can be done in an area of this climatic type. A further indication of the stimulus to growth given by climate here is the rapidity with which vegetation returns when land is lightly stocked or left untouched. It requires, indeed, only a year or two to achieve noticeable results, especially if the land is adequately protected from rabbits.[14]

The climate of Inland South Island, then, itself a product of some of the distinctive features of the area, is expressed in the present-day landscape in many ways. The violence of its destructive powers when nature's balance is upset and its equally powerful encouragement to growth when conservation measures are adopted, impregnate the region with qualities at once unique and compelling in their character. These qualities are well revealed in the view across the Manuherikia valley which can be obtained from the hills near Alexandra. Along the foot of the slopes on the far side of the valley a dark line can be seen, which marks the irrigation channel. Below it the land is green and prosperous, with rich pastures able to support seven sheep on every acre; above the line the land is bare, brown, scarred, and gullied, with rough pastures sufficient for only one sheep on every seven acres. Such a contrast expresses, better than any words or statistics, the essence of the climate of Inland South Island and its manifestation in the region's landscapes.

[13]H. T. Ferrar: 'Soils of the Irrigation Areas of Central Otago', *N.Z. Geol. Surv. Bulln.* (*N.S.*), No. 33, 1929; H. S. Gibbs, J. D. Raeside, *et al.*, op. cit.

[14]L. Cockayne: 'An Economic Investigation of the Montane Tussock Grassland of New Zealand', a series of articles in *N.Z. Journ. Agric.*, Vol. 18 (1919) to Vol. 25 (1922); 'Report of a Committee on the Regrassing Experiments in Central Otago', *N.Z. Journ. Agric.*, Vol. 26, 1923, pp. 97–100.

13

UPLAND SOUTH ISLAND

MORE than half of the South Island of New Zealand consists of mountain ranges. Here are jumbled peaks, massive ice-fields, bare rock slopes, and deeply incised, flat-floored valleys in which fast-flowing streams race over wide beds or between steep rock walls. No other part of New Zealand is so high or so rugged, and no other part has such a powerful physical personality.

Such a distinctive physiographic province must be regarded as a climatic one as well. Although it contains New Zealand's coldest climates, there are also dry, dusty valleys and over remarkably short distances, especially in summer, one may pass from ice and snow to heat and drought. This diversity is caused by the combined effects of physiography and the prevailing atmospheric circumstances over the country.

The region consists of a mountain mass which extends from southwest to northeast for the whole length of the South Island. The central parts are the highest. A large number of peaks there exceed 10,000 ft. of elevation, and the summits of the ranges are over 7,000 ft. To south and north the elevations are somewhat less. From Mount Aspiring southwestwards, in 'Fiordland', the average summit level is in the neighbourhood of 6,000 ft. above the sea, and this is also the general elevation north of the middle sector in the provinces of Nelson and Marlborough, except for the Inland and Seaward Kaikouras. These exceed 8,000 ft. of elevation and enclose deep, longitudinal valleys such as that of the Awatere. The mountains have been intensely dissected by subaerial and glacial denudation. Many of their valleys are over a mile wide in places and from their flat floors 50 per cent or steeper slopes rise 3,000 and 4,000 ft. There is thus a great deal of steep country, in which relative relief commonly exceeds 4,000 ft.

This brief physiographic description is sufficient to show that Upland South Island is high enough and rugged enough to have acquired the climatic characteristics common to mountain regions in general.[1] These characteristics are derived particularly from the rarefaction of the atmosphere and the decrease in the area of land surface at higher elevations, and they are expressed mainly in a reduction of air temperature and an increase in the intensity of insolation. Such conditions are, according to Kendrew, well developed above 6,000 ft. of elevation but are not prominent up to 4,000 ft. so that 'there is an important difference between the zones below 4,000 ft. and above 6,000 ft.'[2] The average elevation of Upland South Island lies above these critical altitudes. There are, nevertheless, some special characteristics derived from its position in the New Zealand milieu. These may be dealt with under three headings: the effect of heavy precipitation, the effect of the orientation of the main ranges, and the effect of the details of the region's relief.

Precipitation in the mountains of the South Island is extremely heavy. Exposure to moisture-laden winds, coupled with the height of the ranges, produces an average of over 150 inches a year in most of the area. Its incidence is typical of New Zealand since it comes in heavy falls on relatively few days

---

[1]Most standard text-books on climate devote some space to discussing these. Probably the most useful general account is still that of Hann. See J. Hann: 'Handbook of Climatology', Vol. 1, Trans. from 2nd edn. by R. de C. Ward, New York, 1903.

[2]W. G. Kendrew: 'Climatology, treated mainly in relation to distribution in time and space, being the 3rd edition of "Climate" ', Oxford, 1949.

and is associated with a relatively large number of hours of bright sunshine (*Fig.* 70). In spite of the high totals, therefore, few recording stations average more than 200 rainy days a year. For example, the mean annual rainfall at Otira is 201 inches, and the mean annual number of rainy days 167. The equivalent figures at Arthur's Pass are 157 inches and 138 days and at Milford Sound 253 inches and 195 days. Individual falls may be very heavy: 5 inches or more in twenty-four hours are not by any means uncommon, even at stations in the upper valleys on the lee-side of mountains such as the Hermitage at Mount Cook, and on the exposed mountain ranges such totals must be more frequent still (*Fig.* 70).[3]

Much of the precipitation falls as snow.[4] This causes extensive fields of snow and ice, so that the permanent snowline is at a comparatively low level for the latitude. Hochstetter, for example, re-marks:[5]

> Thus, it is obvious, as the perpetual snowline, owing to the equable and humid climate, is at the West Coast very low, probably about 6,500 feet near Mount Cook, and as the fall of snow and condensation of moisture must still be greater in those higher regions, where the equatorial currents come into contact with the cold surfaces of the Alps, that all necessary conditions exist not only for the formation of large glaciers, but also for their descent to much lower regions than at the East Coast, where the line of perpetual snow in a latitude from 43 to 44 degrees probably only reaches 7,500 feet.

Others have placed the permanent snowline at between 7,000 ft. and 8,000 ft. above sea-level, and its average elevation in winter as 4,000 ft. in the middle and northern parts of the region and about 3,500 ft. in the southern.[6]

From the snow-fields large glaciers descend to low levels. This is especially so on the west coast where visitors to the country have remarked upon the incongruity of there being subtropical rain-forest growing at the foot of glaciers such as the Fox and the Franz Josef. From the general climatic viewpoint, however, the chief result of extensive fields of snow and ice is a general lowering of tem-perature, especially above an altitude of 4,000 ft. This feature is particularly apparent in the rapid rate at which temperature decreases with altitude above about 3,000 ft. of elevation as compared with its rate below this height—a feature which is more apparent in spring and autumn than at other seasons (see Appendix A).

The heavy precipitation of Upland South Island is to a large extent caused by the orientation of the main ranges. Within the mountain area there is a contrast between areas of western and of eastern exposures, especially below a height of 4,000 ft. or a little lower. Above this altitude precipitation remains heavy on both sides of the ranges due to the tendency for storms to proceed some distance over their crests. There is, however, a marked alteration in precipitation totals down the valleys on the eastern side, which is apparent in mean figures of rainfall as well as in the precipitation distribu-tion of individual falls. For example, on 9 and 10 January 1950 the rainfall at the Hermitage, Mount Cook, totalled 11.9 inches, but at Braemar, less than twenty miles farther down the Tasman valley, the total during the same two days was precisely 10 inches less.

Finally let us consider the effect of the region's diversified relief upon its climate. Its chief conse-quence is to cause a considerable amount of climatic variety. It is possible within a very short distance to pass from a valley-floor which is almost subhumid in appearance into a superhumid mountain landscape of close-growing grasses or, given sufficient soil, of beech forest. As we have seen, however, moisture contrasts of this nature are not uncommon in New Zealand, and a more outstanding feature

[3]C. J. Seelye: 'The Frequency of Heavy Rainfalls . . .', op. cit.

[4]E. Kidson: 'The Frequency of Frost, Snow, and Hail . . .', op. cit.

[5]F. von Hochstetter: 'New Zealand, its physical geography, geology, and natural history', Trans. by E. Sauter, Stuttgart, 1867.

[6]E. Kidson: 'The Elements of New Zealand's Climate', op. cit.; F. W. Hilgendorf: 'The Grasslands of the South Island of New Zealand', *N.Z. Dept. Sci. and Ind. Res. Bulln.*, No. 47, 1935.

PLATE XI. *Snow and ice in Upland South Island*

Heavy precipitation maintains large quantities of snow and ice in much of Upland South Island. Glaciers descend to low levels on the western slopes and mingle with vegetation which is tropical in its luxuriance. Clear, anticyclonic skies enhance the beauty of this view of the Franz Josef Glacier.

PLATE XII. *Cold climate scenes in Upland South Island*
(*a*) Snow and tall tussock in the mountains of Fiordland. (*b*) Where snow and forest meet in Upland South Island; the treeline and winter snowline are clearly defined in this view in the upper reaches of an Otago valley.

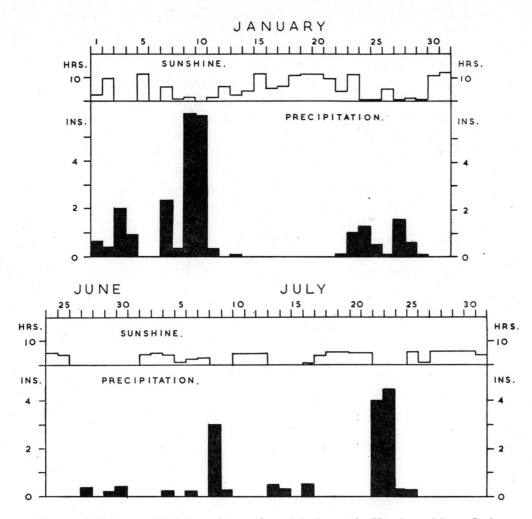

FIG. 70. Daily hours of bright sunshine and precipitation at the Hermitage, Mount Cook, during January, 1950, and part of the winter of 1950.

of this upland region is the amount of difference in the temperature conditions from place to place. This is expressed in general terms by the temperature maps given earlier in this volume. In detail the effect of aspect on temperature and radiation is particularly important. In view of the steep slopes of the area, the contrast between sunny and shady slopes is marked at all seasons and at all times of day. This brings the orientation of individual valleys into prominence.[7] In Fiordland and the middle parts of Upland South Island, this is mainly north to south but farther north, in Marlborough, the valleys follow the main trend of the mountain axis. Such differences further diversify the details of the local climatic pattern. Moreover, the valleys are deep ones and closely connected with nearby fields of snow and ice. Thus, the drainage of cold air at night, and the different rates at which the sides and bottoms of the valleys are warmed by day add still more to an already complex situation.

The foregoing remarks have treated Upland South Island as a single climatic unit, which contains considerable local diversity. It is, however, possible to divide the area broadly into two contrasting

[7]There is room for an interesting study of this matter along the lines developed by Alice Garnett for the European Alps. See A. Garnett: 'Insolation, Topography, and Settlement in the Alps', *Geogr. Rev.*, Vol. 25, 1935, pp. 601–17; *idem*: 'Insolation and Relief, their bearing on the human geography of alpine regions', *Trans. Inst. Brit. Geogrs.*, No. 5, 1937.

parts. South of Lake Wanaka, southwesterly influences predominate. Precipitation variability is less here than elsewhere in the region and is, indeed, as low as anywhere in New Zealand, the mean annual value being in the vicinity of 10 per cent or less.[8] Moreover, since the area is lower and physically more cohesive than the rest, the variation of climate over short distances is reduced, and there is not so much snow on the mountain summits. North of Lake Wanaka, however, relief is more intense and the area is influenced by both northwest and southwest air streams, while at times easterly conditions are effective sources of rainfall, especially from the Rangitata river northwards. Precipitation is consequently more variable than to the south. On the eastern side of the ranges the mean annual variability is over 16 per cent, which helps to distinguish the locality from the south. Here, too, föhn-like winds are felt and climatic diversity is greater owing to the contrast between valleys, many of which may be almost subhumid, and the nearby mountain ice-fields.

Much of the geographic character of Upland South Island, a virtually uninhabited land, is bound up with its climatic character. It combines with the physiography to provide the region with its major distinguishing qualities in a geographic sense. The two are closely connected and together express themselves in other features. Soils, for example, are shallow and acidic in nature.[9] There is also a marked zoning of plants through the area.[10] In Fiordland the forest ends abruptly at the winter snowline, and there is also a striking general contrast between the forests of the west and the open grasslands of the east, whether viewed by the mountaineer straddling a knife-edge ridge on the main divide, or by the traveller who journeys by rail through the Otira tunnel. To the visitor it is perhaps the climatic peculiarities, observed through the different kinds of vegetation, which are the more striking. One expects in mountain areas steep slopes and valleys, but one is not prepared for so much climatic variety. It is indeed an experience to pass in summer along hot dusty valleys, then to climb through grassland into forest, and finally to reach within a remarkably short space of time the myriad of plants which make up the alpine fell field, close above which lies a wilderness of snow and ice. It is, moreover, an experience which arises pre-eminently from the particular combination of climatic qualities existing in Upland South Island.

[8]C. J. Seelye: 'The Variation of Annual Rainfall . . .', op. cit.
[9]H. S. Gibbs, J. D. Raeside, et al., op. cit.
[10]L. Cockayne: 'The Vegetation of New Zealand', op. cit.

CONCLUSION

IN bringing to a close this discussion of the climate of New Zealand, it is well to return to the viewpoint of the opening chapters by considering the area once more as a single unit. In doing so, we shall comment very briefly on climate as an element in the country's geographic personality.

The climate of New Zealand displays considerable diversity within the framework of the common features which bind it together as a whole. It is also a vigorous climate, containing sunshine and and storms, fine weather and heavy rain, stimulating air and sudden change. These qualities have played their part in creating other characteristics of New Zealand. They have etched out the details of its youthful physiography, they have promoted the growth of its unruly native vegetation, and they have accelerated 'normal' erosion so as to produce soils which, in their natural state, are often coarse and infertile. Moreover, the regional variations of climate are paralleled by similar variations in other phenomena, such as the broad distribution of certain native forest species.

But the manifestation of climate in landscape is not confined to its expression in physical phenomena; it is also apparent in other ways. Cumberland has pointed out that the New Zealand countryside derives much of its character from its agricultural features.[1] These have come about through the attempt to spread over the country farm practices which are fundamentally similar, in the sense that they aim to make the maximum use of grassland in order to supply meat, dairy produce, and wool to a distant European market. For this purpose the land has been tamed, and commercial livestock-farming established wherever possible. The resulting regional pattern of agriculture corresponds broadly with that of climate on the one hand and physiography on the other. The major livestock-ranching areas of the country, for example, occupy the more rugged territory, and also those areas where precipitation is either highly variable in its incidence or low in total quantity. On the other hand, the areas of intensive livestock-farming occupy regions where moisture is plentiful and reliable, and where relief is easy. Such correspondences represent the acknowledgement of climatic and physiographic limits in terms of current economic returns.

There are, however, cases in which two areas within a region of uniform climate have markedly different geographic characteristics. The contrasts between north and south Auckland, between inland and western Taranaki, and between central Otago and the rest of Inland South Island, come readily to mind. In the first of these examples, the differences between north and south Auckland are largely man-made, in the sense that they represent the consequences of different stages of development. But in the remaining two examples climate plays an active part, since in these cases the geographic contrasts arise from its varying reaction to the other factors with which it is associated. Thus, it has promoted in inland Taranaki the disorderly landscapes produced by the too-rapid clearing of forest from steep slopes, whereas it has encouraged good pastures on the neighbouring lowlands when they have been cleared and sown with grass-seed. It has also developed erosion forms in central Otago of a different intensity from those it has created outside that area because of its different rate of action on contrasting rock types.

This short summary has emphasized that the distinctive features of New Zealand's climate are

[1] K. B. Cumberland: 'The Agricultural Regions of New Zealand', op. cit.

important to the character of the country as a geographic unit and that, within the land, their significance varies from place to place. Indeed, to exemplify this has been one of the principal aims of this book. As stated in the introduction, such an attitude has been adopted not only to fill a gap in climatological literature but also to illustrate a way of differentiating systematic geography more clearly from other systematic sciences. It is hoped, however, that the book may also have some practical value, in so far as it emphasizes the need to understand the climate of New Zealand in its geographic context. Vigorous, stimulating, and wayward, this climate is one of the country's resources which demands such understanding, but which will repay careful study, for it may be turned to good or bad account with equal facility, according to the way it is regarded and used.

APPENDIX A

The Rate of Change of Mean Temperatures with Altitude in New Zealand

STUDENTS of temperature conditions in New Zealand must interpolate freely from the values of existing climatological stations if they wish to estimate temperatures in the mountainous and inaccessible parts of the country. Most workers have been content to use general figures for this purpose. Kidson, for example, used 2.74F° per 1,000 ft. of elevation as a mean value for the rate at which temperature alters with altitude, although he comments that this is probably too small for most parts of the country.[1] Macky, in a study of temperatures near Wellington, concluded that in that district the rate of change for every 1,000 ft. of altitude was probably as much as 4.4F°, while Bondy and Seelye have used 3.0F° per 1,000 ft. of elevation.[2]

There is, however, enough climatic variety in New Zealand to suggest that single values of this kind fail to provide even an approximately correct indication of conditions in different parts of the country at different seasons. Moreover, in view of the heavy precipitation which maintains large quantities of snow in the mountains, the alteration of temperature with altitude is unlikely to be uniform, but will tend to be greater at higher levels than at lower ones. This is especially so during spring and summer.

There are now nearly a hundred places from which to obtain reasonably reliable values of mean monthly temperatures. Of these, the highest is at the Chateau Tongariro, 3,670 ft. above the sea. No other station exceeds 3,000 ft. of elevation, but there are nine between 2,000 and 3,000 ft., and thirteen others between 1,000 and 2,000 ft. These twenty-three stations above 1,000 ft. of altitude are well distributed among the uplands and ranges of both islands, and all but six of them have records which have been kept for more than fifteen years. They provide, therefore, useful information for the interpolations required not only for an insight into the temperature conditions of the mountains themselves, but also for filling in the blanks caused by the absence of stations on some of the more low-lying parts of the country. All the stations available are grouped in the following table (*Table* 1A) according to their altitude and the climatic regions in which they are found.

Table 1A

NUMBER OF STATIONS USED IN COMPUTING THE RATE OF CHANGE OF MEAN TEMPERATURE WITH ALTITUDE IN NEW ZEALAND

Region	Under 500 ft.	500– 1,000 ft.	1,000– 2,000 ft.	2,000– 3,000 ft.	Over 3,000 ft.	Total
Middle N.Z.	13	2	0	1	0	16
Western Sth. Is.	4	0	1	1	0	6
Northern N.Z.	9	1	1	0	0	11
Southern N.Z.	5	1	1	0	0	7
Eastern Nth. Is.	10	1	1	1	0	13
Eastern Sth. Is.	8	2	4	0	0	14
Central Nth. Is.	5	1	3	2	1	12
Inland Sth. Is.	0	2	5	3	0	10
Upland Sth. Is.	0	3	5	3	0	11

[1] E. Kidson: 'Mean Temperatures in New Zealand', *N.Z. Journ. Sci. and Tech.*, Vol. 13, 1931, pp. 140–53.

[2] W. A. Macky: 'Climatological Observations at Eastbourne, Wellington, and some comparisons', *N.Z. Meteor. Office Notes*, No. 21, 1938; F. Bondy and C. J. Seelye: 'Temperatures Associated with Rainfall in New Zealand', N.Z. *Journ. Sci. and Tech.*, Vol. 28, Sec. B, 1947, pp. 253–8.

The mean annual temperature and the mean temperatures for each season for all these stations were plotted against altitude in a series of graphs. Regression lines were then drawn. The slope of these at lower levels, where observations were plentiful, was checked mathematically by using the method of semi-averages described by Conrad.[3] At upper levels it was 'fitted' to observations of the snowline at different times of the year, making the assumption that such a level also represented a mean temperature of 32°F for the season concerned.[4] As a rule it was felt necessary to change the slope of these regression lines somewhere between an altitude of 1,500 and 3,000 ft., the height of the change varying with the seasons and according to locality. After scrutinizing all the evidence obtained in this way, it was decided to divide the figures for the alteration of mean temperature with altitude into two groups: the rate below 2,000 ft. of elevation and the rate above it. This was done for each season in each region and also for the year, and the final figures chosen as reasonably valid are given in *Table* 2A.

Table 2A

RATE OF CHANGE OF MEAN TEMPERATURE WITH ALTITUDE IN NEW ZEALAND
(F° per 1,000 ft.)

(a) Below 2,000 ft. of elevation.   (b) Above 2,000 ft. of elevation.

Region	Winter (a)	Winter (b)	Spring (a)	Spring (b)	Summer (a)	Summer (b)	Autumn (a)	Autumn (b)	Year (a)	Year (b)
Middle N.Z.	3.6	3.6	3.5	3.5	2.2	3.8	2.0	3.2	3.4	3.4
Western Sth. Is.	4.3	4.3	2.0	4.5	1.0	4.5	2.5	4.0	2.5	4.0
Northern N.Z.	4.0	4.0	3.5	3.5	4.0	4.0	3.6	3.6	3.8	3.8
Southern N.Z.	4.3	4.3	2.2	3.5	1.0	3.7	2.4	3.5	2.2	3.5
Eastern Nth. Is.	3.5	3.5	4.1	4.1	3.8	3.8	3.8	3.8	3.8	3.8
Eastern Sth. Is.	2.6	2.6	2.1	4.2	1.0	4.0	1.8	3.5	2.2	3.5
Central Nth. Is.	3.5	3.5	3.5	3.5	3.2	4.0	3.4	3.4	3.5	3.5
Inland Sth. Is.	2.4	2.4	3.0	4.2	3.0	4.0	2.0	3.3	2.5	3.5
Upland Sth. Is.	1.5	3.8	1.5	4.5	1.5	4.3	1.7	4.2	1.5	4.2

[3] V. Conrad: 'Methods in Climatology', 1st ed., Harvard U.P., 1947.

[4] The limit of tall trees in many areas appears to coincide with a mean annual temperature of 43°F., and this possibility was used in places.

APPENDIX B

Weather Conditions during part of the Summer of 1949—50 and of the Winter of 1950

IN each of the chapters devoted to describing conditions in the climatic regions of New Zealand there appears a diagram illustrating daily conditions of temperature and precipitation during part of the summer of 1949–50 and of the winter of 1950. In nearly every case the summer period chosen is January 1950, and the winter period is from 21 June to the end of July. The main atmospheric situations controlling the weather are shown by lettering and shading at the bottom of each diagram. They have been obtained by examining the chart for 00 hours G.M.T. on each day in question, and on the scale of the diagram it is only possible to indicate the general kind of sequence experienced. The directions of the main air streams over each region are indicated for different days by the appropriate letters, and the other influences by shading: anticyclonic or generally high pressure conditions are shown by dots, the passage of a cold front by a zig-zag line, and a depression (usually with both a cold and a warm front in evidence) by horizontal shading. A depression was only shown to be in control when it actually passed over the area in question in such a way as to preclude the separate designation of individual situations in terms of cold fronts or air streams. Warm fronts are not shown, as they were always attached to depressions, and the lapse of time between the passage of a warm front and a cold one was generally too short for the former to be included in the diagram.

The descriptions of the weather sequences given below refer to the general conditions over the country. They have been copied, with minor modifications, from the official climatological notes published in the *New Zealand Government Gazette*. The notes for January are taken from the *Gazette* of 23 February 1950, page 205, and those for June and July from that of 20 July 1950, page 1000, and 17 August 1950, page 1597 respectively. In addition, a selection of charts for January 1950 and July 1950 follows these notes.

Weather Conditions during January 1950

During the first few days of the month five depressions crossed the Tasman Sea and passed to the south of New Zealand. The associated frontal system moved across the country from the west producing frequent rain in Western South Island and to a lesser extent in Southern New Zealand. Rain became fairly general for a time on the 4th.

On the 6th an anticyclone in the north Tasman Sea extended on to the North Island, where the weather continued fine and warm. It remained unsettled in the south and some heavy rain occurred in Western South Island over several days while an active front progressed slowly up the island. Rain spread to the east coast on the 8th when the front became stationary over north Canterbury, later to move southwards again and gradually to dissipate.

While the cold front from the southwest was crossing the South Island on the 10th, a wave depression developed over Canterbury producing general rain south of Christchurch. Continuing northwards the front crossed the North Island on the 11th.

Following the passage of yet another depression in the south on the 12th, a cold front travelled slowly northwards over the country. With the approach of an anticyclone from the Tasman Sea temperatures became appreciably cooler and the weather gradually improved from the west and south.

A weak front produced brief rain on the coast of Southern New Zealand on the 15th, and about the Kaikouras on the 16th. Pressures rose rapidly behind it and a large high-pressure cell developed east of the South Island. A spell of fine, anticyclonic weather followed, except in the Gisborne district where southeasterly winds and dull, showery weather set in on the 14th and continued for over a week. On the 21st the anticylone moved far away to the east of the South Island, while a disturbance from the north travelled slowly southeastwards past East Cape. Light falls of rain extended to eastern, central and southern portions of the North Island and to Nelson and Marlborough.

Northwesterlies prevailed on the 23rd and rain developed in Western South Island with the approach of a disturbance, the centre of which moved eastwards across Campbell Island on the morning of the 25th. The associated front produced brief rain in most places except in eastern districts from Canterbury to East Cape. Winds turned temporarily to southwest and rose to gale force in the south.

Further rain in moderate amounts fell during the passage of a dying tropical cyclone which, after leaving a trail of damage in New South Wales, moved rapidly across the Tasman Sea to pass over Southland on the night of the 27th. Winds backed to cool southerlies on the 29th and next day the weather cleared generally.

Weather Conditions from June 21st to the end of July 1950

During June a series of six depressions which formed off eastern Queensland, passed over or near to New Zealand. On the 21st the fifth of this series passed well to the north of the country just as the sixth was beginning to form. An intense anticyclone, which had been over southeastern Australia for more than a week, then crossed the Tasman Sea to New Zealand. Thus, on the 24th there came to an end a long spell of showery weather in Southern New Zealand.

The sixth depression of the series followed a more southerly track than any of its predecessors. Deepening steadily, it soon developed into a major storm which produced serious flooding in New South Wales as it moved down the Australian coast. Winds turned northeasterly in New Zealand on the 25th with the approach of the associated warm front. This front was preceded by a very extensive rain-band which reached north Auckland late on the 25th. Barometers fell steadily and rain gradually spread southwards over the whole country. When the original centre was still about 500 miles west of Auckland, a new centre formed east of Hawke's Bay early on the 28th. With a change to northwesterly winds in the north, rain became intermittent there, but the formation of a new centre intensified the rainfall in the Wairarapa and Marlborough, resulting in some local flooding in the latter district.

As the new centre moved away to the east on the 29th, the original centre travelled towards Western South Island where it slowly died away. The weather, however, remained generally unsettled due to the rapid advance of a new and vigorous depression in an east-northeastward direction across from Tasmania.

The centre of this vigorous depression crossed north Auckland at the beginning of July, and heavy rain fell in the northeastern part of the North Island, causing severe flooding in the Gisborne district. The weather was mainly fair in the South Island under the influence of an extensive ridge of high pressure stretching from New South Wales across the South Island and away to the east.

As the northern depression moved away, an anticyclone built up to the east of New Zealand on the 5th. By that time conditions had improved in the North Island, but cloudy, showery weather soon prevailed due to the passage of two weak troughs associated with depressions centred far to the southwest. On that occasion, however, showers did not extend to the east of the main ranges.

An active cold front moved across rapidly from the southwest on the 9th, the associated low pressure centre passing close to Southern New Zealand.

Cold southerlies prevailed on the 11th with the approach of an anticyclone. A brief period of clear frosty weather which followed came to an end on the 13th with the arrival of a trough from the west. A depression formed within this trough, deepened rapidly, and then moved across south Auckland on the morning of the 14th. Rain became general, while the formation of a secondary depression east of Wairarapa accounted for heavier rainfalls and southerly gales about the Cook Strait region. Snow fell on the high country of the North Island and Marlborough. It became colder still after the passage of a secondary cold front on the 16th and showers also developed over the South Island, except Western South Island.

With the approach of a very intense anticyclone, the weather began to improve, and by the 18th it had become fine generally except in the Gisborne district where the clearance was delayed until the next day. Widespread frosts of an unusual severity were recorded for several days during the passage of this remarkable anticyclone in which the central pressure exceeded 1,045 millibars. As the anticyclone began to move away eastwards on the 22nd the frontal system, associated with an extensive disturbance centred far to the southwest, began to advance over the South Island. The development of a wave-depression off Western South Island temporarily retarded the front's progress and this resulted in heavy rain in Westland. There was also widespread rain northwards to Taranaki and Wellington. After the depression had passed across the South Island, the front resumed its journey northwards on the 25th.

Following the passage of an active cold front, southerlies prevailed on the 26th. A large anticyclone approaching from the west then took charge of the weather until the end of the month. Although showers persisted in Southland and Gisborne districts until the 29th, elsewhere clear, frosty weather prevailed after the 26th. The anticyclone was beginning to move off slowly eastwards on the 31st.

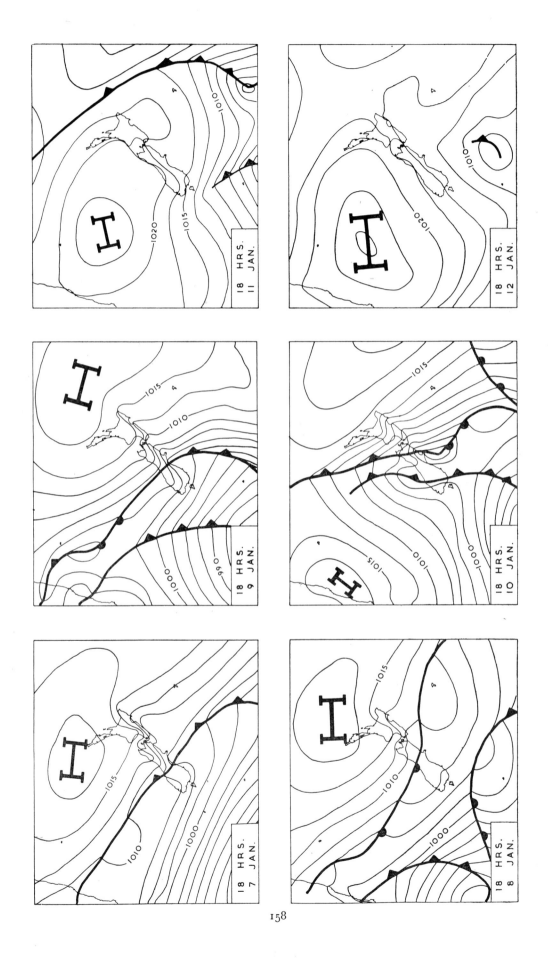

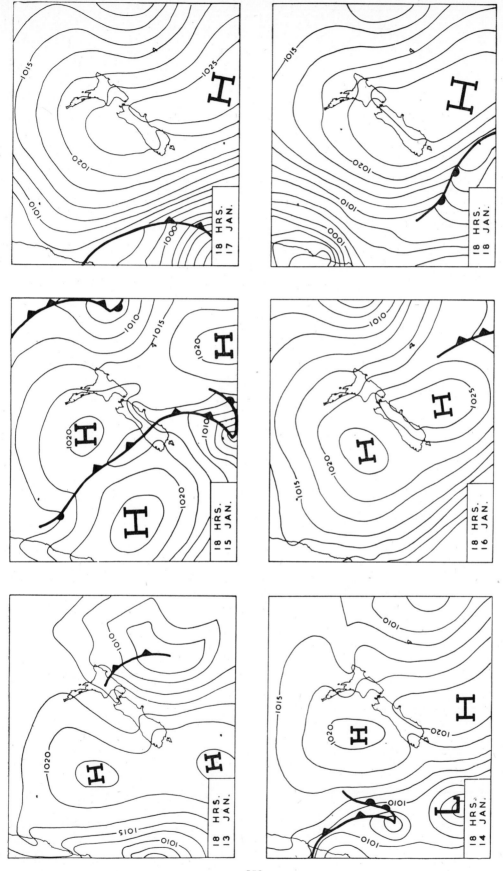

Maps illustrating atmospheric conditions over New Zealand from 7–18 January, 1950.
(All times shown are G.M.T.)

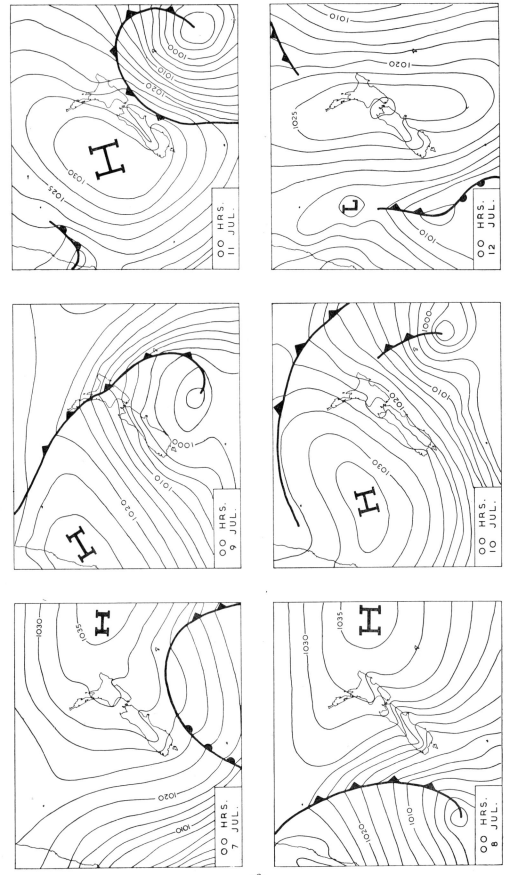

OO HRS.
11 JUL.

OO HRS.
12 JUL.

OO HRS.
9 JUL.

OO HRS.
10 JUL.

OO HRS.
7 JUL.

OO HRS.
8 JUL.

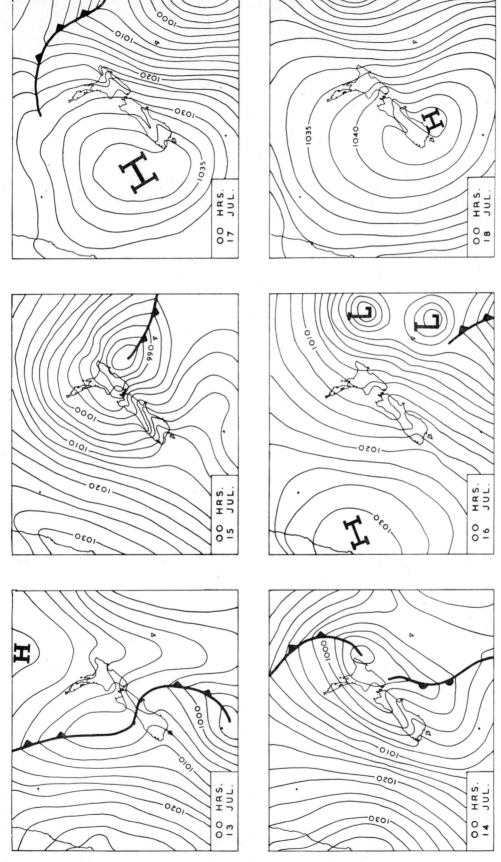

Maps illustrating atmospheric conditions over New Zealand from 7–18 July, 1950.

(All times shown are G.M.T.)

APPENDIX C

Statistical Information

UNLESS otherwise indicated in the text, the statistical information given in this volume has been obtained from the data collected and published by the New Zealand Meteorological Office, Wellington, and also from unpublished statistics in that office which were made available to the author through the courtesy of the Director of Meteorological Services. To appreciate the worth of this material, therefore, it is desirable to outline briefly the growth of climatological observations in New Zealand.[1]

Until the end of the third decade of the present century, the number of climatological stations in the country was limited.[2] The Meteorological Office suffered until then a rather chequered history, being under the control of different Government departments from time to time and having to labour under considerable financial stress. Since 1935, however, there has been a great improvement in the facilities available to it, and expansion from 1940 onwards has been particularly marked. Whereas in 1936 there were only thirty-six climatological stations in the country, by 1939 the number had increased to sixty-three, and today it is in the neighbourhood of 120. The position regarding rainfall stations is somewhat better, however. These include a large number of places where private observers voluntarily supply information to the Meteorological Office in return for the use of standard rain gauges. The number of these stations in 1939 was 520, some of them having records from the earliest days of organized European settlement, and at the present time there are nearly 700 in existence.

From this brief survey it can be seen that, although New Zealand is now well served by stations supplying climatological data, it is difficult to obtain monthly 'normals' for different elements referring to a standard period, except for rainfall where the period 1921–50 can be used as standard in most cases. The statistics quoted in the text, and given in the following tables, therefore, represent averages for all or the greater part of the period during which observations at a given place have been in progress. The length of these records varies as shown in the tables of the Appendix. The data given in them represents but a fraction from what is available.

[1] A full account of this is given in N. G. Robertson: 'The Organization and Development of Weather Observations in New Zealand', in *N.Z. Weather and Climate*, op. cit., pp. 7–25.

[2] A climatological station is one reporting both temperature and rainfall information, and in many cases a great deal more. A rainfall station records rainfall only, generally by means of a standard rain gauge read once a day at 9.30 a.m. local time.

Table 1C

ALTITUDE AND LOCATION OF THE STATIONS FOR WHICH STATISTICS ARE GIVEN IN THE
TABLES OF APPENDIX C

Station	Altitude ft.	Latitude °S	Longitude °E
Akaroa	150	43° 46′	172° 56′
Alexandra	520	45° 15′	169° 24′
Arthur's Pass	2,425	42° 57′	171° 34′
Ashburton	323	43° 54′	171° 46′
Athol	950	45° 31′	168° 35′
Auckland	160	36° 51′	174° 47′
Balclutha	20	46° 14′	169° 44′
Balmoral	743	42° 51′	172° 48′
Benmore	1,600	44° 21′	169° 59′
Blenheim	12	41° 30′	173° 58′
Braemar	1,700	43° 59′	170° 12′
Cape Campbell	10	41° 44′	174° 16′
Castlepoint	154	40° 54′	176° 13′
Château Tongariro	3,670	39° 12′	175° 32′
Christchurch	22	43° 32′	172° 37′
Clyde	600	45° 11′	169° 19′
Darfield	640	43° 29′	172° 07′
Dargaville	80	35° 56′	173° 52′
Dannevirke	684	40° 12′	176° 06′
Dunedin	..*	45° 52′	170° 32′
Duntroon	520	44° 51′	170° 41′
Fairlie	1,004	44° 06′	170° 50′
Farewell Spit	14	40° 33′	173° 00′
Feilding	235	40° 13′	175° 34′
Gisborne	14	38° 40′	177° 59′
Golden Downs	900	41° 33′	172° 53′
Gore	245	46° 05′	168° 58′
Gore Bay	15	42° 51′	173° 18′
Greytown	186	41° 09′	175° 28′
Half Moon Bay	80	46° 54′	168° 08′
Hanmer	1,225	42° 31′	172° 50′
Hastings	45	39° 39′	176° 51′
Hermitage, Mt. Cook	2,510	43° 43′	170° 07′
Hokitika	12	42° 43′	170° 57′
Hunterville	876	39° 56′	175° 34′
Inglewood	657	39° 10′	174° 12′
Invercargill	32	46° 24′	168° 22′
Jackson's Bay	25	43° 59′	168° 37′
Kaikoura	24	42° 24′	173° 41′
Karamea	10	41° 15′	172° 07′
Karioi	2,125	39° 28′	175° 31′
Kawakawa	60	35° 23′	174° 04′
Lake Coleridge	1,195	43° 22′	171° 32′
Lake Tekapo	2,350	44° 00′	170° 29′
Makarora	970	44° 18′	169° 12′
Manorburn Dam	2,448	45° 22′	169° 36′
Masterton	340	40° 59′	175° 37′
Milford Sound	20	44° 41′	167° 55′
Napier	5	39° 29′	176° 55′
Nelson	24	41° 17′	173° 18′
New Plymouth	160	39° 04′	174° 05′
Oamaru	10	45° 05′	170° 59′
Ohakea	167	40° 12′	175° 23′
Ohawe, Hawera	200	39° 35′	174° 13′
Onepoto, Lake Waikaremoana	2,100	38° 48′	177° 08′
Onerahi	125	35° 46′	174° 22′
Ophir	1,000	45° 07′	169° 36′
Otaki	50	40° 44′	175° 07′
Otautau	180	46° 09′	168° 01′

*The figures for Dunedin represent averages for two sites, one at 240 ft. and the other at 690 ft.

Station	Altitude ft.	Latitude °S	Longitude °E
Owaka	120	46° 27'	169° 39'
Pahiatua	384	40° 27'	175° 50'
Palmerston North	110	40° 23'	175° 37'
Patearoa	1,250	45° 13'	170° 02'
Queenstown	1,110	45° 02'	168° 40'
Ranfurly	1,390	45° 08'	170° 06'
Reefton	670	42° 07'	171° 52'
Riverhead	110	36° 42'	174° 33'
Riverton	60	46° 21'	168° 01'
Ross	21	42° 54'	170° 49'
Rotorua	931	38° 09'	176° 15'
Roxburgh	325	45° 32'	169° 19'
Ruakura, Hamilton	131	37° 46'	175° 20'
Rudstone, Methven	1,217	43° 33'	171° 42'
Rukuhia	215	37° 50'	175° 18'
Taieri	80	45° 51'	170° 22'
Taihape	2,157	39° 39'	175° 49'
Takaka	150	41° 01'	172° 52'
Tapanui	550	45° 57'	169° 15'
Tarras	1,428	44° 50'	169° 25'
Taupo	1,232	38° 41'	176° 04'
Tauranga	10	37° 40'	176° 12'
Te Aroha	46	37° 33'	175° 43'
Te Kuiti	179	38° 20'	175° 10'
Te Paki	200	34° 30'	172° 49'
Thames	5	37° 09'	175° 31'
Timaru	56	44° 24'	171° 14'
Tokomaru Bay	57	38° 06'	178° 21'
Tutira	510	39° 12'	176° 53'
Waihi	354	37° 23'	175° 51'
Waimate	200	44° 44'	171° 03'
Waiotapu	1,000	38° 21'	176° 24'
Waipiata	1,550	45° 14'	170° 08'
Waipoua	225	35° 39'	173° 33'
Wanganui	72	39° 55'	175° 03'
Wellington	415	41° 17'	174° 46'
Westport	23	41° 44'	171° 36'
Whakarewarewa	1,000	38° 10'	176° 16'
Whangarei	120	35° 43'	174° 20'
Whitianga	5	36° 51'	175° 41'
Wigram	74	43° 33'	172° 33'

Table 2C

STATIONS FOR WHICH STATISTICS ARE GIVEN IN APPENDIX C LISTED BY CLIMATIC REGIONS

(a) *Middle New Zealand:*

Farewell Spit	Nelson	Otaki
Feilding	New Plymouth	Palmerston North
Hunterville	Ohakea	Takaka
Inglewood	Ohawe, Hawera	Wanganui

(b) *Western South Island:*

Hokitika	Karamea	Ross
Jackson's Bay	Reefton	Westport

(c) *Northern New Zealand:*

Auckland	Ruakura, Hamilton	Te Paki
Dargaville	Rukuhia	Thames
Kawakawa	Tauranga	Waihi
Onerahi	Te Aroha	Waipoua
Riverhead	Te Kuiti	Whangarei
		Whitianga

(d) *Southern New Zealand:*

Athol	Half Moon Bay	Riverton
Balclutha	Invercargill	Taieri
Dunedin	Otautau	Tapanui
Gore	Owaka	

(e) *Eastern North Island:*

Blenheim	Greytown	Pahiatua
Cape Campbell	Hastings	Tokomaru Bay
Castlepoint	Masterton	Tutira
Dannevirke	Napier	Wellington
Gisborne	Onepoto, L. Waikaremoana	

(f) *Eastern South Island:*

Akaroa	Darfield	Oamaru
Ashburton	Duntroon	Rudstone, Methven
Balmoral	Fairlie	Timaru
Christchurch	Gore Bay	Waimate
		Wigram

(g) *Central North Island:*

Château Tongariro	Rotorua	Taupo
Karioi	Taihape	Waiotapu
		Whakarewarewa

(h) *Inland South Island:*

Alexandra	Manorburn Dam	Ranfurly
Benmore	Ophir	Roxburgh
Braemar	Patearoa	Tarras
Clyde	Queenstown	Waipiata
Lake Tekapo		

(i) *Upland South Island:*

Arthur's Pass	Hermitage, Mt. Cook	Makarora
Golden Downs	Kaikoura	Milford Sound
Hanmer	Lake Coleridge	

Table 3C

MEAN MONTHLY TEMPERATURES AT FORTY-NINE STATIONS IN NEW ZEALAND

(°F)

Note: Figures in brackets indicate the number of years of record to 1950.

Station		June	July	Aug.	Sept.	Oct.	Nov.	Dec.	Jan.	Feb.	Mar.	Apr.	May	Year
Akaroa	(15)	45.6	44.6	46.4	50.4	54.3	57.1	60.3	62.0	61.9	59.6	55.5	49.8	54.0
Alexandra	(24)	37.7	36.3	41.4	47.1	52.4	56.4	60.3	61.7	61.4	57.6	51.1	42.9	50.5
Ashburton	(26)	41.8	41.1	43.7	47.9	52.4	55.7	59.1	61.0	61.0	57.8	52.6	46.7	51.7
Auckland	(85)	53.0	51.4	52.2	54.5	57.4	60.4	63.7	66.4	66.7	64.9	61.3	56.6	59.0
Balmoral	(25)	41.3	39.4	42.3	46.2	50.5	53.7	57.3	61.6	61.5	58.0	52.7	46.0	50.9
Blenheim	(20)	45.4	44.6	46.8	50.7	54.2	57.4	61.3	63.1	63.3	60.4	56.0	50.1	54.4
Château Tongariro	(18)	37.3	36.0	37.1	39.7	42.9	46.4	49.8	52.3	53.1	50.7	46.1	41.2	44.7
Christchurch	(65)	43.2	42.3	44.3	48.7	53.1	56.3	59.8	61.4	60.8	58.1	53.5	47.6	52.4
Darfield	(15)	41.8	40.8	42.9	47.0	51.6	55.0	58.9	60.8	60.0	57.1	52.4	46.4	51.2
Dunedin	(20)[1]	44.1	43.2	45.2	48.6	51.9	53.7	56.6	58.6	58.3	56.2	52.6	47.6	51.4
Fairlie	(26)	38.4	37.0	40.2	45.1	50.1	53.7	57.1	59.2	58.6	55.3	50.2	43.5	48.9
Gisborne	(16)	48.8	47.7	49.2	52.1	55.5	59.0	62.7	64.8	65.1	62.0	57.9	52.9	56.5
Golden Downs	(23)	40.8	39.8	42.2	46.0	50.1	53.5	57.1	59.0	58.8	56.5	51.5	45.2	50.0
Gore	(43)	40.3	39.4	42.7	47.3	50.7	53.1	56.3	58.0	57.9	55.1	50.4	44.8	49.7
Hanmer	(32)	39.7	38.5	41.4	46.1	50.6	53.8	57.8	59.7	59.4	56.2	51.5	44.8	49.9
Hastings	(25)	47.1	45.9	48.1	51.0	55.4	59.0	63.1	65.3	65.1	61.7	57.4	51.4	55.8
Hermitage, Mt. Cook	(19)	36.3	34.5	38.0	42.5	47.3	51.4	54.6	55.8	56.1	54.1	48.1	41.2	46.6
Hokitika	(50)[2]	45.7	44.6	45.9	49.3	52.1	54.3	57.7	59.6	59.7	57.8	54.3	49.3	52.5
Invercargill	(44)	42.2	40.9	43.9	47.4	50.7	52.8	55.6	56.9	56.8	54.2	50.5	45.7	49.8
Karioi	(24)	41.5	40.4	42.0	45.0	48.2	51.9	55.2	57.0	57.6	55.1	50.4	45.5	49.2
Lake Coleridge	(33)	40.4	38.8	42.2	46.8	51.4	54.5	57.6	59.4	59.4	56.4	51.6	45.1	50.3
Lake Tekapo	(26)	36.6	34.2	37.4	42.8	47.8	51.2	55.7	57.3	56.8	54.0	48.4	41.4	47.0
Manorburn Dam	(24)	33.0	30.0	34.0	39.6	44.3	48.1	51.5	53.1	53.6	50.4	45.3	38.5	43.5
Masterton	(8)	45.4	44.5	45.9	49.3	52.7	56.1	60.2	62.4	62.4	59.0	54.5	49.5	53.5
Milford Sound	(20)	41.9	41.2	43.2	46.5	49.7	52.3	55.4	57.2	57.2	55.2	51.0	46.3	49.9
Napier	(25)	48.7	47.3	49.1	52.0	56.5	59.6	63.2	65.5	65.4	62.4	58.5	52.8	56.8
Nelson	(32)	46.2	45.3	47.0	50.4	54.1	57.1	60.8	62.8	62.8	60.2	56.4	50.5	54.5
New Plymouth	(31)	50.1	48.9	49.6	51.7	54.4	56.8	60.0	62.2	62.5	61.0	58.1	53.7	55.7
Onepoto	(17)	44.0	42.7	43.9	46.5	50.4	54.0	58.0	60.0	60.2	57.4	52.9	48.0	51.5
Ophir	(25)	35.5	34.8	39.6	45.3	50.5	54.2	58.3	60.2	59.8	55.7	49.3	41.1	48.7
Pahiatua	(25)	46.0	44.8	46.5	49.7	53.2	56.3	60.0	61.9	62.0	59.5	55.4	49.9	53.8
Palmerston Nth.	(40)	47.0	46.1	47.7	50.5	53.9	56.9	60.4	62.4	62.5	60.3	56.6	51.0	54.6
Queenstown	(23)	39.5	38.3	41.6	46.1	50.4	53.9	57.9	59.4	59.6	56.3	50.7	44.3	49.8
Riverhead	(23)	50.0	48.5	49.4	51.0	54.5	57.4	60.3	62.4	63.1	61.2	58.3	53.2	55.8
Rotorua	(53)[3]	46.4	45.2	46.5	48.7	53.0	56.8	60.0	62.8	62.9	60.5	55.4	50.2	54.0
Ruakura	(38)	47.5	46.5	47.8	50.9	54.3	57.4	60.7	63.1	63.3	61.2	56.6	51.4	55.1
Rudstone	(25)	42.7	40.8	43.6	47.0	51.2	54.2	57.5	59.0	59.2	56.7	52.6	46.8	51.0
Taihape	(42)	42.9	41.4	42.7	45.6	49.9	52.4	56.3	59.2	58.9	56.6	52.8	46.6	50.4
Tauranga	(38)	49.9	48.7	49.7	52.6	56.0	58.8	62.1	64.6	65.0	62.6	58.5	53.6	56.9
Te Aroha	(30)	49.9	48.7	50.2	53.6	57.6	60.9	64.0	66.8	66.8	64.0	59.6	53.9	58.0
Te Paki	(20)	54.1	52.6	53.1	54.4	57.1	60.0	63.1	64.7	65.3	64.1	61.6	57.0	58.9
Timaru	(41)	42.4	41.4	43.8	47.9	52.7	55.5	58.7	60.6	60.2	57.4	53.0	46.8	51.7
Waihi	(46)	48.9	47.7	48.7	52.0	55.7	59.0	62.2	64.5	64.4	61.9	57.4	52.5	56.2
Waimate	(46)	43.3	42.0	44.4	48.5	52.2	55.4	57.8	60.2	60.1	57.5	52.6	47.9	51.8
Waipiata	(26)	37.1	36.3	39.7	44.3	48.9	52.4	56.0	58.0	57.8	54.6	49.5	42.6	48.1
Waipoua	(24)	51.6	50.1	50.8	52.4	55.3	58.1	61.1	63.0	63.7	62.4	59.6	54.8	56.9
Wanganui	(15)	48.8	47.6	49.1	52.1	54.8	58.2	61.4	63.5	63.7	61.6	57.5	53.0	56.0
Wellington	(89)	47.7	46.3	47.6	49.9	52.8	55.8	59.1	61.0	61.3	59.4	56.1	51.3	54.0
Westport	(10)[2]	46.4	45.8	46.8	49.4	52.5	55.2	57.7	59.7	59.8	58.2	54.9	50.8	53.1

[1] Years to 1943.
[2] Years to 1945.
[3] Years to 1946.

Table 4C

MEAN DIURNAL RANGE OF TEMPERATURE AT FORTY-NINE STATIONS IN NEW ZEALAND

(F°)

Note: Figures in brackets indicate the number of years of record to 1950.

Station		June	July	Aug.	Sept.	Oct.	Nov.	Dec.	Jan.	Feb.	Mar.	Apr.	May	Year
Akaroa	(15)	11.9	11.6	13.0	15.1	16.6	17.9	17.5	17.7	17.7	16.5	13.8	12.5	15.1
Alexandra	(24)	16.2	16.6	20.4	21.4	21.9	22.2	21.8	21.8	22.5	23.0	21.4	19.4	20.7
Ashburton	(26)	17.4	17.6	18.6	19.1	20.2	20.9	20.0	20.4	20.6	19.3	18.6	19.0	19.3
Auckland	(85)	10.3	10.6	11.4	11.5	11.5	12.2	12.7	12.6	12.7	12.4	11.6	10.7	11.7
Balmoral	(25)	18.5	18.4	19.3	20.4	21.6	22.3	22.6	22.9	23.2	22.8	20.5	20.2	21.1
Blenheim	(20)	18.5	17.9	17.9	18.2	18.5	20.0	20.3	19.8	19.4	20.8	19.2	18.2	19.1
Château Tongariro	(18)	12.3	12.8	12.8	14.8	15.7	16.9	17.7	17.9	17.7	16.5	14.9	13.6	15.3
Christchurch	(65)	15.5	15.3	16.0	16.9	18.0	18.7	18.1	17.9	16.9	16.5	16.5	16.1	16.9
Darfield	(15)	17.6	17.6	19.3	20.6	21.6	23.5	23.3	23.6	24.1	22.8	20.5	18.4	21.0
Dunedin	(20)[1]	11.3	11.9	13.2	15.6	16.6	16.7	16.0	16.7	16.5	15.8	15.8	13.3	14.9
Fairlie	(26)	22.5	21.7	22.9	23.5	24.1	24.6	23.6	24.8	25.0	24.3	23.9	24.3	23.7
Gisborne	(16)	17.0	16.3	16.7	18.1	18.7	20.2	21.9	21.9	20.7	19.5	17.9	17.3	18.8
Golden Downs	(23)	20.4	20.8	20.7	21.9	21.4	22.1	22.8	22.4	22.9	23.4	22.0	21.5	21.9
Gore	(43)	15.3	16.0	18.7	20.1	21.0	21.4	21.6	22.6	22.9	22.3	20.0	18.3	20.0
Hanmer	(32)	19.9	19.2	20.4	21.0	21.9	22.7	23.4	23.8	23.9	23.3	22.1	20.8	21.8
Hastings	(25)	20.5	19.6	20.5	22.2	22.8	23.0	23.5	23.4	22.4	22.3	21.7	20.5	21.9
Hermitage, Mt. Cook	(19)	15.8	15.5	17.2	17.9	19.6	20.2	21.7	20.6	20.1	20.6	18.0	16.9	18.7
Hokitika	(50)[2]	15.3	16.4	15.7	14.5	13.1	12.9	12.9	13.2	13.5	13.8	14.1	15.2	14.2
Invercargill	(44)	13.8	15.0	16.5	17.5	17.1	17.1	17.4	17.9	17.5	17.6	16.1	15.6	16.6
Karioi	(24)	16.8	16.7	18.1	19.0	20.2	21.5	22.3	23.4	22.7	22.5	20.8	18.4	20.1
Lake Coleridge	(33)	19.5	18.3	19.4	19.3	19.9	21.3	21.1	21.6	20.9	21.8	20.0	20.6	20.4
Lake Tekapo	(26)	16.4	15.7	17.7	19.1	20.8	21.7	22.5	24.0	24.2	23.8	20.7	18.3	20.4
Manorburn Dam	(24)	14.9	16.4	17.0	18.0	19.9	20.3	20.7	21.4	21.7	21.1	19.3	16.8	18.9
Masterton	(8)	16.6	17.5	17.2	19.9	19.0	21.7	23.3	23.8	24.5	22.5	21.1	16.9	20.3
Milford Sound	(20)	13.5	14.1	15.4	15.2	15.0	14.8	13.3	14.4	14.7	14.3	15.0	14.2	14.5
Napier	(25)	15.9	15.7	15.4	16.6	16.7	16.4	16.3	16.9	16.0	16.3	16.0	15.8	16.1
Nelson	(32)	17.5	17.1	16.8	16.9	16.3	17.1	16.9	16.7	17.1	17.1	16.5	17.1	16.9
New Plymouth	(31)	12.1	11.9	12.6	12.4	11.9	12.9	13.2	13.9	14.3	14.3	13.1	12.8	12.9
Onepoto	(17)	10.0	9.9	11.0	13.1	14.4	15.0	16.3	16.1	15.3	13.6	11.9	10.4	13.0
Ophir	(25)	17.9	18.0	21.9	22.0	22.4	23.8	23.8	24.6	24.9	25.1	22.9	20.8	22.2
Pahiatua	(25)	15.5	15.8	16.3	16.1	16.4	17.0	17.9	18.0	18.5	18.6	17.0	16.5	16.9
Palmerston Nth.	(40)	14.0	14.0	14.6	14.6	14.6	15.6	16.1	16.2	16.7	16.7	15.3	14.7	15.3
Queenstown	(23)	14.2	14.7	16.2	17.7	18.9	19.8	20.6	20.8	20.4	19.8	16.9	15.6	17.9
Riverhead	(23)	16.9	17.2	17.9	18.6	17.9	18.0	18.9	19.5	19.6	20.0	18.1	18.1	18.4
Rotorua	(53)[3]	16.0	16.7	17.4	18.7	18.4	20.5	20.6	23.0	21.4	21.1	18.6	16.5	19.1
Ruakura	(38)	18.9	18.8	19.9	19.8	19.4	20.4	21.7	22.9	22.9	22.5	21.9	20.4	20.8
Rudstone	(25)	13.4	13.6	14.3	16.1	17.5	19.2	19.4	19.9	19.6	18.6	16.0	15.0	16.8
Taihape	(42)	11.0	11.1	12.4	14.0	15.5	16.4	17.6	18.1	17.7	16.6	14.8	12.0	14.7
Tauranga	(38)	17.4	17.3	17.8	18.2	18.0	18.7	19.9	19.8	19.1	19.3	18.9	17.8	18.5
Te Aroha	(30)	17.3	17.5	18.3	17.6	17.8	19.4	20.4	21.4	21.3	21.3	19.5	18.1	19.1
Te Paki	(20)	13.1	13.3	13.3	13.4	12.9	13.4	14.3	15.8	15.6	15.0	13.4	13.2	13.9
Timaru	(41)	16.3	16.0	17.2	17.9	19.3	19.9	18.3	18.6	18.3	18.0	17.7	17.6	17.9
Waihi	(46)	16.9	16.9	17.9	17.4	17.4	17.5	18.8	18.8	19.0	18.8	18.1	17.2	17.9
Waimate	(46)	17.4	17.4	18.0	19.0	19.4	19.5	17.7	19.6	19.5	18.5	18.3	18.0	17.9
Waipiata	(26)	15.6	15.8	17.5	19.3	19.9	21.3	21.7	22.6	22.2	22.3	20.0	18.2	19.7
Waipoua	(24)	15.6	15.8	16.4	16.3	16.4	16.0	17.7	17.7	18.1	18.5	16.7	16.1	16.7
Wanganui	(15)	12.8	13.2	13.8	13.4	13.7	14.8	14.6	15.3	15.3	15.1	14.5	13.1	14.1
Wellington	(89)	9.7	9.7	10.4	11.2	11.9	12.8	13.1	13.2	13.0	12.3	11.1	10.1	11.5
Westport	(10)[2]	14.1	13.4	13.5	13.7	12.7	14.1	13.0	13.0	13.9	14.4	13.9	13.7	12.8

[1] Years to 1943.
[2] Years to 1945.
[3] Years to 1946.

Table 5C

MEAN EXTREME MAXIMUM TEMPERATURES AT FORTY-NINE STATIONS IN NEW ZEALAND

(°F)

Note: Figures in brackets indicate the number of years of record to 1950.

Station		June	July	Aug.	Sept.	Oct.	Nov.	Dec.	Jan.	Feb.	Mar.	Apr.	May	Year
Akaroa	(15)	63.2	60.0	65.3	70.3	73.6	78.9	83.9	85.5	84.9	81.1	77.9	68.0	88.1
Alexandra	(24)	59.4	57.4	61.1	68.4	74.7	80.1	84.8	86.2	85.2	81.9	75.0	65.4	87.9
Ashburton	(26)	62.2	60.6	64.5	69.9	74.4	79.5	83.1	85.9	86.0	81.4	76.6	69.3	88.6
Auckland	(85)	63.5	62.0	62.6	65.5	68.0	73.0	76.4	78.9	78.9	76.7	72.8	67.3	80.7
Balmoral	(25)	63.4	60.6	64.0	68.9	74.2	79.2	84.2	87.4	85.4	82.3	77.5	69.0	89.4
Blenheim	(20)	64.4	61.8	64.8	70.0	74.5	80.9	85.6	88.5	85.9	82.7	78.4	70.0	90.0
Château Tongariro	(18)	51.0	50.8	52.0	56.0	60.9	64.4	68.9	72.0	69.2	67.4	63.4	56.7	74.2
Christchurch	(65)	62.5	61.1	64.7	70.5	74.5	79.4	84.2	86.2	83.5	81.3	75.9	68.7	88.2
Darfield	(15)	62.9	61.2	64.6	71.3	75.5	81.8	85.5	87.2	89.3	82.7	78.0	68.3	90.8
Dunedin	(20)[1]	59.6	57.7	61.6	67.1	73.0	75.4	78.4	81.5	80.2	75.4	72.3	64.6	84.4
Fairlie	(26)	61.9	58.5	63.8	69.1	75.5	79.4	83.7	86.6	85.0	83.4	77.6	68.6	89.2
Gisborne	(16)	65.4	64.8	66.0	70.2	75.2	82.3	84.8	89.6	85.8	82.9	78.2	70.0	90.2
Golden Downs	(23)	59.1	56.5	60.0	64.1	69.5	74.8	78.5	81.2	78.6	76.7	71.7	63.3	82.4
Gore	(43)	58.7	57.3	62.6	68.9	73.8	78.2	81.9	84.5	84.1	80.3	73.8	65.2	87.5
Hanmer	(32)	62.3	59.3	63.3	69.4	73.6	77.8	82.7	86.3	85.1	80.4	75.9	67.2	88.5
Hastings	(25)	67.7	64.4	68.1	71.6	78.4	82.6	85.9	88.7	86.9	83.2	80.5	71.8	89.8
Hermitage Mt. Cook	(19)	56.8	52.6	57.4	62.8	68.7	74.9	78.3	80.0	79.1	76.7	71.0	59.7	83.3
Hokitika	(50)[2]	59.3	58.6	59.8	62.4	65.0	67.1	71.1	73.2	72.7	71.3	67.9	63.7	76.3
Invercargill	(44)	59.6	57.6	61.2	66.5	72.9	74.6	78.7	80.5	79.7	76.7	71.0	64.2	83.3
Karioi	(24)	59.7	56.4	60.2	62.4	67.2	71.7	75.2	77.4	75.7	74.2	71.1	62.8	78.9
Lake Coleridge	(33)	62.4	60.6	63.8	69.4	74.1	77.7	81.2	84.5	83.2	80.9	75.1	67.3	87.4
Lake Tekapo	(26)	55.3	52.6	56.2	62.9	69.4	73.7	78.6	81.1	79.8	77.5	71.2	62.2	84.3
Manorburn Dam	(24)	51.7	47.7	52.6	58.4	66.2	70.6	74.2	77.2	77.5	73.1	66.1	57.1	79.5
Masterton	(8)	64.3	62.0	64.5	68.0	73.1	79.2	84.2	86.8	85.3	81.5	77.2	69.2	88.8
Milford Sound	(20)	58.7	56.3	58.1	61.8	66.8	68.7	70.8	74.2	73.9	70.6	66.6	61.1	76.2
Napier	(25)	66.6	64.8	66.4	70.6	76.5	81.3	83.6	86.8	84.9	82.3	78.0	70.7	88.2
Nelson	(32)	61.1	60.0	62.1	65.6	70.2	74.1	77.8	79.3	79.1	77.2	72.1	66.0	81.7
New Plymouth	(31)	61.8	60.2	61.2	63.2	66.5	70.2	74.0	76.9	76.9	74.7	71.1	65.6	79.3
Onepoto	(17)	57.3	56.3	57.8	62.3	67.6	72.6	77.2	79.1	77.8	74.2	70.4	61.3	81.1
Ophir	(25)	57.7	55.4	59.9	65.9	72.5	78.8	82.6	85.6	84.4	80.2	72.8	64.1	87.7
Pahiatua	(25)	61.1	60.6	63.0	62.3	70.0	75.6	79.8	81.6	81.1	77.6	73.2	66.8	83.9
Palmerston Nth.	(40)	60.7	59.4	63.1	65.3	68.4	74.1	77.8	79.6	80.0	76.8	73.1	66.5	81.6
Queenstown	(23)	57.0	54.5	59.1	63.8	70.9	74.6	79.7	82.2	81.0	76.7	69.7	61.6	84.1
Riverhead	(23)	64.3	62.3	63.7	66.4	69.8	73.3	76.6	78.9	79.1	76.6	73.7	68.3	80.7
Rotorua	(53)[3]	62.3	60.7	63.1	67.1	72.7	77.7	82.4	84.8	82.9	80.1	74.2	67.8	86.4
Ruakura	(38)	64.5	62.5	64.2	67.8	71.4	76.3	81.0	83.3	83.1	80.1	75.9	68.8	85.2
Rudstone	(25)	61.0	58.2	61.5	67.1	71.6	76.0	79.3	81.9	82.0	79.1	73.7	65.9	85.2
Taihape	(42)	58.2	56.4	57.8	61.7	66.7	70.8	75.1	78.0	77.3	74.5	69.7	61.9	79.4
Tauranga	(38)	65.2	63.4	64.1	69.4	72.0	76.5	81.3	83.3	81.8	80.2	76.6	67.3	85.1
Te Aroha	(30)	66.1	63.4	65.5	68.6	73.7	79.5	84.1	85.5	85.2	82.0	76.9	69.9	87.7
Te Paki	(20)	64.9	62.6	63.6	65.6	67.9	71.4	74.6	76.4	77.0	75.4	73.2	69.1	77.6
Timaru	(41)	60.9	60.0	64.0	70.4	77.3	79.6	83.8	86.5	83.7	80.1	75.2	66.6	89.5
Waihi	(46)	63.8	62.9	64.2	67.5	71.9	76.3	79.7	82.2	81.1	78.8	74.4	67.8	83.3
Waimate	(46)	62.7	60.7	64.6	69.9	75.7	79.0	81.6	85.7	83.4	81.0	75.7	68.8	88.3
Waipiata	(26)	57.8	54.4	58.9	64.5	70.3	76.6	80.7	83.7	82.6	78.6	72.8	64.1	85.4
Waipoua	(24)	66.5	64.3	66.0	67.5	70.1	74.3	77.7	79.7	79.5	78.2	75.2	69.5	81.0
Wanganui	(15)	62.4	61.4	64.6	66.8	70.6	77.5	79.2	80.6	80.3	77.2	76.4	67.1	82.1
Wellington	(89)	60.9	59.4	61.3	64.1	67.5	71.2	75.0	77.8	77.4	74.8	70.3	64.9	79.6
Westport	(10)[2]	59.4	57.2	59.8	60.2	63.0	65.7	68.9	72.9	70.6	70.8	66.9	62.8	75.5

[1]Years to 1943.
[2]Years to 1945.
[3]Years to 1946.

Table 6C

MEAN EXTREME MINIMUM TEMPERATURES AT FORTY-NINE STATIONS IN NEW ZEALAND

(°F)

Note: Figures in brackets indicate the number of years of record to 1950.

Station		June	July	Aug.	Sept.	Oct.	Nov.	Dec.	Jan.	Feb.	Mar.	Apr.	May	Year
Akaroa	(15)	31.8	30.4	31.9	33.4	36.5	39.7	42.7	44.5	44.1	42.4	39.1	34.9	30.4
Alexandra	(24)	21.5	18.2	22.7	26.4	29.8	33.9	38.5	39.8	38.1	34.7	29.6	23.5	17.6
Ashburton	(26)	23.1	20.9	24.8	26.4	30.6	33.5	37.3	39.1	38.7	34.8	31.4	25.8	20.1
Auckland	(85)	39.2	37.6	39.0	41.4	44.2	47.4	49.8	52.5	53.3	51.0	46.7	42.3	36.9
Balmoral	(25)	20.5	18.8	19.8	25.4	28.4	31.8	35.6	35.9	35.8	32.2	29.6	24.4	17.5
Blenheim	(20)	24.2	24.1	25.6	28.6	31.6	35.0	38.6	40.8	41.0	36.5	32.4	26.7	22.8
Château Tongariro	(18)	22.3	18.5	21.5	22.9	25.8	29.2	31.6	33.8	33.6	30.4	28.5	24.8	17.4
Christchurch	(65)	26.1	25.9	26.7	29.7	32.4	35.9	39.6	41.5	40.9	37.3	32.8	28.6	24.7
Darfield	(15)	23.5	21.1	24.0	27.1	29.5	31.5	35.8	37.3	35.9	34.0	30.1	26.1	20.3
Dunedin	(20)[1]	31.1	30.2	30.9	33.0	34.6	36.9	39.9	41.4	41.5	39.0	36.9	33.5	29.4
Fairlie	(26)	16.0	14.1	17.8	22.3	27.5	29.9	34.7	34.4	34.2	30.1	26.0	19.9	12.2
Gisborne	(16)	29.6	28.9	31.4	33.1	36.0	37.0	41.2	44.2	42.7	41.8	37.4	33.5	28.2
Golden Downs	(23)	21.5	20.1	21.1	24.7	29.6	34.1	36.0	39.0	37.8	34.8	30.8	23.9	18.4
Gore	(43)	23.8	22.8	24.8	28.2	30.3	32.8	35.4	36.1	35.5	33.2	30.0	26.2	21.5
Hanmer	(32)	17.9	16.5	18.8	22.9	28.3	30.6	34.0	35.2	34.9	31.2	28.3	21.9	14.7
Hastings	(25)	26.2	25.7	27.4	28.9	32.6	36.0	40.2	42.3	42.4	37.0	33.9	28.4	24.3
Hermitage, Mt. Cook	(19)	18.7	16.7	19.0	23.2	27.3	30.6	33.3	33.6	34.1	30.9	29.0	22.3	14.5
Hokitika	(50)[2]	29.7	28.8	30.0	31.9	35.2	38.4	41.9	43.3	43.3	40.6	36.5	31.9	27.8
Invercargill	(44)	26.0	24.6	26.5	29.6	31.6	34.5	37.1	38.1	37.7	34.8	31.7	27.6	23.7
Karioi	(24)	20.6	18.9	20.3	22.5	25.3	28.7	31.7	33.2	32.8	29.0	27.7	22.8	17.7
Lake Coleridge	(33)	20.6	18.8	21.1	26.5	30.4	33.3	35.7	37.1	37.0	34.1	30.0	23.6	17.2
Lake Tekapo	(26)	18.2	16.3	17.7	22.8	26.2	28.4	32.1	33.7	33.3	30.4	28.1	22.0	13.5
Manorburn Dam	(24)	13.3	7.8	10.1	20.0	24.6	26.5	31.5	32.1	31.3	28.6	26.0	20.3	5.8
Masterton	(8)	26.1	25.2	26.0	28.7	30.7	33.1	36.9	38.9	38.8	35.2	31.8	26.8	24.1
Milford Sound	(20)	28.3	27.2	28.7	31.7	34.7	37.4	40.9	41.8	40.4	38.7	35.0	31.0	26.5
Napier	(25)	31.8	31.0	31.8	34.0	37.8	40.9	45.2	47.7	47.0	45.5	39.3	35.0	30.0
Nelson	(32)	29.4	29.4	30.0	33.0	35.9	39.4	41.7	45.0	44.0	41.4	38.2	32.7	28.0
New Plymouth	(31)	33.6	32.3	33.3	35.0	38.0	40.7	43.1	45.7	45.9	43.5	40.5	36.1	31.2
Onepoto	(17)	31.6	30.4	31.3	32.0	36.5	37.8	41.4	41.6	43.8	41.2	38.7	34.0	29.4
Ophir	(25)	16.3	13.8	18.4	22.5	26.6	29.1	33.6	35.8	34.2	30.2	25.6	19.5	12.4
Pahiatua	(25)	25.0	24.6	25.1	27.9	30.7	33.8	37.8	38.2	39.2	33.0	31.7	27.3	22.6
Palmerston Nth.	(40)	28.0	28.0	29.1	30.6	34.7	38.4	42.1	42.9	43.4	37.5	36.1	30.4	26.5
Queenstown	(23)	25.4	23.6	25.8	29.5	32.6	35.4	38.9	39.7	39.9	36.3	34.6	29.5	22.9
Riverhead	(23)	27.5	26.2	26.9	29.5	32.2	35.7	39.6	40.8	42.2	38.2	35.3	30.6	24.8
Rotorua	(53)[3]	27.0	26.5	27.7	29.5	32.3	36.3	39.6	41.1	41.2	37.9	34.4	30.4	25.8
Ruakura	(38)	24.7	24.0	25.7	29.5	33.1	36.2	38.0	39.8	40.3	36.8	31.9	27.4	20.1
Rudstone	(25)	27.9	26.1	27.3	29.7	31.8	34.3	37.0	39.1	39.0	37.1	34.9	30.6	25.2
Taihape	(42)	28.9	27.5	28.5	29.8	32.4	35.2	38.2	40.0	40.2	37.9	35.0	31.2	26.4
Tauranga	(38)	30.6	29.7	30.6	32.7	35.1	38.7	40.6	43.3	44.7	41.9	37.6	32.9	28.5
Te Aroha	(30)	26.9	26.6	27.8	32.5	36.4	40.6	42.0	44.3	44.1	39.6	35.2	30.0	25.0
Te Paki	(20)	34.3	31.0	32.6	35.1	38.3	42.6	45.8	46.4	46.4	45.1	41.1	37.0	30.2
Timaru	(41)	26.7	25.7	26.7	30.4	33.8	36.1	39.2	41.2	40.6	37.9	34.2	29.1	24.6
Waihi	(46)	26.8	25.3	36.3	29.4	34.1	39.2	40.0	44.3	44.2	40.1	34.6	30.5	24.3
Waimate	(46)	27.0	26.1	27.3	30.4	33.3	35.4	38.8	40.4	39.9	38.1	34.2	29.3	25.3
Waipiata	(26)	19.1	17.3	20.5	24.7	27.7	29.4	33.3	35.8	35.2	32.2	29.4	24.1	15.8
Waipoua	(24)	33.0	30.9	31.6	33.7	36.6	40.3	43.4	45.0	46.4	43.2	39.8	35.6	29.9
Wanganui	(15)	31.6	30.3	32.0	34.5	37.1	40.5	45.8	46.2	47.5	43.2	40.4	35.5	29.8
Wellington	(89)	34.5	33.0	33.7	36.1	38.4	40.9	44.7	46.1	46.7	44.0	41.3	37.4	32.0
Westport	(10)[2]	34.6	32.5	34.3	36.4	40.0	43.1	44.8	47.3	47.4	45.3	41.7	37.4	32.2

[1]Years to 1943.
[2]Years to 1945.
[3]Years to 1946.

Table 7C

AVERAGE NUMBER OF GROUND FROSTS AND SCREEN FROSTS AT DIFFERENT SEASONS AT
FORTY-SEVEN STATIONS IN NEW ZEALAND

Note: Figures in brackets indicate the number of years of record to 1950.

Station		Ground Frosts					Screen Frosts				
		Wi.	*Sp.*	*Su.*	*Au.*	*Year*	*Wi.*	*Sp.*	*Su.*	*Au.*	*Year*
Akaroa	(9)	46.7	12.7	0.3	11.6	71.3	3.9	0.2	..	0.1	4.2
Alexandra	(22)	78.2	38.5	2.4	38.8	157.9	62.4	9.4	..	14.0	85.8
Ashburton	(23)	64.4	23.5	2.6	24.9	115.4	43.3	7.0	..	9.5	59.8
Auckland	(41)	2.7	0.2	..	0.1	3.0	..	..	..	..	Nil.
Balmoral	(23)	59.6	24.4	3.8	26.3	114.1	44.3	12.0	0.2	15.0	71.5
Blenheim	(18)	58.5	21.1	1.5	22.6	103.7	36.0	5.4	0.1	6.6	48.1
Château Tongariro	(21)	57.8	36.1	7.5	23.3	124.7	50.0	24.9	2.3	14.2	91.4
Christchurch	(45)	54.1	19.2	1.4	18.9	93.6	28.9	2.9	..	4.4	36.2
Darfield	(6)	58.8	23.0	0.5	19.7	102.0	45.2	8.8	..	8.7	62.7
Dunedin	(29)¹	34.2	7.0	0.2	6.2	47.6	6.0	0.4	..	0.3	6.7
Fairlie	(25)	79.3	37.1	5.8	39.1	161.3	67.3	18.8	1.0	24.0	111.1
Gisborne	(8)	23.6	7.7	0.3	3.8	35.4	6.4	0.3	..	0.5	7.2
Golden Downs	(21)	64.1	24.2	2.3	27.0	117.6	48.1	10.9	0.3	13.8	73.1
Gore	(42)	64.0	22.1	3.0	24.9	114.0	38.7	5.8	0.3	8.5	53.3
Hanmer	(29)	68.2	28.1	6.1	39.6	142.0	54.4	15.1	0.4	17.5	87.4
Hastings	(22)	45.0	16.1	0.3	12.3	73.7	23.1	4.6	..	4.0	31.7
Hokitika	(56)	42.9	9.5	0.5	11.5	64.4	16.1	1.1	..	0.9	18.1
Invercargill	(45)	37.7	11.5	1.0	11.8	62.0	23.8	3.1	..	4.7	31.6
Karioi	(23)	51.5	25.5	6.0	22.3	105.3	43.2	18.5	1.8	15.3	78.8
Lake Coleridge	(33)	65.1	25.9	3.7	32.0	126.7	47.3	8.4	0.2	12.3	68.2
Lake Tekapo	(25)	81.2	54.7	24.8	57.2	217.9	67.5	22.7	1.9	20.9	113.0
Manorburn Dam	(22)	79.4	41.2	8.4	39.0	168.0	76.1	33.0	2.9	30.6	142.5
Masterton	(8)	41.2	25.3	4.4	22.5	93.4	21.3	5.8	..	4.1	31.2
Napier	(26)	26.6	5.9	0.1	3.8	36.4	6.9	0.6	..	0.4	7.9
Nelson	(30)	44.9	9.1	0.1	6.6	60.7	11.5	0.7	..	0.5	12.7
New Plymouth	(29)	13.4	2.9	..	1.7	18.0	1.1	0.1	..	..	1.2
Onepoto	(15)	18.3	4.8	0.4	1.9	25.4	4.6	1.0	..	0.9	5.9
Ophir	(25)	81.1	43.9	13.9	46.1	185.0	71.1	21.2	1.0	28.9	122.2
Pahiatua	(23)	37.3	12.6	1.2	13.1	64.2	23.0	4.3	..	4.9	32.2
Palmerston North	(22)	38.3	12.7	1.1	12.1	64.2	12.7	1.4	..	1.7	15.8
Queenstown	(21)	76.4	37.3	6.1	34.4	154.2	44.6	0.9	..	5.5	51.0
Riverhead	(22)	28.8	11.1	0.3	8.3	48.5	20.9	3.8	..	2.7	27.6
Ruakura	(29)	42.7	17.7	1.9	17.0	79.3	20.7	3.1	0.1	4.7	28.6
Rudstone	(22)	59.5	32.7	13.2	34.1	139.5	21.9	3.4	..	1.7	27.0
Taihape	(39)	43.6	19.8	2.2	15.4	81.0	15.3	3.1	..	1.5	19.9
Tauranga	(37)	36.7	11.3	0.7	10.0	38.7	7.2	0.7	..	0.8	8.7
Te Aroha	(27)	23.2	2.8	..	5.6	31.6	15.0	0.5	..	2.4	17.9
Te Paki	(20)	6.3	1.2	..	0.3	7.8	1.8	0.1	..	0.1	2.0
Timaru	(41)	58.3	15.8	0.2	16.4	90.7	30.9	2.5	..	3.8	37.2
Waihi	(22)	28.1	6.0	1.1	7.9	43.1	21.5	2.7	..	3.6	27.8
Waimate	(14)	69.6	24.7	1.5	28.8	124.6	25.9	1.9	..	2.5	30.3
Waipiata	(25)	75.8	39.3	8.7	41.6	165.4	63.5	16.1	0.3	16.7	96.6
Waipoua	(22)	10.2	1.5	..	0.6	12.3	2.9	0.1	..	..	3.0
Wanganui	(13)	10.4	1.9	0.1	1.1	13.5	3.1	0.1	..	..	3.2
Wellington	(89)	13.9	3.5	..	1.5	18.9	0.1	..	..	..	0.1
Westport²	(5)	29.7	12.6	0.4	5.9	48.6	1.1	..	..	0.1	1.2
Whakarewarewa	(23)	39.2	12.2	0.2	10.1	61.7	25.4	4.5	..	4.2	34.1

¹Years to 1942.
²Westport Airfield.

Table 8C

MEAN MONTHLY RAINFALL TOTALS FOR THE PERIOD 1921–50 AT FORTY-NINE STATIONS
IN NEW ZEALAND
(in.)

Station	June	July	Aug.	Sept.	Oct.	Nov.	Dec.	Jan.	Feb.	Mar.	Apr.	May	Year
Akaroa	4.63	4.78	3.98	3.28	2.44	2.28	2.70	2.32	2.47	2.65	2.70	4.33	38.56
Alexandra	0.79	0.66	0.63	0.82	1.22	1.08	1.30	1.84	1.47	1.15	1.35	0.91	13.22
Ashburton	2.60	2.62	2.32	2.62	2.42	2.45	3.01	2.63	2.69	2.20	2.41	2.55	30.52
Auckland	5.39	5.46	4.42	3.79	4.09	3.30	2.93	3.18	3.91	3.15	4.39	4.79	48.80
Balmoral	2.30	2.12	2.46	2.28	2.46	2.31	2.30	2.06	2.15	1.72	2.13	2.80	27.09
Blenheim	2.24	2.52	2.35	2.37	2.11	1.68	2.04	1.88	2.47	1.54	1.88	2.16	25.24
Château Tongariro	10.40	9.31	8.32	9.09	10.36	8.42	10.06	8.57	8.87	6.73	9.53	8.55	108.21
Christchurch	2.59	2.60	2.05	2.06	1.95	1.82	2.54	2.23	1.80	1.94	1.85	2.85	26.28
Darfield	3.49	2.17	2.47	2.76	2.69	2.43	2.85	2.78	2.53	2.04	2.29	3.01	31.51
Dunedin[1]	3.31	3.14	2.98	2.85	3.24	3.42	3.76	3.41	3.28	3.27	3.16	3.46	39.28
Fairlie	1.80	1.98	1.90	2.66	2.92	2.39	2.89	3.02	2.92	2.39	2.37	1.95	29.19
Gisborne	4.21	4.41	3.86	2.62	2.43	2.59	1.91	2.54	3.15	3.70	3.66	4.77	39.85
Golden Downs	5.07	4.09	5.18	3.74	4.14	3.89	4.14	4.04	4.00	2.71	4.63	3.75	49.38
Gore	2.75	2.01	2.07	2.46	2.85	3.21	3.08	3.08	2.81	3.11	2.85	2.59	32.87
Hanmer	3.49	4.20	3.58	4.43	3.90	3.48	3.71	3.53	3.65	3.36	3.34	4.48	45.15
Hastings	3.13	3.34	2.84	2.09	2.12	1.97	2.03	2.53	2.56	2.42	2.75	3.47	31.25
Hermitage, Mt. Cook	12.08	9.47	12.43	13.46	17.23	14.31	12.92	18.79	15.18	15.69	17.42	13.46	172.44
Hokitika[2]	9.30	8.87	9.27	9.21	11.83	10.73	10.44	9.89	7.14	9.74	9.29	9.71	115.42
Invercargill[3]	3.75	3.00	3.03	3.43	3.58	4.01	3.84	3.85	3.46	4.16	3.85	3.86	43.82
Karioi	5.10	4.19	4.21	4.27	4.25	3.86	3.91	3.68	4.05	2.34	3.72	4.22	47.80
L. Coleridge	2.46	3.00	2.90	3.12	3.03	2.43	2.58	2.46	2.23	1.93	2.68	2.72	31.54
L. Tekapo	1.98	1.60	1.78	2.05	2.05	1.66	1.82	1.85	1.83	1.56	1.92	2.04	22.14
Manorburn Dam	1.19	0.98	0.98	1.17	1.68	1.82	1.96	2.18	1.76	1.69	1.82	1.62	18.85
Masterton	1.81	1.63	1.92	2.69	3.53	4.45	5.65	6.32	6.32	5.28	4.00	2.73	46.33
Milford Sound	13.95	13.90	17.20	19.80	25.84	24.06	23.36	26.38	15.18	22.18	21.78	21.57	245.20
Napier	3.06	3.43	2.73	1.97	1.90	2.09	1.98	2.61	2.68	2.58	2.63	3.34	31.00
Nelson[3]	3.49	3.43	3.33	3.48	3.54	2.94	3.01	3.00	2.89	2.93	3.04	3.15	38.23
New Plymouth	6.18	5.36	5.75	4.90	5.63	4.71	4.59	4.47	3.98	3.74	4.78	6.07	60.16
Onepoto	7.14	8.07	6.71	6.51	5.13	5.63	4.72	5.74	6.18	6.37	6.74	8.32	77.26
Ophir	0.96	0.78	0.78	1.14	1.70	1.33	1.82	1.84	1.93	1.46	1.47	1.06	16.27
Pahiatua	5.15	4.94	4.43	4.27	5.40	4.56	3.96	3.80	3.12	3.33	4.36	4.68	52.00
Palmerston North	4.35	3.04	3.87	3.01	3.56	2.86	3.28	3.20	3.09	2.23	3.36	3.32	39.17
Queenstown	2.34	2.18	2.22	2.66	3.36	2.72	2.50	3.03	2.41	2.85	3.04	2.72	32.03
Riverhead	6.15	7.21	5.02	4.35	4.36	3.78	3.60	3.95	4.52	3.22	4.85	5.42	56.43
Rotorua[4]	5.31	4.98	5.17	4.89	5.00	4.18	3.79	4.38	4.18	3.57	4.51	5.46	55.42
Ruakura	4.78	4.73	4.09	3.68	4.13	3.68	3.08	3.48	3.08	2.98	3.74	4.50	45.95
Rudstone	2.66	2.99	3.16	3.70	3.63	3.57	4.12	4.07	3.74	3.20	3.24	3.22	41.30
Taihape[3]	3.28	3.07	2.71	3.16	3.36	3.32	3.27	3.31	2.87	2.43	2.80	3.33	36.91
Tauranga	5.55	5.04	4.75	4.22	4.97	3.44	3.53	3.94	3.73	4.10	5.02	5.13	53.42
Te Aroha	5.07	6.44	5.33	4.87	5.01	4.02	3.42	3.72	3.42	3.42	4.68	5.43	55.53
Te Paki	6.81	6.96	6.84	4.41	3.81	3.11	2.94	3.39	3.51	3.43	5.95	3.45	54.61
Timaru	1.87	1.73	1.46	1.95	1.93	1.95	2.66	2.37	2.22	2.13	1.66	1.53	23.46
Waihi	8.58	9.78	8.41	6.78	7.30	5.42	5.32	5.48	5.49	7.20	7.65	8.42	85.83
Waimate	2.02	1.91	1.71	2.25	2.11	2.17	2.93	2.61	2.32	2.24	1.84	1.71	25.82
Waipiata	1.11	0.93	1.03	1.12	1.63	1.55	2.19	2.01	2.00	1.57	1.48	1.21	17.83
Waipoua	7.24	8.09	7.10	5.61	5.06	4.41	4.15	4.42	4.28	3.25	5.73	6.53	65.87
Wanganui	3.00	3.26	2.77	2.87	3.35	3.10	2.76	2.89	2.78	2.42	3.24	3.23	35.67
Wellington	4.65	5.36	4.65	3.84	4.23	3.37	3.46	3.08	3.28	3.18	3.81	4.92	47.83
Westport[2]	7.16	6.63	6.41	6.51	7.03	6.74	6.69	6.84	4.97	5.98	5.27	6.18	76.41

[1]Average of records from various sites over a period of 89 years to 1940.
[2]Average of 70-year period to 1945.
[3]Average of 59-year period to 1950.
[4]Average of 64-year period to 1946.

Table 9C

MEAN MONTHLY POTENTIAL EVAPOTRANSPIRATION AT FORTY-FIVE STATIONS IN NEW ZEALAND
(mm.)

Note: Figures in brackets indicate the number of years of record to 1950.

Station		June	July	Aug.	Sept.	Oct.	Nov.	Dec.	Jan.	Feb.	Mar.	Apr.	May	Year
Akaroa	(15)	22	25	27	40	59	72	92	99	79	72	52	33	672
Alexandra	(24)	10	7	19	38	62	79	100	104	84	72	44	22	641
Ashburton	(26)	16	15	24	36	57	73	92	98	80	71	47	28	637
Auckland	(85)	33	30	35	47	59	72	92	104	91	82	61	44	750
Balmoral	(25)	17	14	22	36	57	75	93	99	81	72	50	25	643
Blenheim	(20)	21	21	29	41	59	74	94	101	86	75	52	34	687
Château Tongariro	(18)	15	12	18	26	43	59	74	83	71	65	44	27	537
Christchurch	(65)	19	18	24	39	60	76	95	99	83	70	48	30	661
Darfield	(15)	17	16	24	37	59	73	92	98	80	70	48	29	643
Dunedin	(20)[1]	21	21	28	41	60	71	87	90	72	67	49	31	638
Fairlie	(26)	12	10	19	34	58	73	92	99	79	69	46	25	616
Gisborne	(16)	25	24	31	40	60	76	97	106	86	76	56	37	714
Golden Downs	(23)	17	15	25	36	56	71	89	95	78	70	48	29	629
Gore	(43)	15	15	25	41	59	71	89	93	77	67	45	28	625
Hanmer	(32)	14	12	22	35	56	71	91	97	79	69	49	26	621
Hastings	(25)	23	22	29	39	60	74	97	107	88	77	54	34	704
Hermitage, Mt. Cook	(19)	9	2	16	31	53	70	92	86	77	71	46	23	576
Invercargill	(44)	20	20	28	40	59	70	86	90	75	66	45	31	630
Karioi	(24)	18	17	23	32	50	64	79	88	71	68	48	29	587
Lake Tekapo	(26)	10	5	13	31	53	70	88	97	78	69	45	23	582
Manorburn Dam	(24)	1	0	8	29	50	69	86	90	77	65	42	20	537
Masterton	(8)	22	22	28	39	57	71	94	100	83	72	50	33	671
Napier	(25)	25	23	30	40	63	86	99	105	86	76	55	37	725
Nelson	(32)	22	22	29	41	58	73	94	99	82	75	53	34	682
New Plymouth	(31)	29	29	33	40	56	70	87	94	79	74	57	55	703
Onepoto	(17)	23	18	25	34	54	68	87	95	79	70	52	33	638
Ophir	(25)	6	4	18	34	59	76	102	102	86	71	45	22	625
Pahiatua	(25)	22	21	29	37	57	70	92	95	81	75	54	34	667
Palmerston Nth.	(40)	24	22	29	41	58	69	88	101	83	73	50	36	674
Queenstown	(23)	14	12	22	35	57	76	95	98	82	70	47	25	633
Riverhead	(23)	29	26	33	41	55	70	84	92	80	74	58	41	683
Rotorua	(53)[2]	23	22	28	40	58	74	92	102	83	76	57	35	690
Ruakura	(38)	24	24	31	41	57	71	91	101	85	76	54	36	691
Rudstone	(25)	18	17	25	36	62	72	89	94	79	70	49	31	642
Taihape	(42)	21	20	26	35	52	66	84	95	73	70	51	32	625
Tauranga	(38)	26	27	31	42	60	73	90	100	86	76	55	38	704
Te Paki	(20)	34	33	34	43	57	72	91	95	81	79	64	46	720
Timaru	(41)	18	17	24	37	62	78	92	98	80	70	49	29	654
Waihi	(46)	27	25	30	42	59	73	88	100	82	76	55	38	695
Waimate	(46)	19	19	25	39	60	72	89	97	79	71	48	30	648
Waipiata	(26)	10	9	20	33	56	72	92	98	83	68	45	24	610
Waipoua	(24)	31	29	34	42	55	69	87	91	79	75	59	41	692
Wanganui	(15)	26	26	32	43	59	73	90	99	84	76	57	40	705
Wellington	(89)	26	24	30	41	56	69	87	94	78	72	52	37	666
Westport	(10)[3]	28	27	31	42	56	67	86	91	77	71	53	38	667

[1] Years to 1943.
[2] Years to 1946.
[3] Years to 1945.

Table 10C

MEAN MONTHLY RELATIVE HUMIDITY AT 9.30 A.M. AT FORTY-EIGHT STATIONS IN NEW ZEALAND

(per cent)

Note: Figures in brackets indicate the number of years of record to 1945.

Station		June	July	Aug.	Sept.	Oct.	Nov.	Dec.	Jan.	Feb.	Mar.	Apr.	May	Year
Akaroa	(10)	77	80	76	70	69	66	68	66	69	71	72	75	72
Alexandra	(19)	87	88	81	68	58	55	56	56	63	68	78	83	70
Ashburton	(21)	78	78	75	70	65	62	66	64	70	73	77	75	71
Auckland	(80)	83	84	80	76	74	71	70	71	72	74	78	80	76
Balmoral	(20)	72	73	68	62	57	54	54	53	57	62	66	69	62
Blenheim	(15)	80	81	77	65	64	58	56	57	61	63	71	76	67
Château Tongariro	(13)	82	86	81	79	77	77	75	75	76	79	79	81	79
Christchurch	(60)	86	86	82	73	66	63	66	66	71	75	81	84	75
Darfield	(10)	85	83	82	77	71	64	63	64	69	75	79	83	75
Dunedin	(20)[1]	77	77	73	70	67	68	72	68	71	73	77	75	72
Fairlie	(21)	77	81	75	71	67	64	69	71	78	81	83	75	74
Gisborne	(11)	81	81	79	71	69	63	60	63	68	71	76	80	72
Golden Downs	(18)	82	82	80	74	72	68	68	69	72	72	77	77	74
Gore	(38)	87	86	84	81	79	77	77	80	83	84	87	86	83
Hanmer	(27)	76	81	74	67	63	62	64	65	68	70	74	74	70
Hastings	(20)	78	77	74	69	65	62	63	63	68	72	75	77	70
Hermitage, Mt. Cook	(14)	74	75	70	59	57	54	54	62	60	62	64	66	63
Hokitika	(50)	88	86	84	80	77	77	78	79	80	83	87	87	82
Invercargill	(39)	84	83	82	80	75	76	81	76	82	83	84	84	81
Karioi	(19)	80	79	76	71	72	71	68	69	71	73	77	79	74
Lake Coleridge	(28)	72	75	68	59	54	51	55	53	58	60	68	67	62
Lake Tekapo	(21)	78	82	78	69	63	60	60	60	65	68	75	74	69
Manorburn Dam	(19)	86	88	83	71	64	60	62	60	63	70	76	81	72
Milford Sound	(15)	87	84	86	85	83	80	77	81	86	88	89	87	84
Napier	(20)	74	82	78	71	68	65	64	63	69	74	77	79	72
Nelson	(27)	85	83	78	68	66	63	65	64	67	68	75	79	72
New Plymouth	(26)	83	83	82	80	81	81	80	81	81	80	81	81	81
Onepoto	(12)	87	89	86	82	77	75	76	77	81	82	84	85	82
Ophir	(20)	86	86	77	66	61	58	59	60	65	70	77	80	70
Pahiatua	(20)	83	83	81	79	79	79	78	78	78	80	82	83	80
Palmerston Nth.	(35)	83	82	79	77	74	74	74	73	74	78	80	82	78
Queenstown	(18)	80	82	76	70	67	66	65	66	71	71	76	79	72
Riverhead	(18)	86	86	84	78	76	74	74	73	74	77	81	83	79
Rotorua	(52)	84	83	80	73	71	68	68	69	72	74	79	81	75
Ruakura	(33)	86	84	78	74	72	72	72	72	73	77	81	85	78
Rudstone	(20)	70	71	70	65	62	62	65	64	66	69	70	68	67
Taihape	(37)	85	84	80	79	74	72	71	70	73	76	79	83	77
Tauranga	(33)	81	82	81	75	72	73	71	71	71	74	78	80	76
Te Aroha	(25)	88	88	83	79	75	73	73	74	77	79	82	85	80
Te Paki	(15)	79	80	77	76	74	74	75	73	75	75	76	77	76
Timaru	(36)	82	81	78	74	69	68	72	72	74	76	83	81	76
Waihi	(41)	83	83	81	77	75	75	73	75	75	79	81	82	78
Waimate	(41)	79	78	77	75	70	71	74	71	76	76	82	79	76
Waipiata	(21)	83	84	78	70	63	60	61	62	67	72	76	77	71
Waipoua	(19)	90	90	87	83	79	77	76	77	80	83	87	89	83
Wanganui	(10)	80	79	75	70	67	65	65	65	68	70	73	76	71
Wellington	(84)	81	82	80	77	76	74	75	74	76	77	78	80	78
Westport	(10)	87	83	82	84	81	82	82	83	86	86	87	88	84

[1]Years to 1942.

Table 11C

MEAN ANNUAL PERCENTAGE FREQUENCY OF WIND DIRECTION AT TWENTY-EIGHT STATIONS
IN NEW ZEALAND

Note: Figures in brackets indicate the number of years of record to 1948.

Station		Total No. of Observations	N	NE	E	SE	S	SW	W	NW	Calms
Alexandra	(9)	9,907	9.1	8.7	1.8	1.0	9.8	11.0	5.1	6.0	47.5
Ashburton	(10)	10,267	11.2	13.1	9.8	8.5	8.4	10.4	5.5	16.2	16.9
Dannevirke	(9)[1]	9,097	3.0	5.7	2.3	4.2	10.7	33.0	12.4	4.2	24.5
Gisborne	(10)	11,026	9.4	5.0	4.5	14.0	11.6	7.7	5.4	27.7	14.7
Hokitika	(12)	11,314	10.1	8.3	13.5	5.3	1.5	14.4	13.5	12.1	21.3
Invercargill	(13)	7,754	9.0	8.4	4.8	5.7	4.5	14.1	19.5	11.9	22.1
Jackson's Bay	(9)	10,515	0.6	7.8	4.2	16.4	0.7	7.3	2.6	19.7	40.7
Kaikoura	(11)	11,286	3.8	13.8	7.4	7.8	7.3	16.1	3.4	5.5	34.9
Karamea	(11)	10,065	2.2	2.3	7.2	2.7	2.1	23.6	8.1	10.8	41.0
Karioi	(14)	8,296	2.1	7.8	8.5	6.2	4.0	5.2	26.8	14.9	24.5
Napier	(13)	11,395	3.8	19.4	7.3	4.5	9.2	16.8	10.9	9.4	18.7
Nelson	(11)	12,035	21.4	16.8	2.2	1.5	2.6	16.1	4.0	6.3	29.1
New Plymouth	(11)	11,803	9.8	7.7	4.6	14.1	6.7	9.8	21.7	14.6	11.0
Oamaru	(9)	8,274	7.7	20.9	2.4	7.1	8.9	14.2	7.0	8.3	23.5
Ohakea	(11)	12,286	8.5	5.0	7.7	11.4	3.8	8.4	17.2	28.5	9.5
Onerahi	(11)	11,616	6.1	5.0	7.1	9.2	3.3	26.5	9.7	10.9	16.3
Ranfurly	(9)	10,158	1.8	2.8	2.3	6.0	2.2	11.9	4.3	20.0	48.7
Rotorua	(12)	11,850	6.9	16.6	1.0	6.1	9.9	23.6	7.1	9.8	19.0
Rukuhia	(11)	10,525	6.6	5.7	3.3	4.4	6.7	12.5	14.7	10.2	35.9
Taieri	(10)	10,997	5.1	12.2	3.4	10.6	5.9	17.5	8.0	6.9	30.4
Takaka	(12)	10,227	9.3	15.3	4.7	5.4	8.1	6.1	6.1	15.5	29.5
Taupo	(10)	8,897	4.9	7.6	2.0	5.9	10.9	26.0	7.8	8.6	26.3
Tauranga	(12)	11,760	9.8	9.1	6.9	4.9	3.0	17.4	16.1	9.4	23.4
Te Kuiti	(9)[1]	7,788	9.4	7.1	3.2	3.5	7.0	19.2	17.9	15.1	17.6
Timaru	(12)	10,770	6.8	17.6	5.6	7.0	10.1	12.3	2.0	7.4	31.2
Wellington	(9)	10,777	14.4	3.2	1.4	11.3	17.5	2.6	1.7	32.2	15.7
Whitianga	(10)	9,080	5.4	13.9	5.3	6.9	2.9	28.0	15.1	11.0	11.5
Wigram	(10)	11,958	4.2	20.7	17.4	1.1	11.1	16.9	4.3	7.1	17.2

[1]Years to 1947.

Table 12C

AVERAGE NUMBER OF GALES AND HAILSTORMS IN DIFFERENT SEASONS AT FORTY-SEVEN STATIONS IN NEW ZEALAND

Note: Figures in brackets indicate the number of years of record to 1950.

Station		Gales					Hailstorms				
		Wi.	Sp.	Su.	Au.	Year	Wi.	Sp.	Su.	Au.	Year
Akaroa	(13)	2.0	3.6	2.8	1.9	10.3	5.2	3.8	1.1	2.3	12.4
Alexandra	(22)	0.1	0.4	0.2	0.1	0.8	0.3	0.7	0.2	0.2	1.4
Ashburton	(23)	0.6	1.5	0.8	0.3	3.2	0.3	0.6	0.3	0.5	1.7
Auckland	(41)	3.5	3.6	2.3	2.5	11.9	2.1	1.3	0.2	0.6	4.2
Balmoral	(22)[1]	0.5	1.4	0.4	0.4	2.7	0.3	0.3	0.2	0.1	0.9
Blenheim	(18)	0.3	0.6	0.8	0.4	2.1	0.3	0.3	0.3	0.3	1.2
Château Tongariro	(21)	1.0	0.7	0.6	0.9	3.2	0.4	0.5	0.3	0.4	1.6
Christchurch	(45)	2.2	4.8	4.0	2.7	13.7	2.4	2.0	0.9	1.1	6.4
Darfield	(11)	1.7	2.6	1.3	1.7	7.3	0.7	0.8	0.9	0.8	3.2
Fairlie	(25)	0.1	0.8	0.6	0.6	2.1	0.2	0.7	0.1	0.4	1.4
Gisborne	(13)	0.1	0.2	0.8	0.4	1.5	0.7	0.7	1.0	1.0	3.4
Golden Downs	(21)	0.9	0.6	0.3	0.5	2.3	0.3	0.7	0.3	0.1	1.4
Gore	(42)	0.7	1.4	1.2	0.9	4.2	0.7	1.6	0.6	0.6	3.5
Hanmer	(29)	0.4	1.3	0.4	0.6	2.7	0.2	1.1	0.1	0.3	1.7
Hastings	(22)	0.3	0.4	0.6	0.2	1.5	0.3	0.4	0.1	Nil	0.8
Hermitage, Mt. Cook	(22)	1.0	1.3	1.3	1.2	4.8	0.3	0.3	0.4	0.2	1.2
Hokitika	(29)	0.5	1.2	0.3	0.8	2.8	3.2	2.8	1.2	1.7	8.9
Invercargill	(45)	5.1	7.1	4.9	6.3	23.4	4.4	2.9	1.7	2.7	11.7
Karioi	(23)	0.9	1.6	0.8	0.8	4.1	6.7	3.2	0.1	1.3	11.3
Lake Coleridge	(22)	0.6	1.4	1.6	0.7	4.3	0.5	1.0	0.4	0.5	2.4
Lake Tekapo	(25)	0.5	1.0	0.2	0.3	2.0	0.1	0.1	Nil	0.2	0.4
Masterton	(8)	3.1	4.8	5.1	3.1	16.1	1.3	1.7	0.4	0.3	3.7
Milford Sound	(16)	1.8	2.2	1.0	1.1	6.1	2.1	2.0	1.0	0.4	5.5
Napier	(26)	0.9	1.1	1.3	0.5	3.8	0.2	0.9	0.3	0.1	1.5
Nelson	(30)	0.4	0.4	0.4	0.2	1.4	0.3	0.9	0.4	0.1	1.7
New Plymouth	(29)	4.4	4.0	2.2	4.0	14.6	2.4	1.8	0.6	0.8	5.6
Onepoto	(15)	1.3	2.0	1.5	0.8	5.6	0.4	1.1	0.1	0.1	1.7
Ophir	(25)	0.8	1.0	0.7	0.7	3.2	0.5	1.3	0.5	0.7	3.0
Pahiatua	(23)	0.5	1.2	1.2	0.9	3.7	0.7	1.0	0.5	0.2	2.4
Palmerston Nth.	(22)	0.5	0.6	0.4	0.3	1.8	0.3	0.6	0.2	0.2	1.3
Queenstown	(21)	0.6	0.8	0.7	0.6	2.7	0.4	0.5	0.4	0.3	1.6
Riverhead	(22)	1.7	1.8	1.4	1.3	6.2	2.1	1.4	0.3	0.6	4.4
Ruakura	(29)	0.6	0.5	0.2	0.7	2.0	1.3	1.2	0.2	0.4	3.1
Rudstone	(22)	1.0	1.7	1.4	1.0	5.1	0.7	2.2	1.4	0.7	5.0
Taihape	(22)	0.7	1.0	1.1	0.5	3.3	1.7	3.0	0.8	1.0	6.5
Tauranga	(37)	1.0	1.3	0.8	1.1	4.2	0.6	0.8	0.2	0.2	1.8
Te Aroha	(27)	1.3	0.7	0.6	0.9	3.5	0.6	0.7	0.2	0.2	1.7
Te Paki	(19)	2.0	1.4	0.7	2.1	6.2	0.4	0.1	0.1	0.1	0.7
Timaru	(41)	0.9	1.9	1.3	1.0	5.1	0.5	1.1	0.9	0.2	2.7
Waihi	(22)	0.5	0.3	0.1	0.5	1.4	1.2	1.6	0.3	0.5	3.6
Waimate	(14)	0.5	1.0	0.6	0.2	2.3	0.1	0.5	0.8	0.3	1.7
Waipiata	(25)	0.6	0.7	0.4	0.4	2.1	0.5	1.7	0.7	0.6	3.5
Waipoua	(22)	1.7	1.3	0.9	0.9	4.8	4.9	2.7	0.3	0.6	8.5
Wanganui	(13)	1.1	1.4	1.3	0.5	4.3	1.4	0.9	0.2	0.7	3.2
Wellington	(89)	4.5	7.7	6.0	4.2	22.4	6.3	3.5	0.7	2.4	12.9
Westport[2]	(5)	0.5	1.0	0.8	0.6	2.9	2.3	2.6	0.8	1.3	7.0
Whakarewarewa	(23)	0.1	0.5	0.2	0.2	1.0	0.1	0.2	Nil	Nil	0.3

[1]Years to 1949.
[2]Westport Airfield.

Table 13C

MEAN MONTHLY HOURS OF BRIGHT SUNSHINE AT TWENTY-FIVE STATIONS IN NEW ZEALAND

Note: Figures in brackets indicate the number of years of record to 1950.

Station		June	July	Aug.	Sept.	Oct.	Nov.	Dec.	Jan.	Feb.	Mar.	Apr.	May	Year
Alexandra	(22)	120	118	158	175	207	230	228	236	206	207	158	127	2,170
Ashburton	(29)	106	115	133	153	168	188	190	194	169	166	127	120	1,829
Auckland	(41)	122	126	152	160	176	200	222	231	195	187	151	137	2,059
Blenheim	(24)	150	153	175	197	219	242	257	261	227	222	176	170	2,449
Christchurch	(22)	108	122	145	163	187	213	200	213	192	177	136	132	1,988
Dunedin	(30)	91	105	128	144	165	176	171	188	164	154	123	106	1,715
Gore	(32)	93	112	142	156	180	196	208	217	177	166	124	114	1,885
Hanmer	(38)	103	108	140	160	179	199	209	212	191	190	151	124	1,966
Hokitika	(38)	110	130	144	148	160	179	198	205	177	177	139	131	1,898
Invercargill	(29)	77	94	120	140	161	174	186	199	157	140	104	88	1,640
Lake Tekapo	(22)	118	130	158	176	216	232	248	262	221	226	172	149	2,308
Masterton	(35)	110	113	144	168	189	217	232	235	206	190	158	129	2,091
Napier	(41)	147	143	176	203	222	235	263	261	212	211	179	154	2,406
Nelson	(29)	155	166	182	201	215	242	257	259	228	227	188	170	2,490
New Plymouth	(34)	128	139	164	167	176	206	228	253	214	212	167	157	2,211
Oamaru	(22)	116	125	143	153	170	191	165	185	166	165	131	129	1,839
Palmerston Nth.	(22)	98	110	131	140	155	184	202	206	185	166	138	124	1,839
Queenstown	(21)	76	94	128	162	198	228	241	248	205	194	134	95	2,003
Rotorua	(38)	120	128	144	157	181	205	220	237	195	186	152	136	2,061
Thames	(45)	117	118	144	157	164	210	218	254	206	202	153	124	2,067
Timaru	(26)	124	128	148	160	177	194	183	199	175	170	133	136	1,927
Waihi	(40)	116	122	148	165	181	205	237	243	198	188	148	136	2,087
Waipiata	(26)	115	129	155	168	196	213	215	233	200	202	161	140	2,127
Waipoua	(22)	84	102	125	136	148	160	185	194	168	163	132	109	1,706
Wellington	(44)	105	108	140	164	181	207	231	230	205	191	154	129	2,045

Table 14C

MEAN PERCENTAGE OF THE POSSIBLE SEASONAL TOTAL OF SUNSHINE RECEIVED AT EACH SEASON AT TWENTY-FIVE STATIONS IN NEW ZEALAND

Note: Figures in brackets indicate the number of years of record to 1950.

Station		Wi.	Sp.	Su.	Au.	Year
Alexandra	(22)	46	50	50	49	49
Ashburton	(29)	40	42	41	40	41
Auckland	(41)	43	45	51	46	46
Blenheim	(24)	53	54	57	56	55
Christchurch	(22)	41	46	45	43	45
Dunedin	(30)	37	39	39	38	39
Gore	(32)	40	43	44	40	43
Hanmer	(38)	39	44	46	47	44
Hokitika	(38)	43	40	45	45	43
Invercargill	(29)	34	39	40	33	37
Lake Tekapo	(22)	46	51	55	57	52
Masterton	(35)	41	47	51	47	47
Napier	(41)	51	55	57	53	54
Nelson	(29)	56	54	57	57	56
New Plymouth	(34)	47	47	53	52	50
Oamaru	(22)	44	42	38	42	41
Palmerston Nth.	(22)	37	38	45	42	41
Queenstown	(21)	34	48	51	41	45
Rotorua	(38)	42	45	51	46	46
Thames	(45)	41	45	53	47	46
Timaru	(26)	45	43	42	43	44
Waihi	(40)	42	46	53	47	47
Waipiata	(26)	46	47	48	49	48
Waipoua	(22)	33	37	43	39	38
Wellington	(44)	39	45	51	46	46

Table 15C

MEAN ANNUAL RAINFALL AND NUMBER OF RAIN DAYS AND MEAN PERCENTAGE SEASONAL
DISTRIBUTION OF RAINFALL AT SELECTED STATIONS IN THE
CLIMATIC REGIONS OF NEW ZEALAND

Note: At stations indicated by an asterisk the record is for the period 1921–50; at other stations, except where indicated by a note, the record is for a period of over twenty years to 1950.

Station	Wi.	Sp.	Su.	Au.	Mean Annual Rainfall (in.)	Rain Days
(a) Middle New Zealand:						
Farewell Spit	30.9	25.2	20.6	23.3	45.72	120
Feilding	26.0	27.4	22.9	23.7	36.43	159
Hunterville	25.0	27.8	24.2	23.0	43.95	157
Inglewood	28.0	27.2	22.4	22.4	92.18	174
Nelson	26.9	26.0	23.2	23.9	38.23	116
New Plymouth*	29.7	25.2	21.7	23.4	60.16	185
Ohawe, Hawera	28.8	23.7	21.6	25.9	42.10	149
Otaki	27.6	25.9	22.0	24.5	38.96	165
Palmerston North*	25.8	26.8	23.2	24.2	39.17	173
(b) Western South Island:						
Hokitika[1]	23.8	26.9	24.7	24.6	115.42	188
Karamea	24.4	27.5	24.0	24.1	73.43	170
Reefton	26.2	28.2	22.0	23.6	75.86	165
Ross	21.1	28.5	26.0	24.4	133.60	170
Westport[2]	26.0	26.4	23.6	24.0	76.41	187
(c) Northern New Zealand:						
Auckland*	32.1	23.3	20.2	24.4	48.80	183
Dargaville	31.6	21.5	22.0	24.9	47.75	178
Kawakawa	32.8	20.7	20.4	26.1	57.81	138
Ruakura*	29.1	24.9	21.5	24.5	45.95	161
Tauranga*	28.6	23.6	22.0	25.8	53.42	152
Te Aroha*	30.6	23.8	19.6	26.0	55.53	158
Te Paki*	32.9	20.8	21.0	25.3	54.61	169
Waihi*	31.6	22.0	19.9	26.5	85.83	179
Waipoua*	33.5	22.1	21.5	22.9	65.87	200
Whangarei	33.4	20.7	19.4	26.5	63.36	181
(d) Southern New Zealand:						
Athol	22.3	24.4	26.0	27.3	33.21	120
Balclutha	22.2	25.2	27.1	25.5	26.25	130
Dunedin[3]	24.0	24.2	26.6	25.2	39.28	160
Half Moon Bay	23.2	27.5	23.4	25.9	58.00	222
Invercargill	21.9	24.6	25.3	28.2	43.82	201
Otautau	23.7	25.1	23.4	27.8	44.79	171
Owaka	26.0	26.0	22.6	25.4	37.10	160
Riverton	24.1	24.4	24.5	27.0	47.04	173
Tapanui	23.5	25.1	25.7	25.7	40.80	163
(e) Eastern North Island:						
Blenheim*	28.0	24.5	25.5	22.0	25.24	111
Cape Campbell	30.0	23.2	23.2	23.6	24.60	82
Castlepoint	31.3	21.6	20.3	26.8	35.31	120
Dannevirke	27.2	26.5	22.6	23.7	43.41	163
Gisborne*	31.5	18.9	19.5	30.1	39.85	146
Greytown	28.7	24.3	22.5	24.5	41.77	147
Napier	30.1	19.1	23.6	27.2	31.00	115
Tokomaru Bay	30.8	17.2	23.4	28.6	64.91	135
Tutira	29.1	19.1	21.7	30.1	54.09	119
Wellington	30.8	23.8	21.0	24.4	47.83	165

[1]Seventy years to 1945.
[2]Eighteen years to 1945.
[3]Eighty-nine years to 1940; record from various sites.

C.N.Z.—M

Station	Wi.	Sp.	Su.	Au.	Mean Annual Rainfall (in.)	Rain days
(f) Eastern South Island:						
Akaroa*	35.6	20.7	19.4	24.3	38.56	94
Ashburton*	24.8	24.2	27.5	23.5	30.52	126
Christchurch*	28.7	21.8	24.9	24.6	26.28	126
Darfield*	23.3	25.2	27.4	24.1	31.51	105
Duntroon	21.0	24.5	30.9	23.6	21.83	97
Gore Bay	25.7	22.6	25.8	25.9	33.15	107
Oamaru	24.0	23.8	28.6	23.6	22.18	111
Rudstone*	21.3	26.0	29.2	23.5	41.30	136
Timaru*	21.5	24.4	30.5	23.6	23.46	114
(g) Central North Island:						
Château Tongariro*	23.2	25.8	27.6	23.4	108.21	191
Karioi*	27.2	25.8	25.9	21.1	47.80	164
Rotorua[1]	27.9	25.4	22.3	24.4	55.42	139
Taupo	28.6	25.2	23.0	23.2	43.32	127
Waiotapu*	27.8	24.2	23.8	24.2	52.12	141
(h) Inland South Island:						
Alexandra*	15.3	23.7	34.3	26.7	13.22	100
Benmore	20.4	25.0	27.7	26.9	24.79	109
Braemar	24.1	27.5	23.4	25.0	35.89	94
Clyde	16.9	25.6	30.7	26.8	15.45	85
Lake Tekapo*	24.7	24.2	25.7	25.4	22.14	76
Patearoa	17.0	23.3	34.7	25.0	14.94	78
Queenstown*	20.4	27.6	24.6	27.4	32.03	104
Roxburgh	18.3	24.1	31.8	25.8	20.76	123
Tarras	18.1	28.8	26.3	26.8	19.64	67
(i) Upland South Island:						
Arthur's Pass	19.3	29.3	25.9	25.5	156.70	139
Hanmer*	24.4	26.1	24.7	24.8	45.15	133
Lake Coleridge*	25.9	27.1	23.3	23.7	31.54	114
Makarora	25.6	23.7	28.2	22.5	72.71	108
Milford Sound*	16.8	27.8	28.2	27.2	253.50	195

[1]Sixty-four years to 1946.

SELECT BIBLIOGRAPHY

THIS bibliography contains only those works which were found especially useful in preparing this book and which have a direct bearing on the character and geographic significance of the climate of New Zealand. References to literature on climate in general are absent and the list given here makes no pretence at being a comprehensive survey of information relating to New Zealand and its climate. It does not include all the works cited as footnotes in the text nor are contributions of individual authors which appear in edited volumes such as *New Zealand Weather and Climate* listed separately. Consequently, this select bibliography should be used as a supplement to the footnotes in the text and not as a substitute for them.

A. *Statistical and Similar Data*:

H. H. Clayton: 'World Weather Records', Smithsonian Institute Misc. Collect., Vol. 79, 1944.

Daily Weather Charts available in New Zealand Meteorological Office, Wellington, for the years 1949 and 1950.

Kidson, E.: 'The Average Annual Rainfall of New Zealand for the period 1891 to 1925', Wellington, 1930.

N.Z. Official Gazette: climatic extracts from January, 1950, to December, 1955.

N.Z. Meteorological Office: Annual Meteorological Observations, published yearly from 1938.

Seelye, C. J.: 'Maps of Average Rainfall in New Zealand', Wellington, 1945.

idem: 'Maps of Extreme Monthly Rainfall in New Zealand', Wellington, 1946.

Unpublished Records in the N.Z. Meteorological Office, Wellington, and also those obtained by visiting runholders, particularly in Otago and South Canterbury.

B. *Books and Monographs*:

Acland, L. G. D.: 'The Early Canterbury Runs', 2nd edn., Christchurch, 1946.

Allen, H. H.: 'An Introduction to the Grasses of New Zealand', *N.Z. Dept. Sci. and Ind. Res. Bulln.*, No. 49, 1939.

Andersen, J. C.: 'Jubilee History of South Canterbury', Christchurch, 1916.

Barker, A. P.: 'An Ecological Study of Tussock Grassland, Hunters Hills, South Canterbury', *N.Z. Dept. Sci. and Ind. Res. Bulln.*, No. 107, 1953.

Beaglehole, J. C.: 'The Discovery of New Zealand', Wellington, 1939.

Belshaw, H., Williams, D. O., and Stephens, F. B.: 'Agricultural Organization in New Zealand', Melbourne, 1936.

Buchanan, R. O.: 'The Pastoral Industries of New Zealand', *Trans. Inst. of Brit. Georgrs.*, No. 2, 1935.

Buck, P.: 'The Coming of the Maori', Wellington, 1950.

Butler, S.: 'A First Year in the Canterbury Settlement', London, 1863.

Clark, A. H.: 'The Invasion of New Zealand by People, Plants, and Animals: the South Island', Rutgers Univ. Press, 1949.

Cockayne, L.: 'New Zealand Plants and Their Story', Wellington, 1910.

idem: 'The Vegetation of New Zealand', Engler-Drude *Die Vegetation der Erde*, 2nd edn., Leipzig, 1928.

Condliffe, J. B.: 'New Zealand in the Making', London, 1930.

Connell, R. P., *et al.*: 'Land Utilization Report on the Heretaunga Plains', *N.Z. Dept. Sci. and Ind. Res. Bulln.*, No. 70, 1939.

Cowan, J. C.: 'Down the Years in the Maniototo', Dunedin, 1948.

Cumberland, K. B.: 'Soil Erosion in New Zealand', 2nd edn., Wellington, 1946.

Dieffenbach, E.: 'Travels in New Zealand, with contributions to the Geography, Geology, Botany, and Natural History of the Country', 2 vols., London, 1843.

Ferrar, H. T.: 'Soils of the Irrigation Areas of Central Otago', *N.Z. Geol. Surv. Bulln.* (n.s.), No. 33, 1929.

Garbell, M. A.: 'Tropical and Equatorial Meteorology', London, 1947.

Garnier, B. J. (ed.): 'The Face of Otago', Dunedin, 1948.

idem: 'New Zealand Weather and Climate', *N.Z. Geogr. Soc. Spec. Pubn. Misc. Ser.*, No. 1, 1950.

Gibbs, H. S., Mercer, A. D., and Collie, J. W.: 'Soils and Agriculture of Westland', *N.Z. Dept. Sci. and Ind. Res. Bulln.*, No. 2 (n.s.), 1950.

Gibbs, H. S., Raeside, J. D., *et al.*: 'Soil Erosion in the High Country of the South Island', *N.Z. Dept. Sci. and Ind. Res. Bulln.*, No. 92, 1945.

Gilkinson, R.: 'Early Days in Central Otago', Dunedin, 1930.

Grimstone, S. E.: 'The Southern Settlements of New Zealand: comprising statistical information from the earliest period to the close of the year 1846, etc. etc.', Wellington, 1847.

Haast, H. F. von: 'The Life and Times of Sir Julius von Haast', Wellington, 1948.

Handbook for Otago and Southland (New Zealand), London, 1862.

Harris, C. S., and Harris, A. C.: 'Soil Survey of the Westport District', *N.Z. Dept. Sci. and Ind. Res. Bulln.*, No. 71, 1939.

Hilgendorf, F. W.: 'The Grasslands of the South Island', *N.Z. Dept. Sci. and Ind. Res. Bulln.*, No. 47, 1935.

Hochstetter, F. von: 'New Zealand, its physical geography, geology, and natural history', Trans. E. Sauter, Stuttgart, 1867.

Jalu, R.: 'Expédition Antarctique Française 1948–49: section météorologique—premier exposé des résultats', Paris, 1950.

Kidson, E.: 'The Climatology of New Zealand', Köppen-Geiger *Handbuch der Klimatologie*, Band IV, Teil S, Berlin, 1932.

idem: 'Daily Weather Charts extending from Australia and New Zealand to the Antarctic Continent', *Austr. Antarct. Exped. 1911–14*, *Sci. Rep. Ser. B.*, Vol. 7, Sydney, 1947.

idem and Holmboe, J.: 'Frontal Methods of Weather Analysis applied to the Australia–New Zealand area', Wellington, 1935.

Macklintock, A. H.: 'The History of Otago', Dunedin, 1949.

McClymont, W. G.: 'The Exploration of New Zealand', Wellington, 1940.

Madden, E. A.: 'The Grasslands of the North Island of New Zealand', *N.Z. Dept. Sci. and Ind. Res. Bulln.*, No. 79, 1940.

New Zealand Department of Agriculture: 'Farming in New Zealand', *N.Z. Dept. Agric. Bulln.*, No. 252, 1946.

idem: 'Farming in New Zealand (second series)', ibid., No. 279, 1947.

idem: 'Studies in Farm Management (second series)', ibid., No. 268, 1948.

idem: 'Farming in New Zealand', Vol. 1, Wellington, 1950.

New Zealand Geological Survey Officers: 'The Outline of the Geology of New Zealand: notes and maps on a scale of 16 miles to the inch', Wellington, 1948.

Palmer, C. E.: 'Synoptic Analysis over the Southern Ocean', *N.Z. Meteor. Off. Prof. Notes.*, No. 1, 1942.

Park, J.: 'The Geology of New Zealand', Christchurch, 1910.

Pohlen, I. J., *et al.*: 'Soils and Some Related Agricultural Aspects of mid-Hawke's Bay', *N.Z. Dept. Sci. and Ind. Res. Bulln.*, No. 94, 1947.

Poole, A. L.: 'Preliminary Reports of the New Zealand–American Fiordland Expedition', *N.Z. Dept. Sci. and Ind. Res. Bulln.*, No. 103, 1951.

Simpson, G. C.: 'British Antarctic Expedition, 1910–13, Meteorology: Vol. 1, Discussion; Vol. II, Weather Maps', Calcutta, 1919.

Speight, R., Wall, A., and Laing, R. A. (eds.): 'The Natural History of Canterbury', Christchurch, 1927.

Taylor, G.: 'Australian Meteorology', Oxford, 1920.

Tennent, R. B., and Marks, J. R.: 'Irrigation in Central Otago', *N.Z. Dept. Sci. and Ind. Res. Bulln.*, No. 20, 1926.

Vaile, E. E.: 'Pioneering the Pumice', Christchurch, 1940.

Wall, A.: 'The Flora of Mount Cook', Christchurch, 1925.

Webster, A. H. H.: 'Teviot Tapestry', Dunedin, 1948.

Wodzicki, K. A.: 'Introduced Mammals of New Zealand: an ecological survey', *N.Z. Dept. Sci. and Ind. Res. Bulln.*, No. 98, 1950.

C.   *Articles in Journals and Shorter Publications*:

Aitken, M.: 'The Maniototo Basin, Central Otago: from natural to cultural vegetation', *N.Z. Geogr.*, Vol. 3, 1947, pp. 59–74.

Barnett, M. A. F.: 'The Cyclonic Storms in Northern New Zealand on the 2nd February and 26th March, 1936', *N.Z. Meteor. Off. Notes*, No. 22, 1938.

Bathgate, A.: 'Some Changes in the Fauna and Flora of Otago in the last sixty years', *N.Z. Journ. Sci. and Tech.*, Vol. 4, 1922, pp. 273–83.

Benson, W. N.: 'An Outline of the Geology of New Zealand', *Journ. Geol.*, Vol. 30, 1922, pp. 1–17.

idem: 'Some Landforms in Southern New Zealand', *Austr. Geogr.*, Vol. 2, No. 7, 1935, pp. 3–22.

Birks, L., and Bates, D. C.: 'Annual Rainfall Fluctuations', *N.Z. Journ. Sci. and Tech.*, Vol. 4, 1921, pp. 173–8.

Bjerknes, J.: 'La Circulation Atmosphérique dans les latitudes soustropicales', *Scientia*, Vol. 36, 1935.

Bondy, F., and Seelye, C. J.: 'Temperatures Associated with Rainfall in New Zealand', *N.Z. Journ. Sci. and Tech.*, Vol. 28, Sec. B, 1947, pp. 253–8.

Bray, F. R.: 'A Survey of Rural Nelson and Marlborough', *N.Z. Journ. Agric.*, Vol. 76, 1948, pp. 49–57; 167–75.

Buchanan, J.: 'Sketch of the Botany of Otago', *Trans. N.Z. Inst.*, Vol. 1, 1875, pp. 181–212.

Cockayne, A. H.: 'Some Economic Considerations concerning Montane Tussock Grassland', *Trans. N.Z. Inst.*, Vol. 48, 1915, pp. 154–65.

Cockayne, L.: 'A Sketch of the Plant Geography of the Waimakariri River Basin, considered chiefly from the Oecological Point of View', *Trans. N.Z. Inst.*, Vol. 32, 1899, pp. 95–136.

idem: 'An Economic Investigation of the Montane Tussock Grassland of New Zealand', series of articles in *N.Z. Journ. Agric.*, Vol. 18, 1919, to Vol. 25, 1922.

Connell, R. P.: 'Farming in New Zealand: the Canterbury District', *N.Z. Journ. Agric.*, Vol. 75, 1947, pp. 369–83; 465–76.

idem: 'Pasture Production in Canterbury', *N.Z. Journ. Agric.*, Vol. 78, 1949, pp. 549–57.

Cotton, C. A.: 'The Structure and Later Geological History of New Zealand', *Geol. Mag.*, Vol. 3, 1916, pp. 243–9; 314–20.

idem: 'The Geomorphic Provinces of New Zealand', *N.Z. Geogr.*, Vol. 1, 1945, pp. 40–47.

Cumberland, K. B.: 'Canterbury Landscapes: a study in New Zealand Geography', *Geogr. Rev.*, Vol. 30, 1940, pp. 19–40.

idem: 'A Century's Change: natural to cultural vegetation in New Zealand', *Geogr. Rev.*, Vol. 31, 1941, pp. 529–54.

idem: 'Contrasting Regional Morphology of Soil Erosion in New Zealand', *Geogr. Rev.*, Vol. 34, 1944, pp. 77–95.

idem: 'Burning Tussock Grassland: a geographic survey', *N.Z. Geogr.*, Vol. 1, 1945, pp. 149–64.

idem: 'The Agricultural Regions of New Zealand', *Geogr. Journ.*, Vol. 112, 1948, pp. 43–63.

idem: 'Aotearoa Maori: New Zealand about 1780', *Geogr. Rev.*, Vol. 39, 1949, pp. 401–24.

Devereux, H. B.: 'The Remarkable Rainfall and Meteorology of Waihi', *N.Z. Inst.*, Vol. 42, 1909, pp. 408–11.

Edie, E. G., Seelye, C. J., and Raeside, J. D.: 'Notes on the Canterbury Floods of February, 1945', *N.Z. Journ. Sci. and Tech.*, Vol. 27, Sec. B, 1946, pp. 406–20.

Edwin, R. A.: 'The Meteorology of New Zealand: on the routes of high and low pressures, and the changes of pressure and wind movement resulting from them', *Trans. N.Z. Inst.*, Vol. 37, 1904, pp. 555–67.

Fox, J. W., and Lister, R. G.: 'The Galatea Basin: a geographic reconnaissance', *N.Z. Geogr.*, Vol. 5, 1949, pp. 19–46.

Gabites, J. F.: 'Mean Westerly Wind Flow in the Upper Levels over the New Zealand Region', *N.Z. Journ. Sci. and Tech.*, Vol. 34, Sec. B, 1953, pp. 384–90.

Garnier, B. J.: 'The Application of the Concept of Potential Evapotranspiration to Moisture Problems in New Zealand', *N.Z. Geogr.*, Vol. 7, 1951, pp. 43–61.

idem: 'Thornthwaite's New System of Climate Classification in its application to New Zealand', *Trans. Proc. Roy. Soc. N.Z.*, Vol. 79, 1951, pp. 87–103.

Gentilli, J.: 'Air Masses of the Southern Hemisphere', *Weather*, Vol. 4, 1949, pp. 258–61; 292–7.

Glanville, E. B.: 'Farming in New Zealand: the North Auckland Peninsula', *N.Z. Journ. Agric.*, Vol. 76, 1948, pp. 549–58; Vol. 77, 1948, pp. 53–8.

Hill, R. P.: 'Farming in New Zealand: Hawke's Bay', *N.Z. Journ. Agric.*, Vol. 80, 1950, pp. 15–26.

Holloway, J. T.: 'Ecological Investigations in the *Nothofagus* forest in New Zealand', *N.Z. Journ. Forest.*, Vol. 5, 1948, pp. 1–10.

Holmes, J. M.: 'The Vegetation of New Zealand', *Scott. Geogr. Mag.*, Vol. 51, 1935, pp. 89–99.

Hutchings, J. W.: 'Orographical Cyclogenesis over New Zealand', *N.Z. Meteor. Off. Notes*, Ser. A., No. 8, 1944.

idem: 'Tropical Cyclones in the southwest Pacific', *N.Z. Geogr.*, Vol. 9, 1953, pp. 37–57.

Kidson, E.: 'The Theory of the Polar Front', *Austr. N.Z. Assn. Adv. Sci.*, Vol. 16, 1923.

idem: 'The Flood Rains of the 11th March, 1924, in Hawke's Bay', *N.Z. Journ. Sci. and Tech.*, Vol. 12, 1930, pp, 53–59.

idem: 'The Annual Variation of Rainfall in New Zealand', *N.Z. Journ. Sci. and Tech.*, Vol. 12, 1931, pp. 268–71.

idem: 'Dry Years in New Zealand', *N.Z. Journ. Sci. and Tech.*, Vol. 13, 1931, pp. 79–84.

idem: 'Mean Temperatures in New Zealand', *N.Z. Journ. Sci. and Tech.*, Vol. 13, 1931, pp. 140–53.

idem: 'The Frequency of Frost, Snow, and Hail in New Zealand', *N.Z. Journ. Sci. and Tech.*, Vol. 14, 1932, pp. 42–53.

idem: 'The Canterbury "Northwester" ', *N.Z. Journ. Sci. and Tech.*, Vol. 14, 1932, pp. 65–75.

idem: 'Problems of Antarctic Meteorology', *Quart. Journ. Roy. Met. Soc.*, Vol. 58, 1932, pp. 219–26.

idem: 'The Wairarapa Floods of August, 1932', *N.Z. Journ. Sci. and Tech.*, Vol. 14, 1933, pp. 220–6.

idem: 'Climatic Notes: New Zealand districts', *N.Z. Meteor. Off. Notes*, No. 17, 1937.

idem: 'The Climate of New Zealand', *Quart. Journ. Roy. Met. Soc.*, Vol. 63, 1937, pp. 83–92.

Lamb, H. H.: 'Topography and Weather in the Antarctic', *Geogr. Journ.*, Vol. 111, 1948, pp. 48–66.

Levy, E. B.: 'The Grasslands of New Zealand', various articles in *N.Z. Journ. Agric.*, Vol. 23, 1921, to Vol. 36, 1928.

Macky, W. A.: 'Some Comparisons of the Invigorating Effect of the Climate in Different Parts of New Zealand', *N.Z. Journ. Sci. and Tech.*, Vol. 19, 1937, pp. 164–72.

idem: 'Climatological Observations at Eastbourne, Wellington, and some comparisons', *N.Z. Meteor. Off. Notes*, No. 21, 1938.

McCaskill, M.: 'The Coromandel Peninsula and the Thames Valley', *N.Z. Geogr.*, Vol. 5, 1949, pp. 47–71.

McGillivray, R.: 'The Mackenzie Country Grasslands: progress of natural regeneration and experimental sowings', *N.Z. Journ. Agric.*, Vol. 39, 1929, pp. 73–78.

McIndoe, K. G.: 'Ecological Study of the Vegetation of the Cromwell District with special reference to root habit', *Trans. N.Z. Inst.*, Vol. 62, 1931, pp. 230–66.

Merry, D. M. E., and Adamson, N. J.: 'Farming in New Zealand: the Nelson District', *N.Z. Journ. Agric.*, Vol. 74, 1947, pp. 449–67.

Meeson, J. T.: 'The Rainfall of New Zealand', *Trans. N.Z. Inst.*, Vol. 23, 1890, pp. 546–69.

New Zealand Soil Bureau Officers: 'Soil Map of New Zealand, 1948', Wellington, 1948.

Packard, W.: 'The Lake Coleridge Catchment Basin: a geographic survey of its problems', *N.Z. Geogr.*, Vol. 3, 1947, pp. 19–40.

Pemberton, B. V.: 'Weather Forecasting in New Zealand', *N.Z. Journ. Sci. and Tech.*, Vol. 2, 1919, pp. 87–94.

Petterssen, S.: 'Some Aspects of the General Circulation of the Atmosphere', *Cent. Proc. Roy. Met. Soc.*, 1950, pp. 120–55.

Poole, A. L.: 'New Zealand—American Fiordland Expedition', *Nature*, Vol. 69, No. 4298, 1952, pp. 434–5.

Raeside, J. D.: 'Some Post-Glacial Climatic Changes in Canterbury and their effect on Soil Formation', *Trans. Proc. Roy. Soc. N.Z.*, Vol. 77, 1948, pp. 153–71.

idem: 'The Origins of the Schist Tors of Central Otago', *N.Z. Geogr.*, Vol. 5, 1949, pp. 72–76.

Report of the Committee on the Re-grassing Experiments in Central Otago, *N.Z. Journ. Agric.*, Vol. 26, 1923, pp. 97–100.

Rose, A. J.: 'The Takaka Valley, northwest Nelson', *N.Z. Geogr.*, Vol. 6, 1950, pp. 154–70.

idem: 'Northwest Nelson: its emptiness and isolation', *N.Z. Geogr.*, Vol. 11, 1955, pp. 139–54.

Russell, H. C.: 'Moving Anticyclones in the Southern Hemisphere', *Quart. Journ. Roy. Met. Soc.*, Vol. 19, 1893, pp. 23–34.

Seelye, C. J.: 'The Variation of Annual Rainfall in New Zealand', *N.Z. Journ. Sci. and Tech.*, Vol. 22, Sec. B, 1940, pp. 18–21.

idem: 'Wellington City Rainfall', *N.Z. Journ. Sci. and Tech.*, Vol. 26, Sec, B, 1944, pp. 36–46.

idem: 'Variations of Monthly Rainfall in New Zealand', *N.Z. Journ. Sci. and Tech.*, Vol. 27, Sec. B, 1946, pp. 397–405.

idem: 'The Frequency of Heavy Rainfalls in New Zealand', *Trans. Proc. Roy. Soc. N.Z.*, Vol. 77, Pt. 5, 1949, pp. 66–70.

Shepherd, J. R.: 'Farming in New Zealand: Westland', *N.Z. Journ. Agric.*, Vol. 79, 1949, pp. 255–66.

Speight, R.: 'The Post-Glacial Climate of Canterbury', *Trans. N.Z. Inst.*, Vol. 43, 1910, pp. 408–20.

Stewart, J. D.: 'Farming in New Zealand: Malvern County', *N.Z. Journ. Agric.*, Vol. 79, 1949, pp. 337–50.

Stuart, A.: 'Farming in New Zealand: Southland', *N.Z. Journ. Agric.*, Vol. 79, 1949, pp. 137–52.

Taylor, N. H.: 'Land Deterioration in the Heavier Rainfall Districts of New Zealand', *N.Z. Journ. Sci. and Tech.*, Vol. 19, 1938, pp. 657–81.

Walker, C.: 'Farming in New Zealand: the South Auckland district', *N.Z. Journ. Agric.*, Vol. 77, 1948, pp. 131–7; 247–54.

Wallace, W. H.: 'New Zealand Landforms', *N.Z. Geogr.*, Vol. 11, 1955, pp. 17–27.

Ward, W. T.: 'The Tors of Central Otago', *N.Z. Journ. Sci. and Tech.*, Vol. 33, Sec. B, 1951, pp. 191–200.

Watts, I. E. M.: 'The Relation of New Zealand Weather and Climate: an analysis of the westerlies', *N.Z. Geogr.*, Vol. 3, 1947, pp. 115–29.

Wheeler, R. H.: 'Expedition into Fiordland', *N.Z. Geogr.*, Vol. 11, 1955, pp. 173–82.

Wood, J.: 'Phenomenal Rainfall and Floods of the North Auckland District', *N.Z. Journ. Sci. and Tech.*, Vol. 1, 1918, pp. 293–6.

Woodcock, J. W.: 'Farming in New Zealand: Otago', *N.Z. Journ. Agric.*, Vol. 74, 1947, pp. 21–33.

Zotov, V. D.: 'Some Correlations between Vegetation and Climate in New Zealand', *N.Z. Journ. Sci. and Tech.*, Vol. 19, 1938, pp. 474–87.

idem: 'Survey of the Tussock Grasslands of the South Island, New Zealand', *N.Z. Journ. Sci. and Tech.*, Vol. 20, Sec. A, 1938, pp. 212–44.

idem, *et al.*: 'The Vegetation of the Tararuas', *Trans. Proc. Roy. Soc. N.Z.*, Vol. 68, 1939, pp. 259–324.

INDEX